Visigothic Routes

DACIA

TLᒋ

DANUBE RIVER

STAIRNON
IN LITTLE
MOESIA

MOESIA

EASTERN EMPIRE

PONTUS EUXINUS
(THE BLACK SEA)

Constantinople

THRACE

PROPONTIS

ALARIC
CROWNED
KING

MACEDONIA

EPIRUS

ÆGEAN SEA

ASIA

WHERE THE GULF
OF CORINTH
FROZE

GREECE

CRETE

0   Miles   100

palacios

THE
FALL
OF
ROME

R. A. Lafferty

THE
FALL
OF
ROME

DOUBLEDAY & COMPANY, INC.
GARDEN CITY, NEW YORK
1971

22107

Contents

Contents

THE
FALL
OF
ROME

Prologue of the Persons

ROME, the city that was the world and the Empire, is the main person of the story: How she came to her end, and how the world ended at the same time.

GOTHIA, the ambulant kingdom of the West Goths who, under her esoteric nobility, returned to the attack across many centuries and thousands of miles.

ALARIC, the Boy Giant, the King of the West Goths, who brought the world to an end in his moment of weakness.

STAIRNON, the first and most magnificent of the Valkyries, the wife of Alaric. And her three brothers:

SINGERICH, the Goth who became a Greek,

SARUS, the Goth who became a Roman,

ATHAULF, who is Cain, the Goth who remained a Goth.

Then:

STILICHO, the great Master General of Rome, a Pannonian German Vandal convert from paganism who was more Roman than the Romans and more Catholic than the Pope.

THEODOSIUS THE EMPEROR, the last who can be called 'Great' without laughing. And his three offspring:

ARCADIUS, the Emperor of the East, who was born an old man.

HONORIUS, the Emperor of the West, with the mind of an eleven-year-old boy.

GALLA PLACIDIA, the goblin child and sister of the two young emperors who, at age seventeen and when all the rest of them were cowed, seized control of the Roman Senate and the City and represented the defiance in the last one hundred days of the world.

These are the high persons of the history, and should be noted.

Then these others, from the strangeness of their ancient names and in the interest of clarity, are given for easy reference:

FRITIGERN, the Gothic leader who defeated and slew the Emperor Valens during the boyhood of Alaric.

ATHANARIC, the Gothic leader who threw away the victory.

EUTROPIUS, the Imperial eunuch who may have been two different men.

ARBOGAST, Count of the Franks, who had the world in his hands, and dropped it.

EUGENIUS, the pretender Emperor, the last of the last of the pagans.

SIRICIUS, the Pope who did nothing.

INNOCENT, the Pope who did next to nothing.

SAUL, who led the switch to the Christian side at Frigidus and so saved the day.

ULDIN, a King of the Huns, who devoted his life to the support of the Roman Empire after the Romans had ceased to care.

ST. AMBROSE in Milan, who believed that the world was to endure.

ST. AUGUSTINE in Hippo Regius who understood why the world must end, and when.

GODIGISEL, the King of the Vandals, who was overmatched by the imperial Vandal Stilicho.

RADAGAIS, the Ogre, the complete barbarian, who convinced the Roman world that it had falsely applied the name to others.

OLYMPIUS, the Defamer, who out-Heroded Herod.

SOLINAS, the Infiltrator.

HERACLIAN, Count of Africa, who, from another viewpoint and in the light of different sympathies, might be considered as great a man as Stilicho whom he killed.

These and many other great men and ladies mingle in the high history of the days just before the world ended.

Prologue of the Picture

Near the end of the fourth century, the Mosaic-of-the-Great-Picture came into its own. Its centers were Constantinople and Ravenna. Like Creation itself, it was built around one grand trick.

The great mosaics were made up of thousands of small cubes or *tesserae* imbedded in a matrix of plaster or cement or clay. The colored cubes formed intricate pictures, one picture merging into another: these smaller pictures, when seen from a distance and in the right aspect, would form one great picture. Most persons could see it clearly: some could not see it at all.

The small glass cubes were clear or naturally colored. The clear cubes were wrapped in gold or silver leaf or colored fabric; over this another thin layer of glass was fused. The cubes were set into the matrix with an unevenness that was an art, so that the light off them shattered and gave a sheen and sparkle to the whole arrangement.

The smaller pictures were of people, animals, actions, furniture and handicrafts, towns, fields, banquets, worships, labors and pleasures, buildings, ships, plows, soldiers, children, courtesans, sheep, and asses. They combined in the great picture (which not everyone could see), the face of Christ.

Among the colored cubes pressed into the matrix to form the mosaic of the end of the fourth century were these: the cities Rome, Constantinople, Ravenna, Brundisium, Syracuse, Zancle which is Messina, Oea which is Tripoli, Massilia, Alexandria,

Artaxata, Caesarea, Camulodunum which is Colchester, Carthage and Cyrene, Corinth and Athens, Damascus and Jerusalem.

There are six hundred mountain peaks that must be pressed in here, and two hundred main rivers. There are fifty million slaves who form a part of the picture. The Adriatic Sea is a person in the complex, and the Euxine.

There are the nations of the Empire whose names read like a litany: Cappadocia and Cappadocia Pontica; Cilicia and Pisidia and Pamphylia; Galatia, Lycia, Bithynia; Arabia Petrae and Arabia Felix; Syria and Coele Syria and Palestine and Armenia; Greece and Thrace and Macedonia; Dalmatia and Dardania and Moesia; the settled nation of the Pannonian Vandals, and the wandering nation of the further Vandals; Raetia and Vindelicia and Decumates; the three nations of Gaul, Aquitania and Lugdunensis and Belgica; Britain and Narbonnensis; Tarraconensis and Cisalpine Gaul; Baetica, Lusitania, Gallaecia, Asturia; Mauretania and Numidia; the Province of Africa which had been Carthage; Libya and Egypt; and the wandering nations of the West Goths (them especially), the Burgundians and Lombards and Alemans and Huns. And many more, for there were two hundred nations involved in the Empire.

There are the translucent tesserae of the saints and martyrs like chips of lapis lazuli; and of the Blessed Virgin who did not die, who is the only yet-living citizen of the Empire. There are the popes of the turning of the century, Damascus, Siricius, Anastasius, Innocent: the Emperors Valentinian and Valens, Gratian and the Second Valentinian, Theodosius the Great, Magnus Maximus the Usurper, Eugenius, Arcadius and Honorius and the Second Theodosius.

There are Goths by the dozens. (We will come to them. The Gothic people were very strong in the mosaic.)

The great Master Generals of the era: Promotus, Nevigastes, Gennerid, Sebastian, Trajan, Frigerid (many of these were Gothic men), Victor, Maximus, Nanienus and Mellobaudes, Hellebicus and Caesarius, Saturninus, Lupicinus, Julius, Heraclian, Bacurius, Stilicho, Arbogast.

There are the Kings: Godigisel and Respendial and Uldin the Hun. The ministers, the heresiarchs, the great ladies were all parts of the big picture. Sometimes the picture of the passion and death of the Empire will be the face of the crucified Christ: but often there will emerge the most fulfilled, the most shatteringly profound image ever, the laughing Christ of Creophylus.

And now we will attend to the business at hand and disclaim all further looseness of thought and word. We will studiously add the colored bits to the matrix of blue clay, and we will be guilty of no more such outbursts. *Dimitte nobis rhapsodia nostra*—forgive us our rhapsodies.

To a great extent, the matrix was Roman, and in that fullness of time, the tesserae were very often Gothic. We consider that perfervid Gothic element now.

1. All About Goths

Tacitus, four lifetimes before, had referred to the Goths as a red-haired nation, but most now called them blond. Their coloration may have changed in their wanderings or with the mixing of blood: or the application of the words may have changed, as Latin Americans today call a blond a *rubia,* a red one.

The Goths were a tall people, that much is agreed upon. They were giants to the Romans, as the Celts and the Scythians and Persians and African Negroes were not. In early illustrations they were a type of German that has changed little in nearly two thousand years: deep-eyed, what can only be described as dished-faced, long of moustache and beard and hair, very tall and straggly, often gaunt, tremendous of hands and feet. The same type appears later, again in popular illustrations, as the Vikings. They are subject to caricature, and their appearance on early murals almost had to be caricatures. Real people could hardly look like that, but we must assume that the caricatures are valid ones. The Goths were of an exaggerated size; and to the Romans they were funny looking.

Strabo, the ancient geographer, writes of two rivers lying near to each other: the Sybaris that makes the horses that drink from it timid; and the Crathis that makes the hair of persons who bathe in it to be yellow. He sets these two rivers in ancient Italy, but the geographer was weak on geography. One of those rivers surely was

in deep Gothia: that which turns the hair of the people yellow.
And in Gothia also there must have been a river of opposite effect
to the Sybaris: one that turned the horses into savage giants.

The elephants that Hannibal had brought over the Alps did not
startle the Romans so much as did the giant horses of the Goths.
The elephants were completely strange, and evoked mere wonder.
The giant horses resembled, to a degree, the Roman horses,
though Pliny believed them of separate species and unable to breed
with each other on account of the great divergence of size. These
giant horses were, to the Romans, a familiar thing gone wrong, an
animal friend cast in a gigantic and frightening aspect—a terror.

The Gothic word for horse, *maran,* cognate to the English mare
though with change of sex, has become an element in the word for
a terror, a nightmare, in several of the Low-Latin languages,
cauchemar, quauquemaire, and has kept its same sense for sixteen
hundred years.

The Roman word for horse, *equus,* was to die out, and *caballus,*
a slang word given by the Romans to the four-footed giants, became the generic word for horse. The new giant men and the new
giant horses came together of necessity. A Roman horse would
have carried with difficulty a heavily armed Gothic knight, and
would not have given sufficient bottom for the using of the heavy
lance. The big northern horse was a draft animal in its development, whereas the Romans used ponies for riding and oxen for
draft. The northern horses were kin to the giant modern draft
horses used into the twentieth century. They were larger than the
Percherons or Clydesdales, as heavy as the Shires and Belgians,
and probably taller than these animals.

The new giant men and horses coming together gave the Romans the impression of a visitation of centaurs; and the male
prowess of the Gothic men went into male legend in terms more
applicable to horses than to men.

The appearance of the new people made one other unusual impression on the Romans. They seemed to the Romans to be furred
animals. The Goths, a very hairy people, dressed to a considerable
extent in furs and skins. They wore the fur of marten, mink, sable,

castor fiber or the old European beaver, fox, wolf, bear. They did not dress in furs from savagery but from something like the modern spirit of advertising. They controlled the fur trade of Europe and they luxuriated in it. But their own extreme hairiness (going from brindled through tawny, roan, red, blond, sandy, tow, straw-colored to nearly white) seemed but a continuation of the furs they wore. There was something artificial-seeming in the wide moustaches and flowing beards and long head hair of the men: and the waist-length, even ankle-length hair of the women. And their coloration seemed too extravagant.

The Goths were not generally referred to as barbarians at their coming, for it was realized that they were no such thing. They were called *Gothi* by the Romans and *Gota* by themselves. In history, they are the West Goths, the Visigoths. And they were not a primitive people.

In many things, especially their handicrafts, the Goths were more advanced than the Greeks and Romans. It is forgotten that in many fields the Greeks and Romans, depending so largely on slavery, did not advance as might have been expected; were sometimes actually adverse to advance. In the larger things, ship-building and military engines and architecture, there had been advance. The Romans had had concrete constructions for nearly five hundred years, while the Goths had been limited to timber and rough stone construction. It is an exaggeration, though, that any of the "barbarians" looked upon the large buildings of the Empire as natural phenomena, like mountains and caves, not built by human hands. It may be that some of them were not properly impressed by this deft hugeness; it may be that some of us are not properly impressed today.

But it was in the smaller and more common things that the Goths and other creative minorities were superior to the Old-Empire people. The wagons and carts of the Goths were better than those of the Romans. Their saddles (with stirrups) and general horsemanship was better. Their rafts and barges and river boats were in advance of those of the Romans—though the Goths had not yet come to lead sheathing of wooden bottoms as the Romans had for

their Mediterranean and other salt-water craft. The carpentry of
the Goths was better, their leatherwork finer, their iron work as
good. Their farming was superior, their plows heavier and de-
signed to turn the deeper furrow required for the heavier northern
land. Their draft animals, their harrow sleds, their scythes and
corn-cradles, their winnows and flails, their corn-drying kilns, were
all superior to anything to be found in the Empire.

The Goths had better axes, shears and scissors, churns, buckets
and barrels, knives and whetstones, forges and anvils, sieves and
querns, better rope and cordage, better harness, better soap and
lye, better spears and lances and armor, better flax and linen, better carpets and cloaks, better shoes and shirts.

They were as good at intrigue and better at logistics than the
Romans.

The cartage of the Goths was so superior that they had become
the haulers and draymen for much of the Roman world. It was the
Gothic firms that controlled the overland freight. They were the
commercial haulers, the expressmen, the wagoners over areas of
thousands of miles. By this enterprise in particular the Goths had
entrée into the Empire for the several centuries before their bulk
colonization.

In another class of trades they were also known. They were the
established—as well as itinerant—blacksmiths, tinkers, sharpeners,
bottomers, peddlers, horse-traders. They served in the capacity of
gypsies to the Romans six hundred years before the gypsies themselves appeared in the same area.

The superiority of the Romans over the Goths would hardly
extend beyond stonemasonry, ship building (but not small-boat
building), wine and olive culture, glassmaking, and the complex
of the arts. But even in these fields it would be found that it was
not the Romans themselves who excelled, but certain specialized
foreign groups within the Empire. If any real superiority of the
Romans over the new races existed, it would seem to be in the
fields of administration, organization, politics, and law. Yet it was
in those very fields that the Goths ultimately defeated and super-
seded the Romans.

The élite among the Goths were literate in about the same per cent as were the Greeks and Romans—somewhere between three and ten men out of a hundred—even during the generations before the Goths crossed the Ister. The surviving account books of the Gothic merchants are in every way better than those of the Greeks and Romans for the same period. The Goths used both Greek and Latin; and also their own language written down variously in Greek, Latin, and Runic letters. The Gothic Bible of Ulfilas used Uncial Greek letters, with several letters from the Latin and Runic alphabets to represent Gothic sounds for which there were no Greek equivalents.

The Goths used a trade-pigin language with a large accretion of Celtic and a barter-equivalent notation that has not been completely unraveled. They were born linguists, as are the Germans and gypsies and Jews and Levantines; as were not the Romans and Greeks, as are not the English and Americans. They are found serving the Romans as translators, of languages other than the Germanic, very early.

The Gothic system of numbers—actually the Runic—was derided by the Romans as no more than notches or tally cuts; yet it was far better than any notation of the classical world. In the fourth century they already had—and it is possible that the whole northern sweep from the Baltic to China had it—a system that would later be introduced into the settled world as the Arabian. Their numbers or marks or tally cuts had *positional value,* as they do with us today, and as they did not with the Romans. A mark could have the value of two or twenty or two hundred, depending on its position. Multiplication could be accomplished in the modern manner, and there was a mark for the zero. With the Romans there was not even an idea of the zero.

The Goths had a seven-day week from their beginning. The Romans had but recently changed from a nine-day to a seven-day week. But the Goths hadn't an accurate calendar; they arbitrarily employed insertion of weeks or longer periods to even up the years.

The Goths had been converted to Christianity in significant numbers about as early as the Romans. At the time of their bulk entry into the Empire—the final third of the fourth century—they stood at about 60 per cent Christian. But with a difference.

There had early been a strong element of Catholic Christianity among the Goths. It would have run to 10 per cent and above in them, as it did also in the Empire in the same early years. But when —early in the fourth century—Christianity moved suddenly to increase its one-tenth to one-half, the increase in the Goths beyond the frontier was in another manner. Ulfilas, a Goth of the Empire and a heretic, appointed himself an apostle to the people of his ancestry. He converted great numbers of them, not to Catholic, but to Arian Christianity.

This is more than a detail. Belloc has written that an Arian world would have been much more like a Mohammedan world than what the European world actually became. Arianism was a rationalizing Unitarian sort of religion, denying the full Godhead of Christ, carefully choosing its nucleus from the great body of Catholic belief. Within the Empire, Arianism was held by a group of intellectuals who maintained a feeling of superiority over the masses. For them it was a half-way house between paganism and Christianity. They would be Christian, but not overwhelmingly so. These intellectuals were a chilly group, but there is one thing that must be said for them. At that time there was still a requirement, since dispensed with, that intellectuals must be intelligent. These were intelligent, as were their Gothic counterparts who also selected Arianism, and for the same reasons. They realized that in accepting Arianism they were not becoming full Christians, and they did not intend to be.

The cult of Arianism—a religion that dies is demoted to a cult —was unsuccessful; but for centuries it served as a compromise between paganism and Christianity. The practice of it can be traced wherever the Goths went, into Provence and Langdoc, Spain and Africa—and the working of it was in truth Mohammedan. Christ was, in effect, the prophet of God, but He was not God. The implications of this difference were great. In action it was as though the women and children were Catholic and the grown men were

Arian; it continues so today in much of Latin Europe and America with the free-thinking husbands and fathers of Catholic families.

One other point about the Goths—they were rich. The Roman officers—assigned to the inspection of the Goths before the Danube crossing—envied them their fringed carpets and their linen garments. Of all the northern people the Goths were richest in cattle. A Roman report claimed, however, that their numerous red cattle had no style to them; were not fine cattle like those of the Romans. The Goths were rich in cattle, horses, sheep and goats, swine, land, and tools. They had wagon loads of gold and silver bar as befitted an organized nation on the march. They had wealth of furs and iron. They had millions of bushels of grain cached along the line of their marches, in caves and earth granaries. The Goths were an anomaly: a pastoral nomadic people who farmed wherever they set down. They had fifty thousand heavy horse wagons. If they had traveled in a single-file caravan, which they did not, their horse-drawn wagons would have stretched out for more than two hundred miles.

The Goths were governed by an oligarchy of noble families, as the Balthi who were descended from bears, and the Amali who were descended from wolves. They elected a king in time of crisis. They did not, however, maintain a king at all times, and it might be several generations between the times of their calling one up.

The early history of the Goths is a fog. Their first sure location was in southern Scandanavia in the last centuries before Christ. Their names are there yet; in Göteborg (Goth town) on the Kattegat at the entrance to the Baltic; and Gothland (Goth land), an island in the Baltic. Gothland in classical times included all of southern and central Sweden and Norway.

The sifting of the legends gives the impression that the basic Goths had been in Scandanavia for many centuries, but that their nobility—which was not entirely of the same stock—had come to them from the sea, and that within generations that could be counted on the fingers of the hand.

A great fermentation was produced by the interaction of the old Goths and the new élite that had arrived overseas. The identity of this refugee nobility defies research. They were even taller, but leaner, than the Goths themselves. They were often dark, and the progeny of the crossed races was often red-haired. The old Goths and the new intrusion did become, more or less, one people; but they became an exceedingly restless people. The sea arrivals, after coming to the Baltic arm of the sea and discovering—to their wonder—that it was fresh water, did not linger more than a century. They were drawn to wander again, and in the ultimate direction of something they remembered strongly. The Gothic nobility, whoever they were and wherever they had come from in the century before the birth of Christ, remembered Rome.

The Goths were one of the few old peoples who had historic memory. The Romans hadn't, in its real sense, until they learned it from the Goths and other outlanders. It is possible that every early people who carried a memory carried it for revenge.

At about the beginning of the Christian era the Goths crossed over to Europe proper and settled in the neighborhood of the mouth of the Vistula. They remained there for more than a century and less than two centuries. Then they began to wander once more, or to scatter. In the two centuries following they occupied land all the way from the German Baltic to the Pontus—the Black Sea. They traveled as a nation of shepherds, farmers, and wagoners. When they set down they would plant barley and spelt. They would remain one, two, or three years in one location—no more; and then move on. There were about a third of a million of them in the main body, which was to be called the West Goths, the Visigoths. The Eastern branch, of identical history before leaving the region of the mouth of the Baltic, wandered even further and were sundered from their Western brothers. This Eastern group became involved with the Huns and went into the composition of that large aggregation of steppe peoples sometimes known as the White Huns.

The heaping up of details may help in comprehending the sort of people the Goths were. They had lived in lands 55° N., and their tradesmen had traveled much further. They were familiar with regions beyond the limits that the classicists had set for the world, and knew there to be mountains and plains where the geographers showed only encompassing ocean. They had seen overhead stars that the Greeks and Romans had seen only in the low north. They may have hunted the last of the European lions, which seem to occur in their mythology. They certainly saw the last of the giant wolves, now extinct. They had known snowfalls of fifty inches, whereas the classical peoples were unfamiliar with anything beyond an inch or two. The Goths were a mountain people to a degree impossible of realization in the south. They knew frozen rivers, torrential floods, tempests, and thunderstorms, and forest fires of thousand-mile fronts. Nature in the south, when they came to it, seemed an incredibly gentle thing.

It is not to be admitted that they were universally behind the classical world in the arts. They carved in wood instead of stone, and so left few remains. The epic poetry, embryonic in them, did not make its full and startling appearance till six hundred years after this time. Though all the epics of Europe, from the *Poema del Cid* through the *Song of Roland* and the *Nibelungen* to the *Eddas,* were strongly Gothic, yet the early development of them either was not written down or was lost; and so cannot be judged.

The Goths were the inspired users of rime. Rime had been grotesque in classical Greek and classical Latin. Yet Low Latin, seeming much the same as classical and having—at first—the identical words and grammar, took to rime as though it were born for it. Vulgate, Low Latin, spoken by a new sort of people, was a new language. It used accent instead of tone and employed a new word order for the new thought pattern behind it. Vulgate Latin, and the Romance languages descended from it, were Gothic languages that happened to be made up of Latin words.

The Goths were not a strange people coming with a strange tongue. They were cousins of the Romans, speaking a language that was a cousin of theirs. It is not known whether the Goths of that day realized the cousinship of their tongues. The Romans certainly never realized it, nor do they to this day. Before the development of Grimm's Law—and the brothers Grimm were the most Gothic of Germans both in their tales and their philology—

the thing could not have been as clear as it is now. But it is seen
more clearly between Gothic and Latin than between modern German and Latin.

The words for close kindred—father, mother, sister, daughter,
brother—would have been recognized as the same; so would the
numbers, and some of the pronouns. Possibly the *k-h* relationship
would have been seen (remembering that Latin *c* was always hard
—a *k*). Latin *caput,* Gothic *haubith;* the head. Latin *cornu,* Gothic
haurna; a horn. Latin *clivus,* Gothic *hlaivas;* a hill. Latin *caecus,*
Gothic *haihas;* blind or purblind.

There are a dozen such corresponding equivalents of letters,
and some of the relationships would have been seen. The Goths,
for all their strangeness, were cousins of the Romans, and their
languages were cousins.

The Goths had no song. This is a Roman statement, and from
the Roman viewpoint it was true. Strabo, the ancient geographer
once more, reported that the Halex River passed through a deep
ravine between the Rhegian and Locrian territories, and that the
grasshoppers on the Locrian bank sing, but the others are mute.
It might be possible that one people would make music and that
an adjacent people would not. It is more likely, however, that
somebody is using a too-narrow definition of song and music. The
Goths did not have song as the Romans had it—odes or canti or
carmines. Their chants were considered a species of shouting, and
their rimed recitations as childish doggerel. They did not have
lyrics—song—in the Roman sense. But they did have tunes; something that the Romans could not comprehend—almost could not
hear.

The Goths had no drama, or none that has left survivals; but
they did have variety shows—almost in the modern manner. These
also the Romans had trouble comprehending. The Goths used
shadow play, hand figures cast by candlelight on linen sheets.
They used ventriloquism in conjunction with this, but they did not
invent it; several ancient peoples used ventriloquism. The Goths
had traveling wagon and tent shows—actual carnivals that followed the great northern fairs. These, and not the bloody busi-

ness in the Circus Maximus and the Coliseum, were the first circuses—as far as the Western World was concerned. The Goths had trained bears and possibly, from one garbled account, trained seals.

The dance is something with no survival, lacking verbal or pictoral record. The Goths may have had it. If they painted, it was not in a medium or on a material that has survived. Their history was unwritten. Their scientific speculation may not have gone beyond mead-table discussions and arguments. There is no record of their early philosophy. Since they were Germans, they must have constructed philosophical systems; and also, since they were Germans, these would have been erroneous.

This is how the Goths came to enter the Roman Empire:

In the second half of the fourth century the movement of the peoples north of the Ister River was complicated by the coming of the Huns out of Asia. The Huns were not more terrible than the West or East Goths, but there were more of them; they were the largest cohesive band of people who had ever appeared on the steppes. They were more mobile than the Goths and others, being basically a movement of horse fighters without families, or with their families left at stations far to the rear. They struck, for a hundred years, in paroxysms of fury interspersed in periods of somnolence.

The agreement now entered into between the West Goths and the Roman Empire concerning the Huns was a simple business agreement and had no foundation of terror or panic. The Romans could have hired troops out of Africa or Spain or Cappadocia or Persia to cope with any sort of situation. They decided to use the West Goths, a people they had not employed before—except for a few thousand adventurers integrated into their legions— a people beginning to have some fame as warriors. Half a century later the Romans would not have been able to arrange support from many sources, but now they could still deal with forces and nations as needed. The Romans contracted with the Goths for a certain job.

The West Goths had offered to maintain the line against the Huns if they were given a topographical basis of operations. They were given the Ister River and the now half-populated provinces directly south of it. They entered on this territory. The Huns, understanding military reality, turned aside at finding the Goths established behind the river. They knew them to be impregnable there; they went and ravaged elsewhere.

It was in the year A.D. 376 of the new era that the Emperor Valens agreed for the nation of the West Goths to cross the Ister River (the Danube) and to settle in Lower Moesia (Bulgaria and Serbia). In the summer and the late summer—the Goths had no word for autumn—of that year, two hundred thousand Goths crossed the river and made their initial settlement near the most southern of the six mouths.

The two hundred thousand Goths were now—by agreement—Romans. This was the largest single entry of outlanders ever to come into the Empire, but actually it was not a great accretion: a fifth of a million people added to the seventy-five million of the Empire.

And in the same year (376) Alaric was born of the Gothic noble family of the Balthi. He must have been born late in that year—after the crossing of the river—for it is always mentioned that he was born a Roman.

It is also said that he was born on an island named Peuce (the fir) at the mouth of the Danube. Whether he was born there or not, it was necessary for his future that he be born there. The coming king of the Goths was to be island born, and he was to come to his people riding on a sorrel mare.

But this was still Roman territory, so he was still born a Roman. The line of the Empire began at the northernmost mouth of the river.

2. About Alaric of Balthi

But if Alaric was born a Roman after the river crossing, how did
he remember the life and the land north of the river? He remembered them from many additional crossings made during his in-
fancy and childhood.

A third of the West Goths had remained in the land north of
the river. The river was an avenue, not a division. Alaric must
have crossed the river many times in his childhood, since his
father was in the business of hauling merchandise and crossing
the river was a main occupation of the family.

The Balthi family, of which Alaric was a member, had been in
the service of the Imperial army even before the Gothic entry
into the Empire. They had been employed in the ferrying and
transportation of whole legions where required. They were contract haulers, of goods, grain, animals, men, or armies.

It was in the transportation of armies that Alaric later came
to excel.

The name of the father of Alaric is in one place given as
Alareidar. This is a doubtful source and nowhere else is he mentioned by name, although he is several times spoken of as the
head of the Balthi family.

Alaric never knew his mother, for one of two reasons. In the
first account she is mentioned as dying in giving birth to him. In
the second account she is mentioned as being taken hostage by the
Romans—along with the wives of a certain number of Gothic

nobles at the time of the river crossing—and as being murdered, along with the other hostages and seized children of the Goths, by the order of Julius, Master General of the Roman troops, in 379 or 380. The theory that Alaric swore an undying hatred of Rome because of the murder of his mother will not stand up. Alaric grew up considering himself a Roman. He considered himself a Roman till the very last, or nearly the last; though he did make symbolic reaffirmation of his Gothic identity before the time of his final assault on the Empire and the City.

Alaric, as a prince of the royal line, was raised by male tutors. But the place of his actual mother was taken by the girl Stairnon in a very peculiar relationship, for she was no more than five or six years his senior. Before it was finished, Stairnon was to be in every relationship to Alaric that it is possible for a woman to be to a man. Stairnon—sometimes called by her Roman-Christian name of Stella or Stella Maris—was a cousin of Alaric. The degree of cousinship is not known. She and her brothers, Athaulf and Sarus and Singerich, were raised in one family with Alaric.

These were all children of extreme talent, and every one was to make a great name in the world. Any one of the five children would have assured for any family remembrance forever. They all set early into a pattern, except Alaric, and what they were in childhood they remained forever.

Singerich, the youngest of all except Alaric—they seemed about the same age—would always be the smallest of the group, though he would be man-sized. He was dark and clever and quick. He was the Goth who became a Greek, and he was born with many of the qualities of that people. It was he who was selected to be taught to read and write, and he learned it in early childhood— later being something of a patron of literary men in Greece. It was felt that even in the noble families one literate member was enough. The others apparently picked up the arts later in life when they had the need for them. Alaric may have learned at the cadets' school, if not before. Stairnon is known to have written many letters and to have aided Alaric in drafting documents. Athaulf, the Goth who remained a Goth, is said to have handled a stylus awkwardly with two hands, and may have mastered no writing but his own name. And there is strong indication that Sarus, when a General, misunderstood the import of written messages more than once. He would half read, half guess, the contents of whatever came to his hand, and he sometimes guessed wrong. The Roman generals, who were sometimes only semi-literate, would always have a scribe trooper by their side; but the Goths were too proud to admit that they did not know everything.

Alaric when small was said to give the impression that he had only two great piercing eyes—no face, legs, arms, body, only eyes. When he developed a body it was at first a very long, stringy one. He was to become the boy giant. He would reach his tremendous height early and then fill out to it, but for the first dozen years of his life he was like an unfledged bird pushed too early from the nest. As a small boy he was a total dunce, despaired of by all except Stairnon, but by the time of his adolescence he developed a tremendous aptitude for learning. He was the only one who learned and changed every day of his life. The rest of them were set in their mold from birth.

Athaulf was huge from childhood—a bear of a boy. When they were grown he was not quite of Alaric's extraordinary height, but seems to have been a much heavier man. He had an amazing intelligence, limited only by his hatreds. In the time of troubles for the disintegrating Empire, he would pull the strings that animated a dozen barbarian nations, and drive the Emperor and Master General frantic. In him most strongly, and in his sister Stairnon to nearly as great an extent, was the old Gothic dream of conquering Rome. But in ordinary things he was a man of fine good humor and amiable nature, a letterless administrator over the affairs of a hundred thousand feral Goths, a military genius in his own right, and the idol of the roughest soldiery in the world. There was never any doubt that he would be and do all these things. He developed in one straight line, and divergence was impossible with him.

Sarus was not to be a giant like his brother Athaulf and his cousin Alaric; but he was as large as the average of his large race and was to be something of a physical marvel. His great strength of hand is mentioned over and over. This is a peculiarity of many very intense men of history who were otherwise but little over the average size. The Emperor Tiberius had it, and William of Falaise. Sarus, when a man, could break horseshoes with his hands. This is a trick which amateur and professional strong men can do today, but the Roman horseshoe—and Sarus was the Goth who became a Roman—was more nearly like a shoe. For reinforcement it had a toe or cusp piece for over the front of the hoof; and from the appearance of surviving shoes it would have taken superhuman strength to bend and break one.

As a man Sarus also performed the feat of lifting a horse, a Roman not a Gothic horse, on his shoulders. He was sometimes called the lion, and he was very cat-like in his motions. His hands and arms were those of Esau, covered with golden hair like fur; and his eyes, like a cat's, are mentioned as looking through, not at one.

Sarus had grave limitations. Though he was to become the finest horseman and the most feared raider in the Empire, he demonstrated a curious incompetence when placed in the command of more than a very few hundred men. In his own specialty he was unequaled, and some of his wild raids were to pass belief. But when he had no clear aim, as when he did not know to whom he owed allegiance as the embodiment of the Empire, he became completely confused. Alaric and Athaulf were to be Kings in their turn. Even Singerich would be King in the weird last seven days of his life; but no one would have offered a kingship to Sarus. In personal combat he was the most feared man in the Empire, but he would not have made a king.

There was great affection among this family—the four cousins of Alaric and himself who grew up with them—with one exception. Stairnon, who was their matriarch from early childhood, loved and was loved by them all. She was an absolute cult with them. It may be for this reason that Sarus and Singerich never married, that Alaric was predestined to marry her, his cousin, and that Athaulf married only after she was dead, though then he married her worst enemy. Between Alaric and his cousins Athaulf and

Singerich and Sarus there was close feeling. This may seem to be contradicted by later conflicts between himself and Sarus, for the conflicts are the stuff of which history is made; but in normal times they were very close. And Singerich, until right at the end, had a real love for all. But there it ended.

The conflict between Athaulf and Sarus was called by Alaric the black shadow over his life. It broke the heart of the Valkyrie Stairnon and helped drive her to her death, and it sent Singerich into fits of weeping—after he had become a Greek. For between the brothers Sarus and Athaulf there was something that went beyond all antipathy and all reason. From the cradle there was red hatred between them. It would be justified later when the two stood as far apart politically as it would be possible for two men to stand—when they represented two different views of a world of which only one could survive.

But in their childhood they had no such reasons. It was a blind and bloody hatred unheard of in children. Three times before they were in their teens they fought to near death. After that it was always assumed that one would kill the other—as was to happen. But they were separated. Athaulf was always thereafter kept with the branch of the family doing business beyond the Danube, while Sarus was kept within the Empire. Stairnon and Alaric and Singerich saw both of them often, but they did not see each other; not until, years later, Athaulf entered the Empire with his army, in the year the world ended, and Sarus followed to kill him before he should reach Alaric at Ravenna—but was unable to overtake him.

These three brothers and their cousin Alaric were the fruit of the Balthi family, one of the most talented kindreds ever.

It is not likely that Alaric would have married Stairnon if they had been within the forbidden degree—closer than third degree of kindred, or second cousin. The Gothic families, particularly the noble ones, were of large accretion, and there were often more than a hundred of them considered as one immediate family. The term brother, also, was used loosely by the Goths. Alaric and Athaulf have been called brothers in several primary sources, though plainly they were not. And several others, of lesser historic importance, have been referred to as brothers of these when only kindred seems to have been meant.

There is also the proposition, which may be the true one, that Athaulf and Stairnon were brother and sister in one family of cousins, that Sarus and Singerich were brothers in a second, and that Alaric was a singleton in a third—therefore, that these were only brothers in the wide Gothic sense. It cannot now be determined, but these five children were all raised in one family, and Singerich and Sarus and Athaulf all called Stairnon their sister; but Alaric called her both sister and wife.

Stairnon, the matriarch of the children, was their undisputed leader. She still dominated Alaric, to a great extent, when he was first put in command of troops and had entered his initial phase of the conquest of the world; when he was just short of eighteen years old.

Stairnon, as the first of the Valkyries, is legendary and so defies description; but it must be attempted. Physically she was magnificent. The Gothic standards, however, were not the modern standards. Alaric was envied for having her, but it is not known if he would be envied today. She was taller than most men of her very tall race, and magnificent of shoulder and arm and breast. The Gothic women went bare in arm and shoulder except for the fur capes in winter weather. She was red-headed, and in her case there was no possibility of the red and the blonde being confused. Her hair was flame-red, and she is spoken of as standing out like a beacon. She wore it to below her waist and it was very heavy. It was once spoken of as of such weight that a Roman woman would not have been able to bear it, but this may have been poetic exaggeration. She was to become a cult with the Goths. But when, in the last years, the goblin girl Galla Placidia called her a holy cow, the blow struck home. But even as a girl she was of this compelling appearance.

Stairnon was the fabulist to the other children. The common heritage of children's stories was already old and known. The Gothic tales were thousands of years old before the latter-day Goths, the brothers Grimm, collected them.

The repertoire of Stairnon consisted of northern fairy tales and Christian legendary, Greek mythos and Hagios and nostos, Gothic airzjanhait—tales of wandering—and Roman fabulae. Storytelling had a large place in a world that was still mostly unlettered, and some of the stories of the steppes had come all the way from China. And all the tales were of lands of wonder.

But, if the lands of wonder to the children of the Empire were the weird exterior lands, those of the Gothic children concerned Rome itself. The Empire was the magic land that they had only begun to taste, the Pandora's Box that would contain all treasures when opened. The glory of the City of the Empire had amazed these northern people for the hundreds of years of their wanderings; and, in some way not understood, they had a folk memory of Rome. The stories of Rome were never entirely believed, just as stories of terrestrial paradises and isles of the blessed are never entirely believed; but much of the stuff of the stories was believed, and much of it was true.

In the tales Rome was always a high-towered city on a tall pinnacle—which it was not; and shone like gold—which it didn't. Rome was mostly built of gray blocks of tufa or slabs of tufa-concrete; sometimes it shone like silver, but not like gold.

But the Goths were never to lose their wonder of Rome, and they have not lost it yet where they remain in Italy, Spain, France, and the Rhineland. Eventually, they made it somewhat into the image they had conceived of it. There was a further element in these stories. The Pandora's Box of the riches of the world belonged to the Goths by right, having anciently been stolen from them. And at the end of their quest the Goths were to recover it.

This is the one fairy tale that really came true. Three of the children, Alaric and Stairnon and Athaulf, would indeed take the city of Rome and open the Pandora's Box of all treasure. But they had misunderstood the ending of the Pandora story. They hadn't known that when the lid of the box was opened the world would come to its end.

But there was still more to this legendry, as created by Stairnon. Alaric was to be the king and conqueror of Rome—Alaric, the most unlikely of them all who was then nothing but an unfledged nester with only a startling pair of eyes. Only a mother or a Stairnon could have preferred the grotesque Alaric in his early stage, but she decided for him; and what she decided was decided for all the children. She decreed that Alaric should be king and conqueror, before he understood what it was to be either. She used the inevitability of this event as a weapon. She was his first oracle, and she gave him his first prophecy that he would take the City. This was some years before a more formal prophecy was given by an official oracle in Latin verse.

She told him that his name Alaric meant the all-powerful, the all-ruling, just as the name of his father, Alareidar, had meant the all-riding, one who excelled in the saddle. She told him that the name Alaric could be given to the scions of only five families in all Gothia. The Balthi were one of the five families from which a king might come.

Stairnon insisted to her brothers, Athaulf and Sarus and Singerich, that they must always defer to Alaric, that he was to be the king and emperor. Neither Athaulf nor Singerich ever swerved in their loyalty to Alaric, or questioned the word of their sister in this, though in many respects both of them had more ability than Alaric. Sarus, however, who had not the high intelligence of his two brothers, was to see a distinction that they missed. Sarus, at one later period acting as spokesman for the generals assembled in Bologna, offered to sponsor Alaric as emperor (and his sponsorship would have made him so), but only on the condition that Alaric *should cease to be King of the Goths.*

If kingship could come to the Balthi, among the five families, it must come to one of these four boys, the princes of Balthi. Stairnon, by her early influence, arranged that the choice should be Alaric. To do this she had to seize on an old legend and make it come true: the legend that the next king of the Goths, island born, would come to his people riding on a sorrel mare.

She announced him King in his eighth year, and fulfilled the legend in this manner:

She had called to him, seeing him on horseback, and he had

cantered to her in a glen. He often dove from the saddle into her arms. He was still a small boy; and she was, too early, a woman.

She told him to come out of the saddle onto her shoulders, and she carried him on her shoulders into camp, announcing that she carried him as King. She had timed it for the afternoon of a great assembly, that he should so come riding the red mare. It was a very Gothic thing to do, but it had Gothic precedent. An early betrothal rite among the Goths had required a girl to carry her man on her shoulders to prove that she was of an age and strength to marry.

The act was accepted absolutely by all the children except one, and the adults remembered it when the time did come to choose a king. Sarus, however, did not accept Alaric completely. Older than Alaric, he had his own ideas about the ultimate kingship. Later, when he became the Empire Goth, he believed that there must not be a Gothic king.

Sarus would several times plant himself as an obstruction in the path of Alaric, and remained unafraid of him. Hafras, writing a few years later, even seems to imply that Alaric was afraid of Sarus. The best of opinion, however, is that Alaric was afraid of no one; that neither of them ever knew fear. The opposition of Sarus and Alaric would become very intricate, and the friendship strained. There would be the accusation of treason; but the question would remain, who was the traitor and who the betrayed? Both boys were to suffer divided allegiance between the Gothic and the Roman in them, but it was Sarus who became entirely Roman when he matured.

There was a strong religious element in the life of the children. The Arian children, like the Catholic, were very close to the Eucharist. This religious element in the life of the Goths and the Romans was more important than it seems, and was the thing that turned many of the Goths into Romans. The Empire had already become a complete Theocracy. It was as totally so as the ancient Jewish state, or as Islam in the years of its explosive activity. It is impossible to get the feel of the period without understanding this. The Empire was Christocentric; though for some, particularly the Arians, Christ was not quite so vividly at the center as for others.

Here it becomes necessary to chronicle briefly the affair between the Goths and the Romans in the early years. The fortunes of the Visigoths, for the first twelve years of the life of Alaric of Balthi (A.D. 376–388), abstracted as simply as possible from the sources, are as follows:

On their entering the Empire the majority of the Goths did not at once settle peacefully on the land of Lower Moesia. Probably neither side expected it to be carried through peacefully. Both the Goths and the Romans defaulted on the terms of their agreement.

The Romans had made the harsh provision, or so it is reported down to us, that the Goths should give up their arms to the Romans on their entry into the Empire, and that the children of the Goths should be taken from them and distributed through the provinces of Asia. The children were to be indoctrinated as Romans, and were to serve both as ambassadors and as hostages of their own people.

The Goths, of course, did not give up their arms. The defence of the border by them was the main part of the agreement for their entry. Neither did they assign all their arms to Roman custody or inspection. For one thing, the Goths were better armorers than the Romans, and a good part of the northern trade had been in arms supplied *by* the Goths *to* the Romans. This mysterious requirement—that the Goths give up their arms—may be a historical misunderstanding of a payment to be made by the Goths in kind—in arms, in the quality of which they exceeded the Romans.

Probably several thousand children of the Goths, but not the fifty or sixty thousand who would have been all the children, were separated from their families for Romanization in groups and centers. It is plain that the Romans intended these to be the children of the noble families, and it is just as plain that the Goths deceived them in this. At least one thousand were taken, for at least one thousand were later murdered by the order of the Master General Julius. It is possible that this taking of the children for a special education was considered as an honor—so considered more by the Romans than the Goths. Provision, apparently, was made for others to be taken at a certain age and for certain periods. Many wives and citizens were also taken as hostages.

The Romans defaulted in their promised treatment of the Gothic settlers. Profiteering at the expense of the Goths was promoted by Lupicinus and Maximus, military officers of Thrace. Instead of assisting in the transition of the Goths, they robbed them and starved them. Supplies brought by the Goths themselves and contributed by their brothers from across the Danube were seized at the inspection points and confiscated or sold at auction for personal profit. Fines were assessed, and Gothic persons were held for money ransom.

At this time Alavivus and Fritigern, called judges, were the leaders of the Visigoths. Fritigern is sometimes spoken of as a kinsman of Alaric, but their relationship, if any, is not known. This Fritigern was an adherent of the Balthi family or party and worked in accord with the Balthi men. The best of belief, however, is that Fritigern was a commoner and not of the Balthi line. He was a man of stubborn ability and much military talent.

Alavivus soon drops out of the picture, and Fritigern becomes the sole effective leader. He did not at once resist with arms, and he forbade the Goths more than local resistance. But he did set up a series of intrigues and was able to reach into the Imperial forces. From the beginning the Goths were able to make contacts where most needed, and they never made a move of any sort before their intelligence system had given an analysis. But it was Fritigern, when he believed that the Goths had absorbed enough abuse, who moved quickly to put a term to the affair.

The first blood of the Gothic revolt was shed at Marcianapolis. Fritigern defeated a Roman force under Lupicinus, and with surprising ease. Fritigern had information that Lupicinus, for all his ability at extortion and deception, was an incompetent general, and that the Roman troops, of adequate quality, would be badly arranged and badly handled. He knew also that Lupicinus was hated by his own men, and that the resistance would be only a token one. Yet the Romans would have been defeated even if

well-generalled and determined. The Goths, in this one action,
established the supremacy of heavy horse troops over even good
infantry, and that supremacy would endure into the time of gunpowder and to the very close of the sixteenth century. Reading
history backwards, it looks as though the events of the next several generations could have been predicted from that one action
alone.

At a little later date, Fritigern won his second victory without
himself being present or his own men being involved. This concerned a move of certain basic Gothic troops of previous intro-
duction into the Empire as mercenaries. There were anti-Gothic
demonstrations, of official or quasi-official instigation, by the
populace of Adrianople. These Gothic troops of the Empire, under
the leadership of Colias and Suerid, swung against the people of
the City and crushed the demonstrations and riots. Then they
came out of the City and joined the forces of Fritigern. This
partly settled the question of where the loyalty of the Roman-
Gothic forces would lie. It would seem that much could have
been predicted by this act also.

A bloody stalemate was then fought between the Romans and
Goths at Salices. This was almost a reversal of the action of
Marcianapolis. Here the Goths encountered Roman soldiers
perfectly commanded, the toughest foot soldiers in the world.
The Goths could not ride them down or run over them as they
had at Marcianapolis; and the old Roman contention was almost
proved—that an absolutely disciplined infantry can stand against
any horse assault whatsoever. It was not conclusive, however; the
Goths had attacked with insufficient forces, and the battle was
fought to a bitter draw. Both sides withdrew in good order to
prepare for the final event. The Emperor Valens collected a size-
able army and moved from Constantinople against the Goths near
Adrianople. And Fritigern assembled his total force for the total
battle.

On August 9 of the year 378 the Goths, under Fritigern, defeated the Romans near Adrianople and killed the Emperor Valens. This should not be told in such a bald fashion, but there exists

no detailed account of the battle. It was surely heavy horse against superb infantry once more, and it was the battle that decided the type of warfare of Europe for more than a thousand years following. The Roman legion in its classical form was made obsolete on that day.

This was one of the most nearly total defeats ever suffered by Roman forces. Its effect on the Roman world was so disorganizing that a gap of several years appears in the chronicles of the Eastern Empire. And the Goths at that time were not keeping chronicles.

The Romans were in total frustration, and in their frustration they now committed a mad-dog act that could have ruined them forever. The Gothic children, and the many Gothic wives and citizens, who had been distributed among the provinces of the East as hostages by order of the Emperor Valens, were now slaughtered in a horrible massacre. The numbers were not great, but something over one thousand. They were executed in a dozen cities by order of Julius, Master General of the Roman troops. The move could have torn the entire Empire apart.

The Roman Empire of the East had had its central army destroyed, and no force had yet been brought from the Western Empire. The Goths were in control of the countryside, and the people of the cities had no defence against slaughter by the Goths. It still is not understood why the Goths forbore.

There were only two things that the Romans could now do. They could mass all the forces of both the Eastern and Western Empires and fight a war that might have lasted a generation and might have finished the Empire forever. They could make the great effort to eradicate and destroy the sudden Gothic power that was now in the middle of them.

Or they could practice the seemingly impossible policy of containment. The policy of containment was decided on, or at least it worked itself to the fore. The Romans could still find the ability to deal with the most difficult situation in the manner that events would prove to be the successful way. And now the perfect instrument for the policy of containment appeared—one Theodosius.

The Emperor Gratian of the West, nephew of Valens the dead Emperor of the East, acting on unknown but sound advice, brought Theodosius from an exile in Spain, and proclaimed him Emperor of the East. Theodosius had been a general and the son of a general. His father had fallen out of favor and been executed but—a sign of the improving of the times which no longer carried death to the descendants—Theodosius had been allowed an honorable exile instead of destruction. It points up either the urgency of the situation or the good sense of the Western Emperor Gratian, that he should call on the son of the man his father had killed a half dozen years before and place complete trust in him. And it is a sign of the hold that the idea of Empire had over the Romans of the day that Theodosius should have been willing to forget past treatment of his family and accept the high office coupled with the nearly impossible task.

Recalled from his Spanish farm to begin his second career, Theodosius was now thirty-three years old and was possibly the most competent man in the Empire.

The historian Gibbon states it simply: "The general or rather the final capitulations of the Goths may be dated four years, one month, and twenty-five days, after the defeat and death of the Emperor Valens."

What happened in the four years, one month, and twenty-five days was a miracle of containment, the perfect use of negotiations and the force of arms available, infinite patience, and the triumph of the still-powerful idea of Empire; and the inculcating in the Goths of that idea. The new Emperor Theodosius fought few battles with the Goths, and won none; but his policy somehow succeeded. He established himself in Thessalonica, the capital of Macedonia, and gave orders for the re-establishment and strengthening of the garrisons of Constantinople and Adrianople. He built up and negotiated and avoided conflict. On the death of the Gothic leader Fritigern—and there has never been a hint that it was other than a natural death—the more stubborn elements of the Goths subsided.

Then came the coup. Athanaric took over the leadership of the Goths; and he listened to the proposals of the Emperor Theodosius. He came as guest to that Emperor in Constantinople, and was given a royal welcome. But two weeks later he was dead. Here, at least, there have been certain hints that the death may not have been a natural one.

However it was done, it was done neatly.

It may have been at that early date that the family of the Balthi moved to the fore in the Gothic esteem. One of the five families of the Goths, the Abrasi, was discredited by Athanaric. The Amali, the first of the families, had remained outside the Empire and had become affiliated with the Huns. The Skeirasi had an impediment in their reputed cruelty and greed, and would not be accepted by the commoners. And the Ansti had remained steadfastly pagan. It would be the Balthi who would next be called upon to raise up a great leader; but first the Goths must doze for a dozen years.

Theodosius, the Emperor, however, did not doze. Athanaric had not been popular, and the intrigues and negotiations of Theodosius began to pay off. The independent secondary leaders of the Goths, first one and then half a dozen of them, came in and made separate treaties with the Emperor. They felt themselves leaderless. As they were now Romans as well as Goths, Theodosius was their Emperor also. They found good faith in the new Emperor; as had not always been the case with the Emperor Valens, and seldom with his deputies. It was late in the year 382 that peace and symbiosis were achieved.

The whole Gothic army, in one form or another, was now enlisted under the Roman standards. The Goths now thought of themselves as Romans, particularly the younger ones. There was not then a strong feeling of nationality among the Goths, only of family among their élite. When Stairnon and Alaric, manipulated by Athaulf from beyond the frontier, brought about a Gothic national feeling a few years later, it was not so much a revival as a creation. And against this would be the strong feeling of the Goths for the Empire—as the motherland of all Christians and as the essence of what was called The World.

The uneasy but workable Gothic-Roman peace was built up for the following several years. The Emperor Theodosius made one very wise move for the Romanization of the Goths, although it was only a revision of a very foolish move that the Emperor Valens had made for the same purpose. We come onto the new device immediately, and the effect it had on Alaric of Balthi and others.

Meanwhile, the Goths achieved stability and thrived on their lands in Moesia. They were probably the best farmers in the Empire when the peaceful spirit was on them.

3. Of the School for Generals

One of the projects for the containment of the Goths which was now set up by the Emperor Theodosius had to do with Gothic youth. This, in a way, was a continuation of an ill-fated project of the Emperor Valens. But, whereas Valens had taken thousands of youths—and those not picked, though he had intended that they should be—Theodosius took only dozens, and those most carefully selected.

Nor were they only Goths. There were Vandal children and youths; Celts and Burgundians and Lombards; Sarmatians, Armenians, Suabians, and "White Huns." There were Saracens and Ideumeans; Africans and Mauretanians and Tarraconese-Spanish, and others. These were the children of the leading families of the new races and the imperfectly assimilated races, taken partly for hostages, but mostly to form them into a mold sympathetic to the Empire. It was realized by the Emperor Theodosius that from these few dozen young men would come the rulers of the world; they would no longer come from the old Roman lines. If these boys could be formed in Christianity, prudence, courage, and foresight, then the Empire would go well.

For all the different nations represented by the youth in the school, however, it was the Goths who came to the fore—as they now came to exceed in all military matters in the Empire. The Goths were few in numbers—a fifth of a million beings among the seventy-five million of the Empire; but even these figures give no

idea of the discrepancy. The great soldiers of the Empire came
only from the élite of the Goths—that strange nobility of great
families. And this élite numbered, in all, less than one thousand
persons.

From this group the names have come down to us, through
fifteen and a half centuries of poorly-kept records, of more than a
hundred Gothic men who were master generals, generals, or soldiers of great note. This is more than one male out of every five
of their group. In that one generation they comprised more than
half of the soldiers of the Empire whose names have survived to
us.

All, of course, did not attend the School for Generals; but at
least one-third of the great Gothic name soldiers did attend.

The Emperor was a good man who was subject to serious failings—physical, mental, and moral. The nature of his physical fail-
ing has not been accounted to us, and the hints are too meager to
establish even a surmise. He was a man of extraordinary strength
and vigor, but there would be days and weeks when he was physically prostrated and could not act at all. He was a man of acute
mind and rapid accurate judgment. Nine times out of ten he would
arrive at a correct decision instantly, implement it, and dispose of
the most difficult affair unerringly. But the tenth time he would arrive at no decision at all—not ever. Hesitation, on the rare occa-
sions that he was subject to it, turned him into a pathetic failure.
The man whom he selected as his first assistant in all matters, the
Pannonian Vandal Stilicho, was to have a touch of the same
failings.

Theodosius was capable of furious anger and of ordering horrifying massacres. He was also capable of the most sincere penance
and restitution. He was never able to restore his victims to life,
but he did pray for their souls and care for their survivors. He did
public penance by the order of the Archbishop Ambrose of Milan,
and thereafter that prelate increased his already strong hold over
the Emperor.

Emperor Theodosius is shown on coin and medallion to be a
handsome man, though somewhat wooden. It is not known how

much of this was the man himself and how much was the convention of representing emperors. All of the fourth-century emperors resemble each other in their faces on coins, and they were not all of one kindred. Theodosius had a clear penetrating voice, but keyed too high. As Emperor he had a mincing way of walking which was incongruous in such a large man, and which was burlesqued by his enemies. He had not had such a mannerism when he was a soldier, and he had been a great soldier. There is some likelihood for the belief that he was often in physical pain when he moved; that perhaps he had suffered rupture or wound or disease and could go in no other way. His movement was clearly not an affectation. He seems to have ridden horseback with more ease than he walked. He had served in Britain and Spain, and may have served in Greece also before his accession to Emperor. His estates were in Spain—he was called Spanish and was known at a later date to have cousins still in Spain; but he could have been of an old Roman line for all that. Area of origin, at that time, had a very loose connection with lineage.

But the basic fact about Theodosius was that he understood himself and all his failings. He was sincere in his wish to build up a nucleus of future leadership that would be more stable than he was himself, though he could not honestly see how it might be more successful than he had been. From the picked youths of the nations within the Empire, he intended to fabricate an instrument that would continue the Empire forever. The Empire, to him, was a main part of religion and the faith; and he believed that the acceptance of the Holy Empire should be a part of the creed.

Alaric of Balthi came to the Imperial School when he was twelve years old. With him were other noble Gothic youths, Hafras and Vargas his friends, and Sarus his cousin who stood in the position of a rather critical older brother. Athaulf and Singerich had been held back. The Balthi family did not intend to give all their princes as hostages. Athaulf, in fact, had already been sent to a branch of the family still living beyond the Danube; and he would not come into the Empire again until he came in to destroy it. The sending of Athaulf was, to the Balthi, as important as the sending of Sarus and Alaric. The family did not neglect its ties with the Goths living beyond the Empire.

Alaric attended the School, along with an extraordinary group of superior students, for about five years. At the end of that time Alaric, still short of eighteen years old, was to be given the command of ten or twelve thousand men in a bloody key operation of a critical civil war. This was not foreseen, but both the material and the instruction had to be superior to make such a thing possible.

The School itself was sometimes at Constantinople, sometimes at Adrianople; in garrisons and barracks and field; and in an academy. It was sometimes on the frontiers and, at least twice, beyond. Part of the courses may have been held in Italy.

When Alaric commanded troops in Italy, in his eighteenth year during the Civil War, it was said that he had been in that country before; just when is not known.

The youths received instruction in all types of warfare and in nearly every sort of weapon. The javelin seems to have been an exception. The Roman *pilum,* the javelin, had last been used at the fiasco of Marcianapolis. The sardonic laughter of the Goths, at the sight of such a weapon, can still be heard by one who has the ear for such things. The javelin had been a survival of the boyhood of the Roman people, and was on par with the slings of the Balearic people. It was a hunting weapon of the early countrymen soldiers, but it had no place in serious warfare. A Roman could throw but one to three javelins, and then stood naked of missiles; a Gothic archer could loose ten arrows in about the same time—more accurate and of much greater penetrating power.

The boys learned the correct use of the lance, pike, halberd-axe, long-sweep sword from horseback, short sword for afoot, heavy mace to break spear-armed infantry squares, short bow, and long bow. They learned horsemanship of the Gothic, Hunnic, and Saracen styles and worked out an effective combination of these. They learned about siege engines and circumvallation and entrenchment.

They were taught by experts of every sort and overseen by men

interested in developing new tactics. The Romans, still the fastest
men with a blade ever, gave instruction to the powerful outlander
youths. There were seasoned Gothic and Hunnic warriors in service at the School who were as good with the long-sweep sword as
the Romans were with the short sword, and who were of the two
peoples who had simultaneously brought horse warfare to a finesse
that it had never known before. There were archers from Scythia
who had made the use of their weapons an art. There were armorers who invented and tested various devices with the youths of the
school.

There was a more-than-Spartan cult of physical culture, with
many of the instructors from old Sparta itself—though the city had
shrunk to a village. Wrestling had always been the soldiers' sport;
now it became a daily occupation of forced excellence. One who
excelled in this was the Gothic boy Sarus, already called the lion.
He had a speed and a ferocity and a strength of hand that would
make any other boy cry out in pain. Years later, after Alaric had
gone from being the Boy Giant to being the gigantic King of the
Goths, Sarus could always make him back off with a good-natured
offer to hand wrestle.

The cadets were instructed in field and by book in every subject
that might be important to a general, in a day when any general
might be called upon to take charge of the entire Empire. They
heard lectures from some very great men; and from one unusual
man who might seem an odd choice to address the future generals.
This was Eutropius, the intricate eunuch of the Eastern Court. He
lectured them in this manner, or in this manner as recollected by
Hafras half a century later, for we have this account from him:

"We will discuss what it is by which a man excells," the eunuch
told them, "and why, out of the forty million men in the Empire,
there are scarce forty of any competence at all; and not one—not
even our Emperors of the East and West, for I am no sycophant—
not one man of complete competence. We will discuss the ideal of
complete competence, the attainment of partial competence, and
the question whether the basis of this competence is of necessity
so narrow as it has been in fact. Competence is merely the man-

agement of men, and the navigation of the tide of affairs. It should
not be so rare as it is. Failure in the management of men cannot
be compensated for by success in all other things.

"A man may be proficient in all the arts and philosophies; he
may have the amenities; he may have scope and balance, and a
strength of hand and mind; he may understand history like the
back and the front of his own hand—what has been, and what will
be; but with all this he may, or may not, have a measure of competence. There are many elements in the complex, and the lightning
cannot be compelled to strike. But remember that it is more likely
to strike the high eminences than the flatlands of humanity. The
more parts of the man there are present in him, the more it is possible that he will be formed into a full man.

"We are most of us Christians—as it is now the fashion to be.
But we must realize that both Fate and Fortune are deities of an
older Theology. We must not believe that our Faith inhibits us from
hazarding for the higher fortune. Every man has an ordained place
in the world. Some of you will have very high places; one or more
of you may some day have the very highest. Now let us understand several things. Cruelty in those of high station may not be
the same thing as in lesser men. Murder is reprehensible in one of
the common sort. To the State itself, or to a judge, or a regent, it
may become a necessary execution. A man of real competence is
entitled to consider himself as a judge, as a regent, as a State. A
man of competence is a public thing. He cannot consider his affairs as private, even to himself.

"Your Christian Faith teaches you why you are in this world—
to serve God. But the thing you must teach yourselves is that the
highest service is to excel. It was to excel in everything that comes
to your hand that you were born into this world. If you do not
excel, then you were born in vain.

"You are all of you born into the Line, or you would not be
here. No well-governing son ever came from inferior parentage.
It cannot happen. You may hear that some sudden General is the
son of thieves and robbers. Believe me, if he is a competent Gen-

eral, then he is the son of competent thieves and robbers, at least."

Eutropius the eunuch talked to them in this fashion and fired in them the desire for competence. The eunuch of uncertain ancestry was enamored with the aristocracy. Not himself born into the Line, he believed that to be born into the Line was everything. It was not an orthodox Christian morality that he preached to the cadets; it was the morality that had been distilled in the mind of the Emperor Theodosius. There is a close similarity between all statements of Theodosius and of Eutropius the eunuch who served him; and for a reason. The thoughts were from the Emperor, but the words from the eunuch. Eutropius was speech-writer for the Emperor for the sixteen years of his reign.

Alaric, coming into his thirteenth year, was a master of horse. He had suddenly changed form and acquired the beginnings of his authority. In their earlier months at the school, while Sarus had already been named the lion, Alaric had been called the *struthio,* the ostrich. This was from his general stringiness and his bird-like head with its piercing eyes set atop his long neck. But now, at the coming of his adolescence, he developed a sort of animal magnetism and became a leader—though still of grotesque appearance. In several years he would become the Boy Giant, but the transition was painful. Alaric was made master of horse for his new qualities of leadership—even over boys of a much greater age. He would never be the horseman his cousin Sarus was, but he was already a leader such as Sarus could never be.

And at the school they were doing things with horses that had never been done before, neither by Goth nor Roman nor Sarmatian. It is said that the heavy mail-clad Sarmatian and Gothic horsemen, armed with heavy lance and long sword, were the true ancestors of the later medieval knights—even having their appearance. They were not the ancestors of the knights, they were the knights themselves; but with a discipline that the medievals would have forgotten. They were stirruped and saddled and pommeled, and mounted on horses heavy enough to make the effective use of heavy lances possible.

It has been written seriously that there were no stirrups before the year 600. But the ornate silver-chased stirrups of that time, the earliest that we possess, had certainly a long ancestry behind them. Rope-sling stirrups, at least, were used from the Baltic to China, as they are still used on much of that steppe land today. Without stirrups a horseman could not retain his mount under the shock of a heavy lance thrust, and the Goths and half a dozen other peoples from the North did use heavy lances.

The technique that was now put together, by the instructors and youths at the School, was superior, not only to anything that had gone before, but to anything that was to come after. The Roman legions had always been insufficient in cavalry; and the Goths had relied on it too heavily. A balance was found now—the perfect employment of heavy and light horse with the orthodox foot legions. The horse-madness of the Goths was a new element. It had broken the Romans at Adrianople and obsoleted the primarily foot legions. The Empire had to adopt it or go down to it.

The tacticians at the School integrated not one but three techniques of cavalry: the very heavy horse of the Goths that could carry heavy men in armor to break the center of a line; the medium horse of the Huns combining speed and power in kaleidoscopic attacks that dazzled and routed; the light horse of the Saracen-Arabs of incomparable speed and ferocity. It is significant that Sarus, when he had become the most feared raider in the Empire, would use all three types in his very small bands.

The boys of Alaric's sort quickly learned the discipline and the patterns and worked well with the diversified groups. They already had the horse-madness.

The Gothic youths learned infantry tactics. They mastered the complete circumvallation of the Romans and walled and trenched camps for even a one night stand. These gave a backing and a sure base for the line. Complete routing of a force with such a camp at its back is almost impossible, and such a camp established the battle site. In the several conflicts between the Romans and the

Goths, it had always been the case that the Goths reached the battle line after a long and brutal uphill charge, to meet the waiting and rested Romans with a fortified camp at their backs. The fact that the Goths had triumphed more times than not was due to their superiority in strength and determination, not to their tactics.

The boys were serious and the instructors, devoted. What was fashioned here, out of the already superior Roman legions and the best of devices from outside the Empire, was a really professional military tactic. The Roman force, at the time of its defeat by the Goths at Adrianople, was not in decline; it was an incomparably finer force than anything that the Republic or the early Empire had devised.

But Alaric and his Goths had intuitive knowledge of military aspects that were completely beyond the scope of the Romans, then or ever. He understood the organization of companies and bands as well as any Roman, being of the race of convoyers and wagon-train masters. He knew the advantage of raiding down from mountains and Alps as a hawk strikes out of a cloud. The Romans could construct no camp as well-walled as a mountain. Of wagoning in mountains he had generations of knowledge—of the wagon winch and windlass and sling-drops that permit baggage vehicles to be lowered down cliffs; of cordage and tackles and hoists; of tall stripped trees to serve as masts and gin poles for the swinging of wagon after wagon over impossible chasms. He knew, as all the Goths knew, that a heavy army with heavy equipment can be moved over any space of land, mountain, swamp, river—or sea.

The Goths could cross country that the Romans could not—that the Romans did not regard as fit habitation for man or army. The Goths would always be able to outflank the Empire by coming at it over the forbidding areas that the Romans did not believe needed guarding. That is why Alaric believed, later, that he could penetrate even the unpenetrable fortress city of Ravenna. There is likelihood that he could have, but for the unforeseen change of status.

The "primitive" Goths of the school now learned another instrument of war from the Romans—a most primitive one—the human voice. None had used the voice quite as the Romans had. Others used heralds, but others did not use the voice of the commander himself to the same extent. The Goths had used horns and trumpets with coded calls and orders. They learned from the classic Romans to go back to the more primitive and effective instrument.

The Roman legions moved to the sound of trumpets, but that was only for the march beat. In conflict they obeyed the human voice of their commander. A legion with auxiliaries, special guards, slaves and dignitaries, followers and provisioners, might total twenty thousand persons. A well-voiced man, even in the open air, can address twenty thousand persons assembled for an oration. It is another matter to have voice command over them in scattered battle array. But it was done by the commander and his centurions. A legion worked better under this direct voice command, and for this reason the cultivation of the voice was given high place. To the Romans, the great voice was a part of complete manhood. Every Roman commander had to be an orator, and every Roman orator had been a commander.

Tully (Cicero) had been proconsul of Cilicia, and concomitant to this office he had commanded troops. Every great orator of the Romans had commanded troops at some time in his career. This ability of voice command of troops was a primitive advantage that the Romans retained to the last.

Alaric, who was now becoming the Boy Giant, had this powerful voice, and it was partly because of this that he was so early given a command over his fellow students. Others of the Goths never acquired it, not even the intrepid Sarus. We shall see how, on the walls of Ravenna, the voice of Sarus broke and he had to turn the invective over to a herald.

The Emperor Theodosius visited the cadets many times and instructed them at length, on at least one occasion giving them the basis of his idea of Empire. He told them simply that the Empire was ordained by God. That God had a representative on earth, and that he sat in Rome, the heart of the Empire. He told them that Christendom *was* the Empire; that it was the world itself, and the highest handiwork of God. He told them that if the Empire should ever fall, it was the world itself that would end: that their life was not their own; that they were the stewards but not the proprietors of their own bodies; that these belonged to the Empire, and through the Empire to God.

This was neither the established nor the universal view; nor was it the Catholic view. But it was the Catholic view as interpreted by the Emperor Theodosius, and perhaps by the Archbishop Ambrose of Milan since these two were very close. St. Ambrose believed the preservation of the Empire to be of the utmost importance, and he had impressed his view on the Emperor—the one person able to implement it. It was an extreme view and would do much mischief in history—when such divine sanction came to be applied to lesser entities than the Empire.

The temporary continuance of a cult is insured by the adherence of even one important convert. Theodosius had already found that convert in one Stilicho. He had impressed his Empire outlook on that great—or soon to be great—Master General. And among the cadets of the school, the Emperor made other converts —assuring that his view would continue for at least another generation.

A young Hun named Uldin and a young Goth named Sarus were possessed of the idea like fire. Both were of the princely line and would be important, and both would give their whole lives to it till it burned them to death.

Bacurinius, the son of a great Spanish general, was likewise captivated by the idea, as was Vargas—another young Goth. They would be the first of the cadet group actually to suffer death for that emblazoned idea of Empire.

Alaric of Balthi was also strongly taken by the idea of the divinely constituted Empire; and he might have followed it as fervidly, as did his cousin Sarus, had not another influence, at the same time, come to bear. This was a reassertion of the oldest influence on him, and it tended to carry him in a divergent direction.

Alaric received letters from his cousin Stairnon, who still considered herself as something of a mother to him. She wrote to him in Greek, possibly to test the knowledge that he had acquired, or was supposed to have acquired, at the Imperial School. These letters, from the portions that are later quoted by the epistolatory Hafras, have a mystic sweep to them. In one of her earliest letters she refers to her "tall sisters" as a part of his mission. Stairnon, as far as is known, had no blood sisters; and Alaric, in all probability, was not yet conscious of having any mission. These sisters were to appear later in the Alaric mythos, sometimes as streaming-haired women in the clouds, sometimes as wraith-like women coming onto the battlefield and swooping up the dead Goths in their arms. They are a prefiguration of the Valkyries; and Stairnon, who employed a passionate mystique in a calculated manner, may have been in the process of inventing a legend. But to complete the invention it would be necessary that she live it through.

In her letters she reminded Alaric constantly that he would be—that he already was—a king. The kingship of Alaric was also an invention of hers and was the one that she would never give up.

Alaric's own ambition was to be *magister militum,* master general, master of troops of the Empire. He considered this the greater thing. In the two halves of the great Empire there should never be more than four *magistri* at one time, though in practice there were sometimes more who used that title, rightly or wrongly. In practice there was no higher office than master general—except emperor.

But Stairnon insisted on the kingship—and the kingship alone—with an intensity that shocked Alaric.

"We are, and shall be, King," she wrote.

This one sentence, in rude Gothic, stood out like a beacon in a graceful Greek letter. The "we" that she used was a peculiar form. It was the most intimate word in any language, more personal even than "thou." It was the Gothic *vit,* the dual-person form—"we two," "the two of us—one." It was a plural or dual form that took singular modifiers and presupposed a relationship so intimate that it could not be expressed in any other language.

It was to the kingship that Stairnon impelled Alaric. And the idea of kingship and that of the divinely constituted Empire were opposed.

The cadets of the School, who were to be so instructed that each should be able to administer the Empire if called upon, had become polyglot. This is a requisite for competent men of every time and place. Two forms of Greek were learned—the Grand, and the Demotic; two forms of Latin—the Classical, and the Low or Vulgate. Aramaic had remained the soldiers' language of the Asian provinces, and Alaric found a certain pride in speaking the language that Christ spoke.

The boys were even reinstructed in their own Gothic—which their nation had begun to let fall into disuse in favor of the Low Latin. They also employed a sort of soldiers' German that was understood by the East and West Goths, the Vandals, the Rhaetans, the Lombards, and the Burgundians; it was even used by the Celts and Scythians and "White Huns"—that mixture of the Asian Huns and the steppe peoples, the East Goths and the Slavs.

Rhetoric and eloquence were taught to the cadets, as was administration. So also were the arts of dissimulation and intrigue. And, as most of them were of courtly families, it was necessary that they know *The* Court.

The cadets became intimates with the Royal Family, with the Emperor himself, and his children and wards. Alaric, the Boy Giant, was a favorite of these. When they dealt with him, later in life, it was not as with an alien stranger or barbarian; but as with a childhood familiar—for good, or for bad.

4. Of Master General and Boy Giant

The cadet group to which Alaric belonged was instructed several times by the Emperor Theodosius himself, and once by a man who may have been even greater than the Emperor—the Master General Stilicho.

Alaric, himself a German and a Vandal, looked at this man Stilicho and knew he had found his equal. Alaric, in his sudden awakening during adolescence, had believed himself to be without equal. To the mind of Alaric, Stilicho was the only equal he would ever encounter, and the confrontation was startling. Stilicho was a man, and Alaric still a boy. But they recognized each other for what they were, and what they would be after the Emperor Theodosius was gone—the only two of first magnitude in the Empire.

They would be allies; they would be conspirators with and against each other; they would be enemies; and, finally, they would be friends. Each was to attempt to hunt the other to his death; but they were to do it openly with a sort of rogues' honor. Alaric knew at once that he would never be able to realize his full goal—the goal that had been insinuated into his mind by Stairnon and the distant Athaulf—so long as this man Stilicho lived. Yet, when it came, the achievement of that goal would be only a side issue to Alaric's revenging the murder of Stilicho.

Achilles, for his fame, had the poet Homer of the Golden Age. Stilicho had his Claudian of the Age of Pewter. It is not certain that Achilles was the abler soldier of the two. And it is not absolutely certain—though it tastes of blasphemy to write it—that Homer was the better of the two poets.

The Master General practiced forms of warfare incomparably more intricate than anything that Achilles could have dreamed of. And the verse of Claudian has meaning on so many levels that it will never be all unraveled. This verse could not have the wide acceptance of that of Homer. It was really for a private audience; but Homer, had he been contemporary of Claudian, would have been of that audience and would have admired it.

In Claudian there are strata of encomiumia, of panegyric, of irony, of satire, of burlesque, of cipher within cipher. And the cellar of his meaning has scarcely been explored at all. Claudian wrote for a private world which, for all its narrowness, may have been the most literate world that even existed. And the barbarian Stilicho was a full member of that world.

Claudian was the unofficial poet laureate when Stilicho was the unofficial Emperor. Countless details of this study are out of Claudian, either direct or at second hand. For many of the events there is no other source.

The Master General Stilicho was by blood a Vandal, of the people who rivaled the Goths as the most intrepid of all the Germans. He is sometimes spoken of as a man without a father, a new man; and yet his father had been an officer of barbarian cavalry serving the Emperor Valens.

Stilicho was a very tall man. His poet Claudian was extravagant in his praises, but he was not foolishly extravagant. Claudian would not have described Stilicho as taller than the demigods if he had not been very tall. He would not have told of crowds gaping in astonishment at Stilicho if Stilicho had not been, to some extent, an astonishing figure. Lacking the measure of them, it is difficult for us to appraise the stature of ancient men—when all the heros were said to be very tall; and when the Romans, who were the standard, were quite short. Athaulf, for instance, is once described as being exceptionally tall, but not so tall as his cousin and brother-in-law Alaric. And Alaric and Stilicho, at the preliminaries to the action of the battle of Aquileia and Frigidus, are described as staring each other in the faces, above the heads of their tall soldiery.

Stilicho—whose forename was Flavius, as whose was not in that day—was raised in the service. As a young man he was famed as a horseman and archer. In Persia he had learned a manner of using the bow that was new to the Romans, and he employed a bow of his own height. He is said to have been able to bend a stronger bow than any other man in the Empire; but the same thing has been said of at least three other men in the same decade.

Stilicho had captured the interest of the Emperor Theodosius, and he may have been known to Theodosius during his first career as General. The Emperor speaks of Stilicho as an old comrade-at-arms, by which he can hardly have referred to the no-battles and intrigues by which they had effected the containment of the Goths. They were comrades once more, though usually separated by several thousand miles. Theodosius, a very peculiar man in his second career as Emperor, had only two real intimates: the Archbishop Ambrose of Milan, and the Master General Stilicho. But it was not for friendship; it was for real ability that Stilicho had been moved up from office to office. The Emperor had recognized him as an indispensable man.

Stilicho had been dispatched to negotiate a treaty with the rulers of Persia. The Roman Empire could no longer maintain any sort of warfare on that far frontier. Although Persia was not, in that generation, as formidable as she had been, the Romans were unable to support real commitments there. It would not have mattered whether the distant Roman adventures resulted in defeats or victories—the results would have been equally weakening. Rome could not afford even cheap victories beyond so distant a frontier.

Stilicho allowed himself a year to it, handling the high dealings with ease, but not with speed. He allowed himself, at this time, the only period of real luxury in his life. And he successfully negotiated a treaty, one that would stand. This was at the time when the Persians were the most skillful negotiators in the world—in the very time that they were feared as soldiers less than formerly. It was also a time, as the Persians pointed out, when the Romans were feared less—due to the loosening of the bonds of Empire and the assaults on a dozen different frontiers.

By this treaty Stilicho secured a quiescent frontier at the time when the maintenance of another legion-consuming frontier would have ruptured the Empire fatally. Stilicho also made a life-long friend of the second most powerful man in the world, the most powerful outside of the Roman Empire, Jezdegerd who would soon inherit as Pad-Shah or Emperor of Persia. Stilicho had dealt with the strong man Jezdegerd as Emperor before he was so in fact; and Jezdegerd would come to consider Stilicho as the only Emperor of Rome, though he was never that in name.

On his return to Constantinople Stilicho received an award, the high office of Master General. And he received a more direct sign of the complete confidence of the Emperor Theodosius—he became a member of the royal family. Stilicho at this time married Serena, the niece and adopted daughter of Theodosius. He thus became son-in-law of the reigning emperor and was considered brother-in-law or uncle extraordinary to the two sons, the two future emperors. To one of these he would also become father-in-law. Stilicho was destined to be the guardian of two emperors and the father of two empresses.

Serena was born in Spain, was the daughter of the first Honorius, who was the brother of Theodosius. Serena came to Constantinople after the death of her father and was adopted as a daughter by her uncle the Emperor Theodosius.

Serena was the oldest and most attractive member of that group of children in the royal household; the others being her step-brethren and cousins—the bewildering girl Galla Placidia and the two future emperors, Arcadius and Honorius. She was called mother by these two young princes, and was to be twice the mother-in-law of one of them as the bonds of the families continued to multiply and tighten.

Serena was to play the role of mother, aunt, cousin, and sister to all three of the children. It was a thankless role, as it happened. She was to be murdered on the secret orders of one of them, with the active connivance of the second, and by the tacit consent of

the third. But now she was married to the Master General Stilicho.
And now that man, during the time of the student days of Alaric,
had come to Constantinople to report to the emperor on the state
of the frontiers.

It was on this visit, during which he instructed the cadets at
the School, that Stilicho was made effective heir to the power of
Theodosius. The Emperor knew that his two young sons would
never be persons of great moment in their own right. For this
reason Theodosius gave a peculiar title to his Master General.
Stilicho was made "guardian" of the two future emperors as well
as "guardian" of the double Empire itself. It is said that Theodosius knew, years in advance, the day and the hour of his own
death. It appears as though he did, for no man ever took such a
series of precautions, progressively over the years, for the care
of his inheritance. But his choice of Stilicho as guardian was a
good one.

Stilicho was an honest man. When every other person involved
in this study—Alaric himself, Athaulf, Emperor Honorius, Emperor Arcadius, Pope Innocent, Sarus, even Serena, Attalus,
Olympius, Galla Palacidia—all showed flaws of character wide
enough to lose an Empire in, Stilicho stood out as the only absolutely honest person in the complex; and he had to die for it.

But now both the Master General Stilicho and the Emperor
Theodosius were still very much alive and were about their business of restoring the World.

Stilicho talked calmly to the cadets one day and night—for the
last part of his discussion was held about a camp fire in a low
creek after dark. They were in the field—off from the city two
dozen miles. Alaric and the other Gothic youths, Sarus and Hafras
and Vargas; the Hun Uldin, the Vandal Respendial, the Spaniard
Bacurinius, the African Heraclian; Gauls and Celts and Arabs, all
got something from the calm and powerful man. Among the
listeners of Stilicho was a boy who, as a man, would kill him; there
were three future kings; there was a young man who would be pretender emperor; and there were two dozen generals in the egg.

Stilicho first talked of himself; and then of the Empire, which was an extension of himself. He gave it as his studied and honest opinion that he was the best horseman in the world, the best archer and targeteer, the best lancer, and that he *had been* the best swordsman; one cannot remain the best with the sword without spending six to eight hours a day in the practice of it. Stilicho attested that he was the greatest foot soldier alive, being able to cover afoot seventy Roman miles over rough country between midnight and midnight under the full weight of arms and provisions —about a hundred pounds in modern weight. Stilicho could endure hunger and thirst and privation beyond all others; he could plan and project more than could another man; he could hold every detail of a countryside in his head, and could recall the underfoot stones of a night path a dozen years later. He could see the pattern of affairs and the pattern behind the pattern.

Stilicho spoke of himself without vainglory, and certainly without modesty. He acknowledged that it was unusual for one man so to excel in everything; but was happy that that one person should be such a responsible person as himself. He gave the opinion that even in himself it would be a short-term affair. Soon his hand and his mind would weaken a little, and soon another man—probably one of them—would move into his place. A dozen years, he told them, is an extreme limit of the time in which a man may serve faultlessly.

He was looking for his successor, he told them bluntly; for one who would fill his place a dozen years from that time. He would carry the qualities of them in his head and weigh them over the years ahead. It may be that he saw Alaric and Heraclian as two with the breadth he desired; that he saw Sarus and Uldin as two with the intensity; but who did he see with everything?

Stilicho stated that every person in the world has his assigned task and that he will know it, whether he admits it to himself or not. Eutropius the eunuch had also told them that every man has his ordained place in the world; but Eutropius had not meant quite the same thing by this as had Stilicho, nor had his statement of it the same effect.

Then Stilicho talked to them of the Empire, as had the Emperor Theodosius. Stilicho gave it to them like the Christian Catechism—an aspect of which it was. He had it, in the basic, from the Emperor, who had it from the Archbishop Ambrose of Milan.

There are even those so base as to state that Ambrose and Theodosius concocted the theory out of political expediency, and then cynically selected the instrument for it, Stilicho, through whom they might bring it to fruit. The big Master General was a single-minded man, and he could be depended on to take the line to its end—once he had swallowed the bait. But those of this opinion are a little less than half right.

Whether or not they concocted the thing out of political expediency, they did not do so cynically. Both the Emperor and the Archbishop were sincere in their belief that the strong idea of Empire must be built up in the people, particularly in the new people who had come into the realm. The cynic is the realist who has given up hope. The Emperor and the Archbishop still had hope that the Empire might endure.

Stilicho stated to the cadets that this world—though it is only a temporary arrangement—is yet a miniature of that which is to come. He swore that it was their bound duty to order the world to the best of their ability.

The Empire, to Stilicho—as to the Archbishop and the Emperor—was itself a religion, and perhaps they gave to it an importance that was unorthodox. Stilicho stated that the Empire was the highest thing in the world, and that it was their duty to make it the only thing in the world—the universal state. He admonished that the perfect ordering of the world was required before we could even consider the ordering of the world to come. He told them that there was divine sanction for Rome, that it was the masterwork of God in this world; and that if Rome should ever fall, the end of the world was at hand. He told them that all things must be ordered in Christ. But he pictured Christ as a sort of master general. It was the Messias of the world that he worshipped as Christ.

Stilicho instructed them that as long as there was one pauper or one slave or one heretic or one rebel remaining, then they had failed at the proper ordering of the Empire—of the world. He did not, however, give specifics for eliminating these things. He left the impression that the strengthening of the Empire would somehow work to the dissolution of all the evils remaining in it.

Yet Stilicho was a good man. If he was a fanatic, he was a calm, even a chilly one. He would live to be the last man in the world who believed that Rome was divine, but a dozen of his sort might have made her so. He was isolated—a Catholic when most of his soldiers and under-officers were Arian. The people of the Empire were Catholic; but Stilicho did not know the people. He was too austere personally to have any real following; a conservative in a world that was prodigal; a unity-man in a civilization that was fragmenting. He was compassionate, a protector of the slaves and the poor, and a restorer of property; but he believed that the giving of bounty and gratuities was what had made slaves in the first place.

He knew that the more African grain was brought into Italy, the more Italy would starve; the more money tribute Asia paid to the Empire, the more the Empire would be pauperized. He preached that the Empire was bleeding to death through usury and impiety—as it was. But others had other ideas as to how to stanch that bleeding, and the majority were willing to let it bleed to death. He was a Christian man more unbending than any pharisee. Like every unbending man, he would have to be broken.

Stilicho's intelligent listeners—and they *were* intelligent—had found little to take exception to in his discourses of military matters during that afternoon. But to his Empire theories—in the night by the fire—many took their own exceptions. To most of them the Empire was a thing that might be owned; and it was a rising idea in several of them that they might be the ones to own it. Most would take it as it was, and have the use of it. To them the high office was that of emperor. Except for Alaric, the boys of the nations thought little of mere kingships; even Uldin who was born a king considered it lightly.

Alaric, perhaps, was the only one who wanted to change the Empire, to take it from the outside and not from the inside.

His developing idea at this time, inspired by the letters from his cousin Stairnon and her brothers Athaulf and Singerich, was to found a *Gothia* in place of a *Romania;* to conquer Rome, not to rise to the highest place in her defence. He was unsettled in his own mind as to this, however. He was as yet undecided whether he was a Roman or a Goth.

Alaric believed that he had it in himself to equal Stilicho—the man sixteen years his senior, who was already, or soon to be, the most powerful man in the world. They were both of them exterior Germans—but the approach of Alaric differed from that of Stilicho. Stilicho had a most extravagant loyalty to the thing he had adopted; he had no doubt at all as to what he was. He was a Roman.

But all of the cadets had caught one fever from Stilicho—the idea that there is no limit to what a single determined man can do. If that overgrown, one-minded German could do it, they could do it.

In the meantime the main study of the cadets—though it was fragmented under a dozen names—was civil engineering. One half of all warfare and all peaceful enterprise consists of this. It was the clearing, moving, building, reinforcing, provisioning, maneuvering in wheeled strength, sanitation and swamp draining, containment of epidemic and anticipation of harvests; bridge, harbor, and road building; armory, overland navigation, topography as a way of considering the world. All engineering, with the Romans, was military engineering. Even the architects of the cities were drawn from the military. This was field engineering, and it was the main study at the School for Generals.

There is one point that must be made clear here. The soldiers and the armies of that period were the real professionals. The integration of new techniques and the experiments carried out, as at the School, were in the long line of constant improvement of the military. The armies now reached a level of military excellence—right at the end of the fourth century—that was never to be surpassed till the age of gunpowder. Real proficiency and tactical sophistication had become the norm. To compare the earlier legions of Caesar or Pompey with those of Stilicho or Arbogast would be like, in the United States of today, comparing high-school football teams with professionals. Stilicho could have given Caesar three to one in numbers and broken his forces like sticks. These men of Stilicho's time were not summer soldiers of citizen levies. They were the final professional forces, and they had spent four hundred years in gaining their proficiency.

There was one very important person met by Alaric at this time of his life, though her importance was not yet realized. At the Eastern Court he had met the goblin child, Galla Placidia, two years old and already fabulous. Galla Placidia was never to be called beautiful, not even by the flatterers of the Eastern Court —the most sycophantic in the world. The silence on the subject of her charms makes it difficult to know just how she failed in the way of appearance. Though she was to grow up without beauty, every man would want her—and not only because she was the daughter and sister of emperors. They were infatuated with her when she was a discredited captive, and there were a million fair women for the taking.

It is said that she was small and dark. It may be that she was before her time; that she would be rated a beauty today, and the magnificent Gothic women would be looked upon as so many cattle. Fashions changed. She spoke when she was three days old, but in a speech that nobody could understand, in the speech of goblins—this happening is on as good authority as much else that passes in history.

She was the last child of the Emperor Theodosius, born of his second wife Galla. Galla Placidia is always written of as extremely intelligent and as achieving her will at the end. She was considered a saint, especially in her later years, and won universal admiration for her kindness. Yet she ordered the murder of her cousin, foster-sister, step-mother, Serena, who was guiltless of any crime.

Alaric, the Boy Giant of the cadets, knew the two young sons of the Emperor; now he met his small daughter. He was friends with Galla Placidia at once; and even at two years old she claimed him as one of hers. She sat on his lap and they talked—two characters out of a fairy tale, the Boy Giant, and the Goblin Child.

There would come the day when Galla Placidia, then seventeen years old, when all the royalty and officials had fled, would reorganize the Roman Senate on her own authority, and would defy Alaric and his Gothic nation while Rome tottered; that was to happen on the day the world ended.

Now, however, they were friends.

This phase of the life of Alaric ended suddenly. The School was terminated temporarily and, as it happened, forever. The cadets took their places in the active legions for a most grave emergency of the Empire. Several of the young men were given startlingly high commands; but none received such orders as did Alaric of Balthi.

He received his orders, rather strange orders for a boy of seventeen—even one of his known ability. He was given the command of an uncertain number of men—twelve to fourteen thousand of them, it is believed. They could not have been far short of that number, for ten thousand of them were to die in a single day only a few weeks afterward. But these numbers were not given to him as a ready force.

Alaric was ordered to alert and mobilize these men from certain sources, and to levy for additional numbers to come to the designated strength. He was to arm, provision, and transport them by his own device—transport them more than one thousand miles through hostile and rebellious territory, and following a route of incredible terraine. He was ordered to do this, though provided with no authority but verbal orders; though given no funds at all; and though the men designated were irregulars settled on farms, and with no pressing desire to leave them at the behest of a young boy.

It would be found also that the numbers of men available were nowise like represented; and that it would be necessary—using these unwilling irregulars for compulsive force—to levy and impress three times their number to complete the army. Arms likewise must be taken by force, and equipment requisitioned on doubtful authority.

Alaric had to find and form an army, transport it through hard going over a distance of more than a thousand miles, evade or defeat four different forces in his path, and arrive at a rendezvous point all within six weeks, with forces battle-ready.

Nor was even this the worst of his assignment. Luckily, he did not foresee the worst part, or even he might have hesitated. Nevertheless, he carried out the assignment. He would arrive with the requisite forces—however acquired—at That Place and at That Time, to take part in one of the most important battles of the Empire.

It was near the end of July, harvest time in Moesia, and of the year 394, that Alaric received his challenging orders.

5. Being a History of the World

Atrox Fabulinus, the Roman Rabelais, once broke off the account of his hero Raphaelus in the act of opening a giant goose egg to fry it in an iron skillet of six yards' span. Fabulinus interrupted the action with these words: "Here it becomes necessary to pause for a moment and to recount to you the history of the world up to this point."

After Fabulinus had given the history of the world up to that point, he took up the action of Raphaelus once more. It happened that the giant goose egg contained a nubile young girl. This revelation would have been startling to a reader who had not just read the history of the world up to that point; which history—being Fabulinian in its treatment—prepared him for the event.

And here it becomes necessary—for the understanding of the coming action—to pause and give the history of the world up to the time when Alaric of Balthi received his forbidding orders. Fortunately, it is not a long history, fifty-seven years and some months from the death of the Emperor Constantine to the preliminaries of the great battle of the Emperor Theodosius against the usurpers.

Some will give a longer term to the world, but actually it was only from the beginning of that Late Empire period that the world and the Roman Empire became identical, and the world takes on our special meaning. The Roman Empire did not, at that time, become identical with the world because of any new aggrandizement of the Empire, but because of the bewildering collapse of all the surrounding nations. It must be realized that the "barbarian" invasions of the Empire were not due to the strengthening of the exterior nations, but to their sudden break-up—turning their peoples into wandering hordes. The Empire was now the world, and outside the world there was only confusion.

Later we will give a much longer period to the world in this meaning, and we will be inconsistent; but it cannot be helped. This short history should have something to satisfy every taste and perversion: action, treachery, fratricide and regicide, corruption, and bloodshed. It contains thirteen murders, the victims being mostly of one family. It lists the ways in which a man or an Empire may be surrounded and destroyed; and contains a veritable catalog of subversions and finely wrought treacheries—which the reader may be able to make use of in his own life. And after this short interruption, we will return to our main action—the opening of the giant egg of the legendary Gothic bird.

Constantine had been the last clear and absolute Emperor of all the Roman regions. Constantine was not the first Christian Emperor—that had been Philip the Arab a hundred years before —but he was the first Emperor who declared the Empire to be Christian; though he did not himself become a Christian till on his deathbed.

There were certain advantages in Constantine's advocating a Christianity for others that he was not yet ready to practice himself. Nobody would question the sincerity of Constantine, but it was a sincerity that ran off in several opposite directions. He left, at his death, a rich heritage, and too many heirs.

Constantine had himself set the example of the blood attrition. He had executed by his own hand Crispus, his son by his first wife—to please his second wife. This left, when he died on May 22 of the year 337, three sons and two nephews to inherit the Empire.

The three sons, with their confusing and too-similar names, were to receive these territories:

Constantinus—Italy and Gaul.

Constantius—the East; that which was to become Byzantium. Constans—Illyricum and Africa.

The territories which the two nephews, Dalmatius and Annibalianus, were to receive are not known for certain, but they are believed to have been Spain and Pannonia. This would have fragmented the Empire intolerably, but a rude sort of process was soon to simplify the holdings. These were not all the nephews—and possibly not all the sons—of Constantine, but they were the inheriting ones.

Keep your eye now on the three sons, Constantinus, Constantius, and Constans, as the shell game is played out. The three are very alike, but one of them will end up with the pea, and the others with nothing at all—not even their lives.

Constantius took it upon himself to correct his father's error of judgment in one thing; he had his two inheriting cousins murdered in the interest of practicality. Nobody objected, certainly not his two brothers. The ground was now cleared, and the main action could begin.

Constantius, partly to give his two brothers a chance to show their hands, but mainly for reasons of real urgency, went off to secure the Persian frontier. The Persians needed to be told that Rome was now the same thing as the world, and that they themselves must subside. Without this preventive action against Persia there might not have been left an Empire to dispute over.

In the meanwhile, Constantinus—the ruler of Italy and Gaul—attacked his brother Constans—the ruler of Illyricum and Africa—at Aquileia in Italy, near the present Jugoslav border. This first battle of Aquileia, in the year 340, was almost identical with the battle of Aquileia and the River Frigidus fought on the same site fifty-four years later. The battle site was a two-way trap, and it was impossible for a victor to withdraw from it victorious. In this first battle of Aquileia, Constantinus won the battle, but lost his life.

There were now two brothers left—Constantius and Constans.

Constans was killed by the usurper Magnus Magnentius in the year 350. Constantius then defeated Magnentius on the Danube, and the usurper was either killed or killed himself in the year 353.

There was now only one brother left, supreme in the Empire—Constantius. He had inherited the pea.

But the Empire could no more be ruled in one part than in five parts. The device of using the master generals for administrators had not yet appeared. The Empire had grown too unwieldy to be ruled by a single man, and there had to be the Eastern and Western subdivisions for actual administration—whatever name the apparatus went by.

In the year 351, Constantius chose his cousin Gallus as a co-Emperor to administer the West. Three years later, Constantius thought better of it, and murdered Gallus.

In the following year, Constantius chose his cousin Julian (a half-brother of Gallus) as co-Emperor of the West. Julian anticipated any second thoughts on the part of Constantius by striking first. Constantius died before Julian's attack had reached him in the East, but he may have died of a weapon called the Dagger with the Very Long Handle. Julian was a canny man, and often sent his emissaries far out in advance.

Julian the "Apostate" took up the campaign of the Persian border, but died near Ctesiphon.

The blood of Constantine had all run out in the twenty-six years following his death. Constantine had been the last clear and absolute Emperor of Rome. Julian had been the last Emperor with any blood claim at all to the honor.

There followed now a new sort of emperors, and a new concept of the office. The new rulers would be men raised by the troops—or at least approved by the troops. The office would not go, of necessity, by blood succession; and would not go in a direct line if a variant line bore better fruit. The selection of the emperors would depend on many factors, of which ability and blood would be only two. The Empire became all important; but the emperor might be almost anonymous, a changing face filling an unchanging office.

The first of the new Emperors—raised by the soldiers and circumstances—was Jovianus. He was elected Emperor in the year

363. He performed one major act in his reign; he surrendered Mesopotamia to the Persians. Then he died in 364 without effective issue.

Valentinian I was elected Emperor by the troops in 364. His election put a favorable aspect on things for the first time in a generation. He was a sound man, and he began to gather very capable men around him. One of his first acts was to appoint his brother Valens to be co-Emperor for the East. Valens was as capable a man as was his brother Valentinian, and there was no fratricide in this family. There was real affection and trust between the brother Emperors.

The two brothers were—as well as it was possible to be at that time—great restorers; of men, of morals, of land. There was a return of stability to the Empire, and the air was full of great expectations. It seemed that they might be able to override a primary force that had been in the ascendant—the tendency of the unwieldy Empire to fragmentize. The brother Emperors employed radical devices to cope with some of the more urgent problems of the day, and to prop up the crumbling frontiers and the heart of the Empire.

It was the Emperor Valens who admitted the West Goths into the Empire in the year of the birth of Alaric of Balthi. This decision of Valens may have been a good one, though it cost him his life. The Goths would have come in, invited or uninvited. Valens gambled that it would be possible to make Romans of them.

In the West, Valentinian had raised his son Gratian to be co-Emperor in the year 367. Valentinian himself was killed in 375 on an expedition against the Quadi and Sarmatians.

The new Emperor Gratian, sixteen years old at the time of his father's death, after consulting with his uncle the Emperor Valens in the East, appointed his four-year-old half-brother Valentinian II to be co-Emperor of the West. Gratian was interested in maintaining the legitimacy of the line and preserving the public order.

After the death of the Eastern Emperor Valens, at the hands of the Goths in 378, Gratian appointed Theodosius—a general of service in Britain and Spain—to be Emperor of the East. Gratian also, in well-placed trust, appointed Theodosius to be guardian of himself and his young half-brother Valentinian II, the two Western Emperors.

This helped to insure stability, but it was not enough. Theodosius was busied for many years in saving and restoring the Eastern Empire. The trouble in the West came in waves that could not all be contained. Gratian gave signs of being a strong man, but he was not given time enough to gain experience.

A new pretender—a splinter Emperor, Magnus Maximus—was raised by the British legions. Maximus took Gaul, and killed the Emperor Gratian at Lugdunum in 383. The details of the action are not to be had. Maximus defeated and killed the Emperor, that is all we know of it.

This was a savage blow to the West, and the Emperor Theodosius was bound to avenge it. It had been Gratian who had raised him up to be Emperor, and who had placed him as guardian over both halves of the Empire.

It seemed that Theodosius hesitated a very long time before moving against Maximus; but this was just at the time when the Goths in the East had finally been contained, and Theodosius had stretched his resources to their limit to bring that about. He must have prayed for a few years grace to allow him to stabilize and re-order the Empire; but the time was never given to him.

Maximus drove the young Emperor Valentinian II out of Italy in 387; and Theodosius finally came to the defence of the family that had raised him to power. There was special inducement for this. Theodosius had now married Galla, the sister of the young Valentinian II, and they were a very close family.

When Theodosius struck, it was with incredible force and rapidity, which betokened careful preparation beforehand. The Emperor was aided in this action by two fine Generals; Arbogast, an established man, and Stilicho, a younger man of great promise.

It had to be done in a single battle. Theodosius was not yet able to wage a sustained campaign from the East. A single battle it was, and the Emperor Theodosius captured and killed Maximus at Aquileia on July 28, 388.

This was the second battle of Aquileia—the first had been fought between two sons of Constantine in 340—and a third terrible battle would be fought on the same site just over six years later. Why it was that Aquileia should three times be such a battle site will be detailed in a moment. It is worth noting that, in all three engagements, the *commanders,* coming from the East out of the Julian Alps, prevailed in their final aims; though in two cases they suffered stunning military defeats, and in the third case the military engagement was a stalemate.

The commanders from the West, fighting from the narrow plains, lost their lives in all three cases, but won great victories in two of them and a partial victory in the third.

At this battle, the second for Aquileia, it was a case of Maximus absorbing and defeating the quick-striking troops of Theodosius, but being killed in the action. The death of Maximus voided his victory, which was turning into a rout of the Easterners, and his troops defected to the Emperor Theodosius.

Maximus, the splinter Emperor, was dead, and it would appear that the Empire, both East and West, was secure. Years of restoration were badly needed. But the Empire was not secure, and the time to make it secure was denied to the Emperor Theodosius. Maximus had been but one wave of a new sort of assault. Arbogast now rose as a most threatening second wave; and the third and fourth waves had already begun to gather in unknown places.

Arbogast was the Count of the Franks. The title still maintains itself sixteen hundred years later, but the title and the man were one. Arbogast was the one and only Count—*Comes*—of the Franks. He was a good soldier and had held second rank in the service of Gratian. After the defeat and death of Gratian at the hands of Maximus, Arbogast had escaped from the West and entered the services of the Eastern Emperor Theodosius—loudly vowing vengeance on the usurper Emperor. It is not known how far Arbogast was then looking into the future, but he seems to have been completely loyal at the time. He had been foremost in urging the Emperor Theodosius to avenge the death of Gratian and the expulsion of Valentinian II.

Arbogast had been a valiant leader in Theodosius' battle against Maximus, and nobody doubted that he was a fine soldier. It was after this action that Arbogast was appointed to be Master General of the armies of Gaul. The appointment was not made by the orders of the young Valentinian, but by the power of Theodosius. It was then that Arbogast fell prey to a disease that had afflicted many of the master generals; treason was endemic to all the master generals except Stilicho. Under a certain combination of circumstances it would come out, and it did now.

Arbogast came under the influence of one of his subordinates, a man named Solinas. This man was of evil prompting, and the opportunity very rich. Arbogast made his decision under the urging of Solinas—a decision that he might have resisted but for this man. Once he had made up his mind, it became easier for him; it is so promising a road that one wonders that everyone does not try it.

The Count Arbogast, having the trust of both Valentinian and Theodosius, began his moves carefully. He worked his own favorites into positions of command in the army—men Frankish for the most part. Arbogast, with the aid of the talented Solinas, did this so skillfully that Valentinian believed the new men were also his own favorites and were of his own selection. The young Valentinian was short of acumen in dealing with his great Master General.

Valentinian is always excused as being a very young man. But he was either twenty-one or twenty-two years old at the time of his death, and by the standards of that time he would have been a full man if he was ever going to be one. The young Emperor was not a coward nor was he physically insignificant. He was a man somewhat above the average in size and courage. He was not a fool. He was guilty of no rash act; nor of any particular negligence. He was intelligent, honorable, good-natured, and whimsically humorous. He made good selections of men and policies, but the man he selected as master general of Gaul developed a policy of treason. Valentinian was a good man, but he failed being a great man. And the Emperor Theodosius remained very seriously involved in the East. Theodosius had spared more men and more months than he could afford in dealing with the usurper Magnus Maximus. He had to trust young Valentinian to rule the West, and he trusted completely Arbogast, the Frankish Count.

Arbogast worked until every leading man in the army and in the Western Court was his own man. In this infiltration and subversion he was aided by Solinas who practiced these matters as a form of art. They were able men who were intruded. Their Court seemed more stable than the Court of the East; more flexible, more able to move against the barbarians.

It was to increase this flexibility that the Western Court was moved temporarily to Vienne in Gaul. Valentinian had been persuaded to move his Imperial residence to that place to give it greater weight and authority. Vienne was in Gaul, and Arbogast was Count of Gaul, and of the Franks.

Either suddenly or slowly Valentinian realized that he was the captive of his Master General. It may be that he would have been allowed to live out his life as puppet. More likely he would have been killed when Arbogast felt secure in his power. But Valentinian was man enough to take up the challenge.

There is a colorful story of the showdown between Count Arbogast and the Emperor Valentinian. After a formal meeting in full view of the Court, Valentinian calmly handed Arbogast a paper telling him that he was relieved of all his commands and offices. Arbogast read it through; then laughed blackly and tore it up and threw it down.

Arbogast motioned to his guards to take the Emperor. Valentinian overpowered the first guard, took his sword from him, and attempted to use it against Arbogast. Such a grand gesture was of no avail there. Arbogast was too well prepared. The Emperor was pinioned and taken away.

Shortly afterwards Valentinian was found strangled in his own apartment. There is no doubt that it was either by the orders or at the hand of Arbogast.

The word came to the Emperor Theodosius that his young Western colleague had died by an accident. The word came from Arbogast, who pledged eternal fealty to the Empire and the Emperor; but who announced that, for the public order, he was himself taking the reins of the Western lands into his unworthy hands. The true account of the affair came to Theodosius, of course; Emperors have long ears. It may have come verbally by the same messenger who brought the official announcement.

Arbogast did not officially make himself Emperor of the West. Instead, he appointed Eugenius, to be Emperor and puppet—the famous pagan rhetorician of Rome—Arbogast now owned the West. He had the full armies of Rome, and the armies of Gaul— of the Franks, his own people. The Franks, the Gauls—half-Celtic, half-German—were the threat to the Western Empire that the Goths had been to the Eastern. But this threat was now made his instrument by Arbogast. He was native Count—leader of that restive people; he was victorious Master General, and he owned his own Emperor. He held Gaul, as well as Rome and all Italy, and all the Western provinces.

Theodosius would be compelled to move against Arbogast, though his resources were still exhausted from his move against Magnus Maximus and his settling of various border disputes. It is said that Theodosius knew that this would be the last campaign of his life; that his unknown physical disability would put an end to his life in the near future; *and that he knew the day of his death*. It is believed that it was at this time that he appointed Stilicho the guardian of the Emperor and of the two young sons, the future emperors. Theodosius had just been betrayed by one Master General, but he had no fear of betrayal by Stilicho.

It is certain that they were planning the campaign while they maintained the fiction that they were taking Arbogast's account of the death of Valentinian at face value. But Theodosius simply did not have the troops to combat the traitor immediately. He dissembled and swallowed his anger for two years while he built up his forces. The Eastern Empire had been bled of troops for service in both the East and West.

Finally, when time itself was running strongly against him and some sort of move would have to be made soon or not at all— when he considered the day of his coming death and realized how short a period he had remaining—Theodosius erupted into galvanizing action and set the thing into motion, naming the date of the battle. He had two Master Generals in the East, Stilicho and Timasius, one of them as great as Arbogast, the other nearly as outstanding. They had the brains and the flair to ignite an action. Between them they would have to find a device to make up for the deficiency in numbers.

Theodosius gave the orders to his Master Generals, and they in their turn gave more detailed and motivating orders. Some of the orders were wild and unheard-of. The orders given to the gawky and impossibly tall Gothic teen-ager, Alaric of Balthi, were orders as wild as could be imagined. But by such devices the Emperor and the two Master Generals put together a final army and began to move it to Italy.

There was one complicating detail in the line-up, which would turn out to be the detail of final effect. The pseudo-Emperor Eugenius had been openly pagan, and the Count Arbogast secretly so. Both believed—and Eugenius had been chosen Emperor by Arbogast because of the skillful phrasing he gave the belief—that Christianity was a parasite on the Empire; and that corporate health could only be restored by the elimination of that new religion. This now became the declared policy. It was a very chauvinistic movement, and it gathered adherents as it became apparent that it was in full power.

The Pope at that time was Siricius, later sainted. He was known for his wide tolerance—which was often given a harsher name by the zealots. He judged correctly that the thunder of excommunication would hold no terrors for those already outside the Faith; that the returned paganism was not an interior heresy but an exterior menace. He found himself powerless to move against the pagan usurpers. The only loud protest came, not from Pope Siricius, but from Archbishop Ambrose in Milan; and it was the one voice that even Arbogast did not dare to still.

The force of Arbogast the Count was now essentially pagan, and that of Theodosius coming against him was Catholic and Arian. This made for deeply divided loyalties in each force: among the Frankish Catholics who followed Arbogast with greatly qualified support, and among the old Eastern Empire army pagans who marched with Theodosius and Stilicho and hoped for the victory of Arbogast.

Several bitter contemporary references to the pseudo-Emperor Eugenius had puzzled us. They asked how a man of such an appearance could attempt the pagan re-establishment. They asked it in horror, for there were certain horrifying aspects to this particular pagan reversion. It was not the old disinterested paganism; it was impassioned and very nearly diabolical in some of its manifestations.

The meaning of the references came clear with the examination of reproductions of coins and medallions of the pseudo-Emperor. Eugenius, who affected an old oriental style in hair and beard, had the face of Jesus Christ.

6. About Little Moesia

Alaric demanded of the tribune of the academy, a very grizzled old General, that he should be assigned three of his fellow cadets to accompany him in the carrying out of his orders. This, Alaric insisted, was the absolute minimum. He could not even begin with nothing at all to go on.

Alaric was assigned three cadets, but not the three he had requested. He had asked for Sarus his cousin, for Uldin the Hun, and for Heraclian. But these were all considered young men of ability on a par with that of Alaric, and they would have their own very important assignments. The four most talented cadets in the school could not be assigned to a single project—however important it might be.

The three who were assigned to Alaric were Hafras and Vargas, fellow Goths, and Bacurinius, the son of a great Spanish General. These three were the best friends of Alaric at the school, but he was not pleased. The three had much ability, and they would follow him forever; but Alaric knew that he could get followers and good ones. He wanted leaders of high caliber, and he would have to find them for himself.

There was but one thing that Alaric could do with his impossible orders: he could go to his people with them. He was still a boy but he must find the Gothic men and one Gothic woman—Stairnon. He did not know where she was, nor her brothers Athaulf and Singerich, nor his—her—family. People, at that time, did not have addresses. The letters from Stairnon and Athaulf and Singerich had been brought to Alaric by Gothic wagoners who were passing his way.

Alaric simply mounted his horse and with his three aides, rode out on the first road, without caring where it should lead. However, this was not the aimless procedure that it seemed.

The Goths were a horse, mule, wagon, cart, and saddle sort of people. The stage-houses and the way-stables were mostly owned by the Goths, as were the houses that passed for inns. The roads were the newspapers of the Goths; and every report could be found out by one who traveled, for every Gothic groom or wagoner or provisioner was a source of information. Tidings of every Goth would come over the roads, but it was not always understood who carried the information. There were some who said that the news of distant Goths was brought by the mules. For the rumor-of-the-roads there was indeed a saying: *Talimodo narrant-id muli*—The mules narrate it so.

The mules told Alaric that Stairnon was still to the north and west of them. They were already on the westerly road when they came out of Constantinople by its southernmost or Golden Gate. Alaric rode with his three friends, though he would have preferred three youths of higher ability who need not be such close friends. Yet, for us, it is an advantage. Had it been one of Alaric's first selection instead of Hafras, we would not have had the account of the affair. Hafras—the other two, Vargas and Bacurinius, would be dead within the six weeks—was to live a long life and become an indefatigable letter writer and reminiscenser. He lived through the greatest things and paid them no mind; but he remembered the little things.

Alaric, as he rode, picked up support and spread the word of the mobilization. After three days and nearly two hundred miles, they came to Stairnon on a farm on the Maritza River in the Thracian Plain, in the region that had come to be known as Little Moesia.

The retinue of Alaric had by this time increased from three men to nearly one hundred—the additions being both green boys and trained soldiers. They would pick up many more by their appearance, for they had barely entered the Gothic countryside. Alaric had his three tribunes—unless he should come upon any better—in his first three companions, Bacurinius, Hafras, and Vargas. He selected a dozen of his centurions and a number of his horse commanders from the men who had joined him early. There had been many of these seasoned men, in full arms, waiting to join him on the road, and Alaric understood how it had been brought about.

The mysterious telegraph had gone out—either from a Roman official or a Goth in Roman service—that the Gothic army would be raised once more, and under the young hereditary ruler. There must have been many who heard the orders of Alaric before he had heard them himself; there was a nucleus of Gothic soldiers and commanders who had gotten them in advance. The Master General Stilicho, from whom the orders originated, had not given Alaric cold orders; they had already been implemented to some extent. Stilicho had intended to test the young Goth with the apparently impossible instructions; but even with the apparatus set in motion, the execution of the project would be very difficult.

Stairnon was on a large farm with none of her family with her. She had about two dozen free Goths and a hundred or so slaves on the land. Hafras recounts, with some surprise, that there were several chained slaves. Both the Romans and the Goths kept slaves, though the Goths to a less extent. The chaining of slaves seems not to have been normal to the Goths; to have been accounted an act of cruelty. But there was no doubt that Stairnon was in complete charge of the enterprise.

The descriptions we have of the farm in Little Moesia—from Hafras—must mostly refer to this first visit and sojourn; but there were subsequent visits of Alaric to the farmstead at which Hafras was also present.

Alaric and Stairnon spoke to each other in Low Latin, and by formula.

"God bless the people and the land," Alaric greeted her.

"God bless the people and the arms of the people," was the an-

swer of Stairnon. So she understood his mission. She had known
of it before he had—that he was to raise the Goths to arms again.

Hafras tells of their party coming to the farmstead between
dusk and dark; of pine knots burning in open iron buckets for
torches, and of the homey smell of warm cows' milk. The Goths
did not share the Greek—and later Turkish—abhorrence for cows'
milk and cows' cheese. In their settled state the Goths used cows
more than ewes or goats or mares for milking. The warm milk was
in wooden buckets.

Stairnon had come to them, very tall and happy, with a long
bull whip coiled on her arm. There was a bell clanging, an evening or supper bell, or a slave bell.

The men of Alaric camped in the farmstead, and considerably
raised the surrounding earth walls, working into the late dark.
Though Goths, they were Roman soldiers, and they would follow Roman camp discipline.

Stairnon was prodigal in caring for them and completely unper-
turbed by their numbers. The feast that began a little after midnight lasted throughout the following day. She slaughtered steers,
sheep, and goats, and also prepared that old Gothic delicacy—foal
colt. They had mead and grape wine. There were bread loaves
the size of cart wheels.

The meal of the Christian Goths could not begin with other than
bread and wine, though they believed all food to be holy. To them
every meal must be a form of the Eucharist, though they had the
Eucharist itself and were not confused between the reality and
the symbol.

They had honey with mare's milk, goat cheese, curds from cows'
milk, fowl and hare, fish of the Pontus and the Maritza, Euxine
sturgeon, roast dog, wheat and barley cakes, pigs fatted on acorns
and hazel nuts. They had old apples and pomegranates, and new
melons and garlic and onions. They had plums, pears, and figs; al-
monds, chestnuts, walnuts, cherries, peaches, and apricots. They
had—and theirs was the first generation north of Greece to have
such—citrus fruit. They had olives and oysters and butter, duck

and goose eggs and flesh. They drank a heavy beer much like the porter of later centuries.

There has been some misunderstanding as to the food of the near-ancient people, and those of the Low Middle Ages. They ate well; they had to eat well, if at all. This was before the appearance of the artificial foods; there was no food but the genuine.

The low-born potato and the turnip, those latter-day degradations to afflict fallen man, were not known. Corn and oats were eaten by animals, as was proper; but not by men. The ranker vegetables had not yet substituted themselves in place of the nobler fruits. Mankind, in its nobler races, had not fallen to peas or beans (which were slave foods); nor commonly to beets, radishes, cabbages, cress, or weeds. Vegetables, some of them, might be used in compounding relishes, but they were *not* used as basic foods. Meat, fruit, nuts, milk, cheese, wheat and barley cakes and bread, were the food of the people. Oats were for horses; millet and semolina for the poor of the Romans.

The drink of the Goths was wine, beer, and mead. Christian men had not yet been seduced by the oriental impostors tea and coffee; the nothing drinks. They knew that only the drink that moves itself, that undergoes a form of metamorphosis or fermentation, can be the resurrection and the life.

The farmstead was one of the more than one thousand such large steads as the Goths established wherever they set down. The Goths had no small farms and could not have conceived of them. The farmstead would comprise from fifty to two hundred persons, and the buildings were encircled with earthen walls, for every farm was likewise a fortress. The farmstead included shops and smithies for carpentry and armory and tanning and fulling and weaving. The wooden and iron implements of the farm were made on the farm. The shoes and the clothing were made there. *The manorial life of the Middle Ages had already begun* with the settlement of the Goths. The Goths had already done for themselves what Stilicho, not knowing the details of their lives, had dreamed of doing for the Romans in the resettlement of the lands.

It is not known just what was the personal relationship of

Stairnon and Alaric at this time. The Goths married much later than did the Greeks and Romans, though Alaric and Stairnon did marry either one or three years later; whether before or after the Greek adventure, it is not known. But Alaric at seventeen was not in a hurry for the thing. He was not as precocious in marital as in martial ways. They did not have the first of their several children till either five or seven years after their marriage; and it may have been a policy marriage, not a marriage of fact, in the early years of it. Stairnon did not reveal too early all the roles that she intended to play in the life and legend of Alaric.

Alaric learned the news of his family. Stairnon's brother Singerich was at Constantia on the Black Sea. Her older brother, Athaulf, had gone feral and was across the Danube near the Barcea Complex with his new father, who was not the father of Stairnon and Singerich and Sarus. And Alaric gave Stairnon the news of her brother Sarus—that he had gone directly into the Roman inner service from the Academy; that Sarus was a Roman now and nevermore a Goth.

On the first morning of the feasting, Alaric called together the Gothic men from the countryside. These were likewise operators of the great farms, and their sons and nephews and kindred. He told them to prepare and arm and be ready to leave within twenty-four hours.

They told him that their harvests would not be completed for ten days; that they would follow him then.

Their harvests should have been completed, Alaric insisted. The harvests had been finished in the land he had traversed in the three days previous. The Roman orders that Alaric had received had assumed that the harvests would be completed in Little Moesia.

The harvests were always a little later here on the Thracian Plain, the Gothic men told him. They knew that the harvests were completed down around Constantinople, what little grain they grew there. The men would follow Alaric as soon as they had finished their harvest.

Alaric said that they would follow him now, on the following morning, or that he would burn them out. Stairnon told Alaric that he would not burn any of the Goths out. She told him that the Gothic men were right, and he was wrong; she won him over on it.

The plan decided on for Alaric and his growing forces was that they should ride to his cousin Singerich in Constantia, in which region he was already raising and arming forces. After joining with the Gothic and Greek forces of Singerich, the army would cross the narrow Dobruja Plain to the Ister—the Danube—where Athaulf would meet them. Athaulf would accompany them for much of their journey and would give them such troops as he could find; but he would not accompany them all the way. He would not re-enter the Empire at this time; he would not re-enter till the decision for the final solution of the Empire had been made, so his message ran—which Alaric did not understand.

Alaric was no fool; he realized that the time element in the whole business was distorted. It was less than four days since he had received his own orders. For messages to go to his two cousins, Singerich and Athaulf, and their answers received back, would have taken no less than ten days. Yet messages of the situation had gone to them from someone, and their answers had already been received.

His selection, Alaric knew, had not only been discussed by the Romans, but had been settled by the Romans with his own people, the Goths. Alaric was a tool and had been the last one to receive the word of his own assignment. He had been selected by the Roman Master General Stilicho to play a role. He had also been selected by the elders of the Goths, both those within the Empire and those outside it, to play a role. He had the feeling, however, that the Romans and the Goths had not selected him for exactly the same role.

It isn't known how deep the Gothic intrigue ran. There were certainly parties and divisions among them—and there were the beginnings of the real Gothic nationalists, and an anti-Empire group. It had been discussed whether the Goths should not soon raise up a king, as they had not done for several generations.

There were those among the Gothic elders, especially beyond the Empire, who inclined to the young Athaulf for the ultimate leadership, as being more intelligent and more what they called wide-seeing than Alaric. The difficulty was that Athaulf, from a childhood fixation and the influence of his sister, Stairnon, supported Alaric and would not consider himself or any other as final leader. Athaulf always stated that he would remain beyond the Danube until the development of certain events; and that he would aid in their development if they seemed tardy.

There were also some among the Gothic leaders who preferred Singerich as leader. Singerich was an easy and urbane boy with an intelligence far beyond his years. He had comprehended the thought of the Gothic interviewers without their having to go into embarrassing explanations. He was scholar and scribe and notary and lawyer, though only of the age of Alaric. He was a commission agent in the Port City of Constantia, and was acquainted with the shipping and business of every part of the Empire. He was a friend of the Emperor and a very close friend of the Eastern ministers, and had become so on his own, without influence and without favor. He had a genius for affairs, and even had a fine understanding of military affairs, which many men of that sort do not have. The Gothic elders were amazed at this young prodigy who had been hatched from their nest, and were very impressed by his achievements. But here there was the same impediment: Singerich was committed to Alaric forever. His mind, that could see nearly every side of every problem, could see only one side of this. It had to be Alaric for Singerich.

Sarus would have been the natural choice of the Gothic men. But they understood what had happened to the boy. It had come to them by too many reports to allow doubt of it. Sarus was a Roman and would be so forever. He could no longer be considered as a Goth.

As for Alaric the Boy Giant, he had talked very little to the Gothic emissaries—not identified as such—who had visited him at the school. It was not even certain that Alaric was intelligent. But the selection of Alaric to lead the Gothic levy, made by the Roman Master General Stilicho, could not be set aside. The leading Goths knew Stilicho, and respected him and his judgment. They

finally agreed with the Master General that the leader should be
Alaric. This was several weeks before Alaric himself received his
orders.

There had been campaigning in Alaric's behalf from other
sources. Bacurius the Spanish General had visited his son at the
School, and had been greatly impressed by Alaric. He had insisted
to Stilicho, again and again, that Alaric would be a great power in
the Empire. The father of Uldin the boy King of Huns, himself
both King and General, had made the same recommendations to
Stilicho. These men, of other race, saw something in Alaric that
his own people did not yet see.

It is not to take anything from Alaric to point out that he had
considerable help in raising, arming, and transporting his troops.
The orders of Alaric were often only the confirmation of orders
that the men had already received from the Gothic elders. Alaric
had soldiers from the great force of Fritigern that had broken the
best of the Romans and killed their Emperor Valens sixteen years
before. He had veterans of every Empire action of the ensuing sixteen years. There were young men who, like Alaric, had been born
in the camps. There were the Goths who were also trained Roman
soldiers, most of them with from six to sixteen years service in the
legions.

They had settled and farmed in the meantime. But they would
rather soldier. They had been waiting impatiently for the blast of
the war horn. Now they began to respond before Alaric had quite
got it raised to his lips.

But another wind was blowing through them when they came to
arms this time. And when they now took up their arms they would
not put them down for more than a thousand years—until they had
lost their identity as a people. The new wind was a non-Roman
thing. The Empire was calling on them to take arms for one great
battle in the civil war; but many of the Goths were looking far
beyond the one battle in the service of Rome.

Rumor is persistent that Stairnon was inextricably involved in
this new feeling. She became a legend-molder, both before and
after the facts. She was either a willing creature or one of the bril-

liant originators of the Gothic National Movement. The Romans did not know what they had started. Any amateur magician can call up a wind, but can he shut it off when he wishes?

It was at the farmstead in Little Moesia that Alaric, in discussion with Stairnon and the Gothic men of the countryside and uneasy at the old Gothic basis of their thought, put forward some of the ideas of Stilicho. He did this badly, being not yet a talker, but he did it with conviction. He was half-Roman now, believed himself to be completely Roman, and he wanted them to understand. He quoted Stilicho to the effect that as long as there was one pauper or one slave or one heretic or one rebel remaining, they had failed at the proper ordering of the world and the Empire.

The answer to this, as Hafras reports, was the rich red laughter of Stairnon. She reminded Alaric that all of them present, except Bacurinius, were heretics in the eyes of Stilicho, being Arians. She told him that they were paupers as to the possession of town things. That they were slaves of the Empire and owners of slaves in their turn. And that they might very well be rebels before the earth had made its full journey. So perhaps it was they themselves who were standing in the way of the proper ordering of the Empire and the world, and they who should be eliminated.

Alaric sincerely believed the thesis of Stilicho, however; and he recognized the answer of Stairnon as no more than a cheerful sophism. Alaric would have effected it all if he had lived long enough—if he had lived for a thousand years, and the Goths and the Romans, and people generally, had been other than they were. The Stilicho dream of restoring the Empire came too late, and to too few men.

After the time of their stay at the farmstead, probably only two days, Alaric and his band—grown to some six or seven hundred men now—rode off to Constantia (anciently named Tomi, where Ovid had lived) to find the cousin Singerich and pick up the troops he had raised. Appointment was made with the Goths of the countryside for a meeting at the cataracts of the Danube—modernly called the Iron Gate—to which place they were to proceed as soon as their harvest was completed.

From the farmstead in Little Moesia it was five days—two hundred miles—to Constantia. The speed was necessarily less than formerly. There was a greater force to move, and horses could not so easily be changed in such numbers.

It was at Constantia that Alaric was almost perturbed *to find how well things were going*. The small fleet of Singerich, Black Sea and river boats, had already sailed. Singerich had answered the question some days before it had been put to him. The boats had sailed north twelve days before, which was prior to Alaric's receiving his orders. The fleet would go, had in fact already gone, north to the southernmost mouth of the Danube (today known as St. George Mouth); it would cruise the south shore of Fir Island (where Alaric had been born), and there it would pick up further Goths. The boats would then proceed around the great bend of the river and south to the Barcea Complex. Somewhere in those lakes and side rivers and swamps there would be Athaulf waiting. The river men would surely be there before the land men.

Singerich had initiated certain financial transactions at Constantia, and these he now confirmed to Alaric. It was an extremely simple business as he presented it. He had raised funds and boats and arms and equipment by mortgages on the basis of warrant claims, which he now executed on the authority of Alaric, who did not understand that he had such authority. It was not Alaric who was so bonded, Singerich explained, but the Empire by his name. Alaric, as the commander of auxiliaries, was so entitled to requisition. Nor should he feel uneasy as to the success of the moneylenders and provisioners. For the risk that they took their mark-up was high, more than 50 per cent. It would not have been possible, of course, had not the word come to the financial men of the port city that Alaric held legitimate appointment from the Master General Stilicho.

There were discrepancies in the matter, however. Singerich and Alaric had received fewer boats and wagons than they had signed for, but they had received a quantity of gold bar that made up the balance. Singerich would go far in his line. Besides, the gold would buy more arms and wagons and provisions on the Gothic border than it would in the Greek port city.

After they had rested for one day and transacted such business, Alaric and Singerich, with their forces joined, traveled on the second day to the Barcea—for it was no more than thirty miles overland—there to meet Athaulf.

The plan thereafter was to proceed up the river (which was then called the Ister as far up as the cataracts—the Iron Gate—and only above the cataracts was named the Danube), traveling by the river and on both shores, with one foot always in the Empire and the other one outside. They would travel the Danube upstream till they came to the Savo Branch (at modern Belgrade); and there Athaulf would give them such troops as he could, but he would not come with them further. He would not enter the Empire. They would follow the Savo Branch up to its source—its ultimate source where it came out of the mountains as a spring that a man could divert with his two hands.

When Alaric should come to that place he would be high in the Julian Alps and not a hundred strides from the divide. From the top of the divide it would be possible for him to see, distantly, the army that he with his forces was to join and support. It would be no more than twenty Roman miles away, to the south, near the passes out of the Julians.

And coming down from the Julians they would be at the gates of Italy and already on the battle field that was the scene of two previous carnages. Five weeks they had left for the rendezvous, or a little less.

Alaric rode out from Constantia with his cousin Singerich, the Goth who had become a Greek, starting early while it was still dark, and came to the river on the same day, while it was high afternoon. There were many who called to Alaric by name as he went by, those who could never have seen him before. Alaric was one of those rare persons—all of them are great, but not all great persons have the attribute—who will be known by name and face wherever they go. Before the age of produced pictures and general literacy, the thing was more noticed than it is now. One king would ride among the people and be known. Another would not be known. There are persons of such a striking image that the rumor of them describes them exactly, and they will be everywhere recognized. Alaric was such a man, and it was partly for this reason that he was selected as leader. Sarus and Athaulf, for all their great ability, were not such men. They would not be known popularly either by face or by name.

Alaric, on coming to the river, was told to enter a boat with only a single oarsman. He did so, and was transported across nearly a mile of slanting water to a small wooded island. This was to be, Alaric knew, an important meeting—one that might explain the motivation of his whole mission. He expected the meeting to be with his cousin Athaulf.

Instead, Alaric was met by a rough-looking, weird, giant of an old man, who told Alaric that he was his father.

7. Of Gothic Lightning and Frankish Thunder

Alaric remembered the death of his father seven years before—the death, but not the burial. The body of the father of Alaric had been taken out by boat, across the slanting water of the river where all things seem to diminish in the sudden shine, to be left on an island in that same Danube River. This was where all the Goths of the horde, who died at that particular time of swarming, were taken to be buried. Some Goths had been buried there from as much as two lifetimes before, and earlier peoples had been buried there from the beginning of time.

There was, however, a strangeness in the traveling to this Shade Island. Nowhere else did the water seem to slant as on this queer journey. Nowhere else did objects seem to diminish, and oneself also if going there, as on crossing an invisible mid-water barrier. It was as though all things going there passed through a mirror and into the land beyond. Alaric had had this impression on seeing the body of his father taken there for burial seven years before; he had the same impression now.

The place itself, the neighborhood of the cemetery island, was well known. It was a familiar crossing where the river, flowing from the west, turned to the north to find its mouths. Alaric had been to the region many times in childhood, as it was a famous Gothic rendezvous. The shore about was familiar from previous visits; the island itself could never become familiar. There was a chilling remembrance of the island, but out of stories, not out of experience. This was the Shade Island of the early ghost stories of Stairnon.

The island, she had told, was not there all the time; or if there, was not always visible. Boats, in fact, could drift right through it when the island was in its unseen state; but every boat that should do so unwittingly would lose one man. He would disappear from the boat and be never seen again, but he would repose in a new grave on Shade Island, a grave that was not dug by hands. And the island was never knowingly approached except by one small boat capable of carrying but two men, usually a dead man and the live one who would give him burial. Sometimes, however, when it was wished to consult the dead, the oarsman would take another live man as special emissary, as in this case Alaric.

The island was clearly older than the river, and older than the land of the surrounding shores; this was certain from the evidence of the senses, evidence which was quite clear, but which could not be put into words.

The cemetery island held a whole labyrinth of dead, and a vast multitude of markers. There were rune stones and seven stones; caverns raised above ground, and those dug into the ground; rock piles; stepped pyramids twice the height of a man; genuine monuments and dressed-stone tombs; and Christian crosses.

Of these there were rude stick crosses, but also ornate carved wood and stone crosses of Greek, Roman, and Celtic design. The Greek crosses had all four pieces of equal length. The Roman crosses had a long vertical piece and a shorter cross-piece high upon it, as has generally the modern cross. The Celtic cross was similar to the Roman, but surrounding the intersection of the pieces was the large wheel, the circle, the halo that was meant to represent Christ. The Goths did not then have their own characteristic cross form, but most often used the Celtic cross.

This was the Island of the Dead, but not of the irrevocably dead. As Christians, the Goths could not believe in eternal death.

There was an adit on the island—though Alaric did not see it— an entrance by which one came to the downward passage to Hell. This was on the early word of Stairnon, as was that of the Mound.

The Mound was in the center of the island; and there the blessed, having made restitution for their sins, should assemble (usually on a Thursday afternoon) and be taken thence to Heaven. To the unbelievers or to the pagans they would look like a flight of eagles, but the true believers would see them as ascending saints.

This habit of the Goths of burying their dead in the river—on islands in the river—may have been the basis for the final legend that was to attach to Alaric. But the dead Shades did indeed walk on the Island of the Shades. This was known to Alaric, not only from the childhood stories of Stairnon, but from later accounts given to him by grown and mature Gothic men—men who had actually seen the old dead walk and talk.

But was this large rough old man actually the dead father of Alaric? Alaric did not believe so. There was a certain intimacy struck between them, but not the very close intimacy that had been between young Alaric and his father. This man looked much like the father of Alaric, but was much older than Alaric's father would have been—unless it is that the dead age more rapidly than do the living. The father of Alaric had been cut down in full early manhood; not in war, but by an accident with the horses. This old man could hardly be Alaric's father, but he might well be his father's father.

Then Alaric shivered as he realized that he was actually living out one of the ghost stories of Stairnon. For this old man must be no other than the last Balthi to have been king of the Goths, the first old giant who had reigned six generations before. Alaric, who was a boy hardly to be intimidated by a dead man of his own ancestry, asked the old giant who he was, and in what way he might be his father.

The old man averred that he was both Alaric's father and his father's father, and the grandfather of his grandfather. He also stated that he would be the father of Alaric's children; that there was no seed in the Balthi but his own. He had been for a long time, the old man said, and when he was a boy the great mountains had been but hillocks.

Had he then been dead quite a long time? Alaric asked him.

It did not matter whether he was alive or dead, the ancient man told Alaric. The differences between the two states are less than one might imagine. But he let it be understood that he spoke with the authority of the dead, and he would be heard as one from the ancient days.

The scene becomes a little bit eerie and we have only an indirect report of it—things that Alaric later told to Singerich and to Hafras, or things that they came to believe that he had told them. Alaric was to take a conscious part in building up the Alaric Legend, and he may already have begun to do so.

The old Balthi grandfather made Alaric swear a series of oaths, not all of them of the Christian sort, owing eternal fealty to the Gothic nation and an enduring enmity for the Roman Thing.

Alaric argued—inasmuch as it is possible to argue with a Gothic great-grandfather who may or may not be dead—that he himself was both a Goth and a Roman, as well as a Christian; and that the Roman Thing was his mother.

The ancient Shade spat angrily, and there was some bitterness between them. Alaric insisted that he would continue to be both a Goth and a Roman, and that his aim in life was to bring it about so that the two should be one thing.

Only as the fox and the hare become one thing after the fox has eaten the hare, the old man told him.

There was much more to it, an elaborate ritual and mystique—with the old man sometimes breaking off and going into the area of the tombs to consult with the other dead on certain points. But, in the end, Alaric had the full blessing of the old man, his mystic Gothic father.

Others had sometimes been intimidated, even frightened, in speech with him—the old man told Alaric—and they had been inclined to agree to things without thinking them through. There is something to be said for a boy who will stand his ground and argue with the ancient dead, even though the boy—in the rashness of his youth—might be wrong on the particular point of argument. Such a boy will some day be a man—the old grandfather told him—

and having been at the same time respectful and unafraid of the dead, he will be competent to deal with the living as well.

The old man went back into the monuments and returned with a broken-hafted old blade that was nearly rusted through, as was he himself. He gave the ruined sword to Alaric, and told him that it was for him, and that no other man would ever be able to wield it. It passed from the hand of the old giant—for the grandfather was towering—to the hand of the young giant.

The sword would not be useful in battle, but Alaric would find it impressive as a talisman. It was recognized as a symbol of authority; and it was this rusty old blade that Alaric would hold in his hand when the Goths would raise him to be king.

Now the old man raised his right hand as if compelling the skies, and Alaric shivered with sudden memory. This would be the test. If Alaric were living through an old Gothic ghost story, then this was the test by which he might know if the story were a true one. The giant king of the tale had a way of ending an interview, of dismissing one from his presence. Alaric froze in anticipation; and as the second doubled itself, he nearly lost faith. But it was no more than two seconds that the old man raised his hand to heaven. Then it came.

A blinding white flash of lightning! The legendary king had been wont to call down lightning from the skies for a sign, and he had done so now. There had never been so sudden and stark a lightning stroke as this.

Alaric, when his sight returned, started to ask the grandfather how it was done, but the old man was gone. Alaric was forced to take the lightning as dismissal, and he returned to the boat where the lone oarsman was waiting for him.

Such, at least, is the account of the happenings on Shade Island as Alaric told it to his cousin Singerich and his friend Hafras on the same day. They have written their separate Gospels of it, and they agree closely. Alaric himself would not have been capable of fabricating this account of talking to his dead ancestor, but there were others with a talent equal to it: Stairnon, it might be, or her brother Athaulf. It is possible that Stairnon, after agreeing on the details with Athaulf, might have coached Alaric in the story before he left the farm in Little Moesia; and Athaulf could well have had the lone boatsman waiting.

But it is possible that it happened just as Alaric said that it did. It is far from the most impossible thing that ever happened to him.

Alaric *did* bring from the cemetery island the old rusted sword, the same that he would hold when he was crowned King. This sword had a name and was remembered by the old Goths by certain signs; or they came to believe that they recognized it by old signs. A mystique was created. If a man is great enough this will gather around him like clouds.

This giant old man seems also to be the mysterious "father" of Athaulf, of whom he had written several times in recent years.

Alaric and the lone oarsman went to the north bank of the river as the storm broke. There was a terrific rainstorm that was introduced by the fantastic lightning. The storm would have been memorable even without the unearthly story associated with the first lightning bolt of it.

On reaching land, the real point of rendezvous, Alaric met his waiting cousin Athaulf. These two, though they had not seen each other for five years, were very close and would always be close—closer than actual brothers. Theirs was the one friendship that would never turn sour; nor has the complete openness of it ever been suspected during the ensuing fifteen and a half centuries.

Athaulf may have been Cain in another connection, but he could not have been so in connection with Alaric; nor while Alaric still lived and had influence over him. Athaulf was not then a bad man, and it is disputed at what point he became bad; or if he ever did so except from one partisan viewpoint. The horrifying double fratricide that was later to engulf the family could not have happened until after the death of Alaric.

With any two men other than Alaric and Athaulf, there might have been suspicion of foul play at one point. For it is a fact that, a little more than a dozen years later, the two of them—with five hundred wagon loads of the richest booty that the world had ever known—went into South Italy together. After some weeks Athaulf came back, himself the new King of the Goths, and neither Alaric nor the booty was ever seen again.

The later Gothic troops of Athaulf, who had been the troops of Alaric, seemed uncomprehending or hard of hearing when asked by outsiders for an account of the events in the South. The story, as given out to the world by Athaulf, of the death, and particularly of the disposal of the body, of Alaric is simply not acceptable as having happened in fact. What it was that did happen will not be known by us until the afternoon of the day of the last judgment, but it was not the murder of Alaric at the hand of Athaulf. That would not have been possible of these two, and history has never considered it possible.

The two were one. Alaric could not make his telling and world-turning moves till he had Athaulf with him in Italy. And Athaulf, though he was the more intelligent of the two, was nothing without Alaric. Together they would bring the world down; but Athaulf, after the death of Alaric, became a very ordinary sort of man and was the leader of a never-again-distinguished force.

But their joining of forces on this day on the north bank of the river was only partial. Athaulf would support Alaric with men and arms and supplies as well as with a sweeping border-sort of diplomacy. But he would not yet re-enter the Empire, nor would he permit the élite of his forces to re-enter. They would come in only some years later, when it was time to put the Empire itself to death.

However, it was the other cousin, Singerich, who kept Alaric amused on their torturous march up the river, and his Greek salt was almost a new thing to Alaric. Here we are indebted to Hafras for almost the only episodic and daily details of Alaric that we are able to come on. Other accounts give a small space to the large things and nothing at all to the trivial; but Hafras has recorded scraps of the conversations of Alaric and Singerich on this campaign.

Singerich was a mocker and a self-mocker. There was very little of the earnestness of the Goths in him; nor was he a heavily religious man as were the Goths of the day. Though he would swear

by the Blood of the Martyrs and by the Wound of the Side of
Christ, as they all did, there was something very light about it with
Singerich. The Christ accepted by Singerich was the Laughing
Christ as carved by Creophylus, surely a more true Christ than
He of the Puritans and Manichees.

Singerich may have had in him a Gothic element that had not
yet come to the surface in the main body of solemn Goths. All the
Goths were grotesque, but Singerich seemed to be the only one
who realized their grotesqueness and made game of it. It would
come to the fore in the next century and the next, when the Goths,
in their new kingdoms in south France and Spain, would begin to
carve and rime and build with that high Gothic humor. It would
come to the fore strongly eight hundred years later when they built
the great cathedrals of Europe, which are *not* misnamed Gothic—
with apes and deformed angels and gargoyles and monsters crawl-
ing all over them inside and out—and when there would be another
Laughing Christ, in France, by a Gothic hand.

Now Singerich ran on in easy anecdote. He told Alaric of the
time when he had visited his sister Stairnon at the farm in Little
Moesia. He had gone to the baths, well built in the Roman style
before the farm was first abandoned and still operable as such. But
Stairnon was using them as a place for storing fruit; the Goths had
not used the baths after the novelty had worn off. Stairnon had
told him that it is not necessary for a person to wash more than the
face and the hands and the feet, and that a basin would suffice for
that. Alaric could see nothing funny in the account and was puzzled at the merriment of Singerich. He explained to Singerich that
at the time of his own recent visit the baths were being used as
an icehouse and a smokehouse.

Singerich also told of the Gothic countryman who came to the
city of Constantia and entered a room of a private building, the
guest of a suspected Greek-Roman with whom he had business.
When the Goth turned to leave the room he could not make the
door opener work. He believed himself to be ambushed and
trapped in a strange place, and he set up a great outcry and beat

his head on the floor. He was about to turn his sword on himself and have it done with, when his host opened the door and came in to see what was wrong. The Goths, to open doors, turn all clasps, handles, and hafts to the left; but the Romans to the right. But the Goth left the city at once and did not transact his business; for who can trust one of a people that does all things backwards.

Singerich told of another Gothic clodhopper coming into an Empire city and being unable to tell the shaven and plucked men from the women. The Gothic men wore trousers and usually beards; but the Romans and Greeks, both the men and the women, were a clouted, skirted, and robed people, close-cropped and usually scented. The story of Singerich had a Greek denouement, and Alaric is reported to have flushed with shame.

Singerich told his stories in dialect, and Alaric for the first time was painfully aware that he himself spoke both Latin and Greek with an intolerable Gothic accent. Previously he had assumed that it was the old Empire people who spoke their own tongues in a peculiar manner.

Singerich caused Alaric himself, who was a familiar of the Royal Family, to feel like a clod. But there was no meanness in the jibes and satire of Singerich. They took a little flesh off, but not much; and the new contact with his cousin Singerich would broaden Alaric's outlook. Still, it is difficult to ungoth a Goth; and culture —the turning into the Greek—is not brought about in one afternoon.

The epic element kept creeping in, in spite of the banter of Singerich, and it took hold even of that Greek-Goth. Singerich was a man of the world too early, but he was still boy enough to abandon his prospects and business in Constantia and go off soldiering with his ungainly cousin. Singerich could as well have been a general as a lawyer or minister; he could have been anything. He had traveled by boat to both Asia and Africa, but he had never traversed such an exhilarating course as that sea of trees and mountains.

It was an august and epic journey up the river, great hardship in travel and extreme beauty in landscape, some bloodshed and death in involvements with both settled and unsettled peoples, and the gathering thunderheads of the building Gothic storm. There were portents, as there are at the inception of every great undertaking. Ravens cried out to them in human voice at Corabia and at Severia, near the cataracts, stones fell on them from the moon. It was Gothic country, and here the Goths were not uncouth.

Singerich, the Goth-turned-Greek, sometimes felt that he was the one who had missed the significance. He came once on Alaric praying at sundown, kneeling and facing his saddle atop its saddle bags on the ground, as the pious in more settled places had now adopted the practice of praying kneeling and facing a household chair. Singerich wished, for a moment, that he had not left off being a Goth.

This was not empty country. There were skirmishes with the settled peoples of Dacia and Dalmatia and Pannonia; and with the unsettled peoples of Noricum. It was at the junction of the Savo and the Danube rivers that Alaric and Athaulf parted company for that time. Athaulf still would not enter the Empire. He would not actively support the Roman thing, and his friendship for Alaric prevented his opposing it. He was waiting for a special sort of call and would brew his own brand of Gothic thunder beyond the precincts of the Empire; when the time came he would add his own forces to the building storm. Nevertheless, he was never entirely out of contact with Alaric. There would be runners and emissaries between Alaric on the Savo and his cousin Athaulf on the Danube.

Stairnon had joined the party briefly at some point, coming with the Gothic farmer warriors from Little Moesia, their harvest now completed. She was sometimes near the forces of her brother Athaulf, sometimes with those of her brother Singerich and her betrothed (at this time it seemed to be accepted by some at least) Alaric. Many of the runners and contacts between the two forces were of her personal party. But a few days after her arrival with the Gothic farmers, and the separation of the groups of Alaric and Athaulf, she returned to Little Moesia.

From here on one could smell the coming battle, one of the turning points of the world. Alaric, naïve though he might seem to his cousin Singerich, was militarily sophisticated. Several hundred miles before reaching their destination, he felt one force strongly, the compelling force of the enemy he would face. This influence was leading him and guiding him, and he knew that it was also channeling the main army of the Emperor Theodosius to follow a preset route. They must follow a certain set of paths, and not others. It seemed as though it was the nature of the country that was guiding them, but there was another nature involved. There were mountains showing themselves forbidding, and mountains showing themselves hospitable. There were streams and trails beckoning to Alaric, and others that refused all passage.

Alaric knew, by signs just beyond the direct apprehension of the senses, which passes would be guarded by fanatical fighters and which passes would be left open to him. He was sure that Theodosius and Stilicho and Timasius were being similarly guided and would be unable to resist taking the selected ways. They were being led into a trap, and they could go no other way.

Alaric was in admiration of the Frankish Count Arbogast, the man who had devised this, their coming antagonist whom he had never seen. The rebel was orchestrating the natural setting of the entire Empire with scattered hundreds of men here and there. He would fight his battle in one place and no other; and at his own time; and under his own conditions. He forced the very mountains and rivers into his own plan, and arranged it that his enemies could come at him by only one way. He would draw the advancing forces towards him at the pace he would set and by the passes he wished, and there would be no other way whatsoever by which they could attack him. There would be only one battlefield possible—the environs of Aquileia—on which an army coming from the east could not win.

How had the Frankish Count Arbogast become so powerful? And why was it of the highest moment that he should be crushed? And why was it maintained that the entire future turned on this one civil conflict, when there had been such conflicts beyond number in the history of the Republic and the Empire?

Arbogast and his Emperor Eugenius were not destroyers of the Empire. They were Empire men as fervid as were the Emperor Theodosius and his master generals. The paganism of Arbogast and Eugenius was not the old paganism of the classic times. It was a new cult paganism, and the Empire was the very center of the cult. It was to this that the deified Emperors had led. It was against this that the idea of the divinely constituted Christian Empire, as understood by Ambrose and Theodosius and Stilicho, had arisen as counterpoise.

The Empire following the victory of Arbogast would not be at all the same sort as the Empire following the victory of Theodosius. The Arbogastian Empire might not have fallen, but it would have frozen. It would have made a China of Europe. For better or worse, we today would not be the same men we are, nor live the same lives, had Arbogast been the victor—as it seemed he must be. That the battle was crucial for all the future was realized at the time.

It was believed by the Emperor Theodosius, by his mentor the Archbishop Ambrose, by the master generals and by the lesser generals that, should the pagan forces of Arbogast and Eugenius be victorious, it would mean the reign of Hell over the Empire; and that the reign would endure for a thousand years. Whether it was truly Hell is a matter of viewpoint. Many moderns have welcomed the Arbogastian thing on its reappearance in our own time.

But to Arbogast and to Eugenius, and to their opponents Theodosius and Stilicho and Timasius and others, this was not an ordinary civil war.

The strength of Arbogast was that he had fought the battle of the narrow plains of Aquileia before and now had with him commanders who had taken part, on both sides, in that previous peculiar battle. He had fought with and against every sort of soldier who would be involved. He had been assistant to the Emperor

Theodosius in the campaign for the containment of the Goths, and he believed that he still knew how to contain them. He had had a large part in the struggle against the Western barbarians and the forces of the Western Empire as led by the usurper Magnus Maximus.

Now he commanded those same Western forces—greatly increased in number and resources—and opposed his old Eastern army—greatly diminished. Arbogast had the advantage of every mistake that Magnus Maximus had made, though Magnus had been in the way of winning the battle when he lost his life. Arbogast would be very careful with his own life, and he would fight a narrow battle where Magnus had fought a broad one.

Arbogast was supreme on the Adriatic. He had more ships than Theodosius, better fitted, better situated. He had finer harbors, particularly that of the great fortress city of Ravenna; the richer Italian Adriatic coast with the better provisioned country behind it. He held the interceptors' angle over any sea force that Theodosius could send against him.

But Arbogast did not intend that there should be any sea action; and there would not be. His whole marine tactic was to preclude any action there by a clear show of supremacy. Arbogast would keep the battle narrow and set it in the place and under the terms of his own choosing.

Arbogast concentrated his great forces in north Italy, except for certain harrowing and guarding details that would guide his enemy by one way only into north Italy. The resistance of the force of Arbogast to that of Theodosius was very selective. He let Theodosius and his auxiliaries occupy all of Pannonia and Noricum as far as the Julian Alps. In the Julians he blocked some passes with picked troops who were sworn to stand and die and not be moved. Other passes he left open, the token resistance that he had set in them melting away at the first contact with the troops of the Eastern Emperor, melting away according to previous plan.

Theodosius, his great Master Generals Stilicho and Timasius, the commanders of the special detachments, as Alaric of the Gothic group and Bacurius of the Spanish Horse, the tribunes, the centurions, the soldiers down to the basics, all knew that they were being led into a trap and exactly what sort of trap it was. They knew it, but they had to enter. There was no choice.

Arbogast had studied in a school for generals under Theodosius in a more true sense than had Alaric and his fellow cadets. Now his treachery turned all his resources against his old master. It was a battle that Arbogast, under no conceivable circumstances, could lose.

Here a footnote must be intruded into the middle of the text. The topographical key to the action is not to be found in the old sources. We are told what happened, but are left dumbfounded as to why such a sequence was possible. What froze the Goths where they stood and let them be slaughtered? Why did Stilicho attack on such a hopelessly narrow front? Why could not the Eastern reserves be used through the long first day of the battle? And what was the meaning of the mad cavalry charges led by Sarus and others far upstream from the main field of battle? Expert military analysis of the compulsion of the topography on the action is needed, and it is not to be found in the ancient accounts.

Fortunately—for the purposes of this study but not for those involved, for it was a bloody affair—the battle was fought all over again fifteen hundred years later on the exact site; and in this modern connection there exists voluminous expert military analysis of the relation of topography to battle action. Many of the anomalies of the great struggle between the forces of Theodosius and Arbogast are explained by comparison with the Italian-Austrian engagement on exactly the same site on August 12, 1916 and the several days following.

For this reason many of the features of that landscape have been given modern names only. We will confess it: we do not, in many cases, know the ancient names, nor have we been able to find them out.

8. As Good a Graveyard as Any

We come soon to our main action. There are men to be killed and Principalities to be demolished. We are now at the time and place of the battle of the River Frigidus—the third battle of Aquileia—the battle that did make a difference. In earlier centuries, it might not have mattered so much whether Rome or Carthage had conquered. In the same fourth century, it did not matter too much whether the Romans or the "barbarians" conquered, for the "barbarians" were also Romans. But it did make a difference whether Theodosius or Arbogast conquered. The issue either way would have produced a different world for the future. Had it gone with Arbogast, it would have been the end of the Church in the world, for better or worse.

But we have divine sanction and assurance that the Church will endure to the end of the world, it is said. No, we do not have assurance that it will endure in effective external form, nor in popularly recognized identity, nor by name or ritual, nor openly at all. The reassurance that the Church will endure does not apply to the furniture of the Church in this world.

Stilicho tried to impress the importance of the event upon his army. He addressed his tribunes and commanders and the commanders of the federated forces, probably the day before the battle. The point is obscured, coming to us through the verse of Claudian, but Stilicho speaks of the time as being memorable, as being the end of the *first century*. But *saeculum,* the word he

employed, means more than century. It has a special meaning
that is related to the word sacred, a meaning more like millennium.
He also used an involved phrase—"years of the days of the years."
It is known that there were Adventists who expected the second
coming of Christ at the end of the Greater Century, the years of
the days, the three hundred and sixty-five years after the Crucifixion. There were others who expected the coming of Antichrist
and the battle of Armagedon. To Stilicho and to his Emperor,
Arbogast and Eugenius were the two faces of Antichrist, and this
was Armagedon.

Stilicho was neither an Adventist nor a Mystic, but he was a
soldier and an orator who would employ what devices he could
discover for the exhortation of his men. He told them that this
was the end of the Greater Century and that this was the most
dread of all battles. The year 394 being taken as the end of the
Grand Century would have placed the Crucifixion in the year
29—but this does not do extreme violence to the records. It is
known that there is an error of from two to five years at the beginning of the era.

To the site of the battle then, where the secondary results will
be more important than the immediate and intended.

Gibbon writes: "He [Theodosius] descended from the hills,
and beheld, with some astonishment, the formidable camp of the
Gauls and Germans [the army of Eugenius and Arbogast] that
covered with arms and tents the open country which extended
to the walls of Aquileia and the banks of the Frigidus, or Cold
River." But Gibbon, who was never wrong, had to be wrong here.

It is thirteen miles from Aquileia to the nearest point of the
Frigidus—where it flows into the Sontius. But it is not now, and
could not have been then, open country. The only open country
is immediately around Aquileia, and the distance to Frigidus
covers some of the most forbidding terrain in the world.

A short sketch of the battle site is required to understand why
the fighting was so straited; why the forces of Arbogast and Eugenius were able to maneuver, and those of Theodosius and his

master generals were not; and why those forces, coming from the East, had to enter that narrow trap.

The uneven south face of the battle site is the Adriatic Sea and the Gulf of Trieste. The vertical axis is the Sontius River—later called the Isonzo and today the Sonzo—flowing generally from the north and into the Trieste Gulf about four miles east of Aquileia. The horizontal axis is the Frigidus River—later called the Wippach and the Vipao and today the Vipacco—flowing generally out of the east and into the Sontius River about ten miles north of the Trieste Gulf.

It was by the pass of the Frigidus River that the armies of Theodosius came down from the Julian Alps, to find the armies of Arbogast occupying the west bank of the Sontius upstream, and both banks of that river downstream, below the juncture of the Frigidus.

The Frigidus is a narrow river, descending rapidly from the high Alps and deserving its name of "cold." The river and the valley of it pass between the peaks of Mount St. Gabriel on the north, and Mount St. Michael on the south. The mountain of St. Michael, at the south bank of the Frigidus and very near the Sontius juncture, was the cork in the bottle that imprisoned the Eastern armies. They would have to fight their way through the narrow passage between the shoulder of the mountain and the rivers, before they could come out onto the plains and into Italy at all.

North of the River Frigidus were the mountains, including the St. Gabriel peak, and extending even to the western side of the Sontius River—the shore held by the forces of Arbogast.

South of the Frigidus was the forbidding Carso Plateau, with only two breaks in its impenetrable shield. There was a deep dry valley, the Vallone, cutting through south to the Adriatic between heights on either side; and there was the narrow way along the east bank of the Sontius, between that river and the abrupt west face of the Plateau.

The portion of the Carso that is to the west of the Vallone is

called the Doberdo Plateau, but it is only a continuation of the
Carso.

The forces of Theodosius must drive against those of Arbogast
through the narrow valley between the Sontius River and the
Doberdo Plateau; or they must drive against them down the Vallone, between the Doberdo Plateau and the Carso. There was
no other possible way to go. Actually, it was necessary that they
proceed on both ways. Abandoning either would allow them to
be outflanked and taken.

There was this pass of the Frigidus River that the forces of
Theodosius used—the pass of modern Gorizia. And there was the
fine Roman Road coming up along the Adriatic from the south-
east—and controlled by the forces of Arbogast—which entered
by way of modern Trieste. There was not, and is not, any other
practical way for an army to come into Italy from the east.

The army of Arbogast held what open country there was—
around Aquileia, on both shores of the Sontius for its final few
miles, and a fair open corner between the Sontius, the Doberdo,
and the Trieste Gulf. The Eastern armies could come into these
open areas only by forcing one or the other of the narrow ways.
The way between the Doberdo and the Sontius would leave them
strung out in narrow file and in range of broadsides of missiles
shot by expert archers arrayed in depth on the west bank of the
Sontius—the river was a narrow one. There were exceptionally
narrow ways where the men of the East must pass in absolute
single file, and the attrition on their forces would be terrible before
they ever came to immediate conflict.

The only other way by which the Eastern armies could come
down was through the Vallone, which had never been forced.
It had been known for centuries as a graveyard.

Arbogast had the walled city of Aquileia for a final refuge, and
a number of walled camps. Arbogast had waited and provisioned
for the six weeks during which the Eastern armies had come by
forced marches. He had, in fact, been dug in and waiting for several years. It was impossible that anyone should have prepared
more thoroughly than did Arbogast.

He could make the battle as narrow or as wide as he wished by meeting the Eastern forces higher or lower in the space between the Doberdo Plateau and the Carso. He could let the Easterners come through in a trickle, and then shut off that trickle when he had gathered enough of them in the pocket to swallow at one time. The choosing of the type of battle was up to Arbogast, and he could alter his choice at any time he wished.

All the commanders concerned, on both sides, except the very young ones such as Alaric, had fought this same battle before. It was known to all of them that, except for the intervention of Fate, the army attacking from the east could not win. This advantage of defense had helped keep Italy secure for centuries.

Of the Carso Plateau—all these high places are actually a part of the Julian Alps—there is a local legend of its beginning. God, after He had finished making the world, gathered up all the stones that were left over, and was going to dump them into the sea. But the Devil, catching up with Him there, slit open the bag that held the stones, and they spilled out. This made the Carso: and it made it a Devil's area; the stones, the boulders, were really worthless and should have been cast into the sea. They remain an abomination on the earth. The story is told of other high places, one in Mexico and one in New Guinea, so it must be assumed that the Devil played the trick more than once.

A feature of the Carso is the occurrence of what the modern Italians call the *doline,* huge cup-shaped hollows that can hold a man or a horse hidden. Parties of archers could be set in these, to cover large areas with their field of shot.

The earth of the Carso is red, the limestone white. There is no vegetation greater than grass or low brush in the whole of the formation. The Vallone, cutting like a fissure through the high Carso, is a dry gulch murderously hot and breathless in the summer, and there is no water at all in its ten mile length.

These barren crags of the Doberdo and the Carso, the farthest south thrust of the Julian Alps, form their own mosaic of rocks, and combine to produce the effect of their own great face. It is the face of the Devil.

Except for the intervention of Fate, an army attacking from the east could not win. But the Emperor Theodosius and his Master General Stilicho *intended* to win. And both had previously demonstrated a masterful way with Fate. As Catholic men, or as Arians, their strategists and themselves could not believe in Fate. But as practical manipulators they understood the allegorical meaning of Fate as applied to political efforts. But Fate was plural: the *Moerae,* called the *Parcae* by the Romans.

The first of the Fates was Clotho, the spinner who spun out the thread of life. The threads of Clotho, however, could be counterfeited; and man-made threads could be wafted out to serve as the stuff of life and affairs. Theodosius and Stilicho had already counterfeited some of them in preparation for the grand action.

The second of the *Moerae* was Lachesis, who dealt out chance and luck and fortune. But Lachesis was a vacillating woman who could be compelled by the intrepid. Should one present a draft for a certain amount of luck, and present it with enough assurance, it might very well be honored. Lachesis is short-sighted and cannot read the fine print of the credentials, only the bold heading. Theodosius and Stilicho had presented such credentials.

The third of the Fates, the *Parcae,* was Atropos who irrevocably cut all the threads of life, and from whom there was no appeal. But Atropos, though she could not be reversed, could yet be anticipated. The threads could very well be cut before she got there; and there was no appeal from this prior cutting, either. Theodosius and Stilicho both practiced judicious assassination from a distance, when it would serve their high cause. By this they had somewhat thinned out the more competent men about Arbogast, and warned others—men who, had they lived till they were disposed of by the Fates, might have been troublesome.

Clotho who spun the thread of life; Lachesis who measured it and gave it fortune; Atropos who cut it off—the Three Fates. But the Christian men believed themselves to be the masters and not the servitors of these Fates. The threads that Theodosius and Stilicho had spread out were long and numerous ones, and they wafted several thousand miles across the Empire like webs of giant spiders. To every treason there is a counter; and to the intricate treason of Arbogast they had responded with their own manifold intrigue. They had set out their seeds, and they believed that enough of them would grow. This seed would root beyond their sight, but there should be a harvest ready to their hand when they came.

Theodosius believed that he would be able to predict that harvest. It was an unfortunate delay in it that made him believe it had failed entirely. It was for this reason that the Emperor was sick with sorrow when he came out above the battle site and saw the vast army opposing him. His harvest had not grown. There was nothing of the good wheat at all, nothing but the pagan cockle.

Theodosius had not received a single emissary coming covertly from the enemy forces, and he had expected half a hundred. He had failed, and his project had failed.

When the turning in their favor did come, some twenty hours later, Theodosius and Stilicho had already given up and despaired of it; and had resigned themselves to defeat and death. But when it did come, it was as the delayed fruit of their preparation and intrigue. Luck and fortune do not always come in prescribed form, nor on time.

But the Emperor Theodosius was without hope on that first morning of the battle. He ordered that the Viaticum—the Holy Eucharist for those at the hour of their death—should be administered to all his men, Catholic and Arian.

Alaric and his Gothic contingent were ordered by Stilicho to advance down the Vallone. It was then that Alaric and Stilicho gazed at each other over the heads of their tall soldiery. The whole action would be a death trap, but Alaric had enough apperception to realize that the Vallone would be a charnel house beyond anything else.

It could be that Stilicho had already recognized Alaric as a threat to the Empire and would not be sorry to see him dead—if it would serve the Empire, of course. It could also be that they would all be dead that day, and it would not too much matter who went first.

The main force, generaled by Theodosius and Stilicho and Timasius, would move into the narrow passage between the River Sontius and the Doberdo Plateau. The right wing, led by the Spanish commander Bacurius and including the raiding parties of Arabians, Scythians, and the dare-devil Gothic élite of horsemen under Sarus, would raid across the Sontius high above the main battle, and harry and disconcert the flankers of Arbogast. They had no real hope of establishing themselves in numbers across the Sontius. Their moves were diversionary, madly and successfully so in the circus antics of Sarus and his select Goths, and defensive, though seeming to be a precipitous offense. The move was to draw as many Western men as possible off from the terrible array that would be punishing the Theodosian force as it filed through the vulnerable narrow passage.

Alaric, commanding the left wing of the army, led his Goths sullenly down the Vallone to die. They livened up quickly, however. They did not know the name of defeat—certainly not of defeat before the battle was even joined.

The flutes and the trumpets were perfunctory. The sound of command quickly became the voices of the commanders—echoing like the cries of so many muleteers over the rocks.

The sun had not yet reached the floor of the Vallone when the men of Alaric entered its length and engaged the advance guards of Arbogast. Neither had the wind that gathered about the heights penetrated down into the gulch; nor would it do so all day. The breath of the Vallone was stale, and its history for thousands of years could be read in its stench.

This was not actually the third battle of Aquileia; it was more like the three hundredth. And in every one of them there must have been deadly flank action in the Vallone. One could have assembled a skeleton in short minutes from the wealth of old human bones there, though wagon loads of them had been hauled off and used for fertilizer. Doomed forces had passed their final very long day here before. There was the smell of bruised weeds and boscage, and of hot rocks and curling dust. The Vallone is a desert where the mountains nearly meet overhead.

There was a whisper and a cry, and the first Gothic foot soldier was transfixed by the first arrow.

A German gentleman in the time of Frederick II complained that his son had been five years to the wars and had killed, for his share, only a probable one fifth of a man. The gentleman thought that the thing should be put on a more efficient footing. But the proportion holds roughly, and has always held.

The killing in warfare goes monstrously slow. If every man got his man there would be none left to tell about it. It is the epics and the presentations and dramas that give the idea that it is an accelerated business—that each man gets a dozen in half as many minutes.

Even in a carnage like that in the Vallone—and it was a carnage almost without equal—the killing seemed to go slowly. There were, perhaps, fourteen thousand Goths strung out; by midafternoon they held most of the ten-mile length of the gulch. They were subject to shot of arrow and catapult and Frankish spear and rocks from above; and they were opposed by a series of barricades which they had to take one by one for ten miles. The further they advanced, the more they were exposed; for both heights were held by their enemy who shot down vertically on them from two hundred feet. There was no question of their finding cover at all; even the cover of overhanging rocks could be penetrated from the opposite side.

The Goths died every inch of the way and on every side, yet it would seem that they died slowly. Should only one die every quarter minute during that ten-mile melee, they would still be one-fourth of them dead by dark. Actually, three-quarters of them would be dead in the lengthy affair.

Alaric had more horse available than he chose to use. He would bring in several hundred horsemen every hour or so, to break the front of the opposing Western army details and to harry them another quarter mile down the gulch. But every assault must be prepared by foot soldiers, and every gain must be secured and maintained by them. In the rough course, the horses were more often led in than ridden in and were mounted only for the assault on the barricades. Provision wagons were drawn in where not normally needed, to give the Goths protection under them, not from the Western men facing them, but from the Western archers overhead on the heights of the Carso. Fire arrows set many of these blazing, and low-hanging, choking smoke added to the displeasures of the Vallone.

There were no troops in either force so green as to be intimidated by the charge of horse, even heavy horse. The Western footmen had repeatedly stood to horse before. But the mounted lancers of the Goths could slant in and cut swathes by their very weight, and permit Gothic foot soldiers to get behind groups of their opponents. The Goths all longed for the open plains where they could really use their horses; but open plains were the one thing that the astute Arbogast would not allow them.

The range was much shorter then, before gunfire. Though an arrow could kill a man at a hundred yards—a lucky lofted shaft could hit its mark at three times that distance—the swordsmen and lancemen would stand and size up their opponents, well out of range at fifty feet. It was engagement and disengagement. One man against one man was a draw, until one should fall by accident or weariness. It had to be suddenly two to one, or three to two, or four to three. Even with twelve to fifteen thousand men on either side in the Vallone there was no maintaining a solid front. It was a melee in depth with the front commonly a hundred yards wide (though sometimes less than fifty feet) and some two hundred yards deep. More than half of the Goths who were killed that day were killed by missiles showered down on them from the two opposite heights. The only safety from this rain of missiles was in the area of close combat with the Arbogastian troops, and the Goths were eager to take their chances in that area.

There were no particular heroics, no great chief rushing in to cut down a dozen or a hundred of the enemy. Nearly all the men present were superior fighting men. The very best of them—as

Alaric might rate himself—would hardly be worth two of the worst
of them, the minimum being very high. In the close fighting of
the Vallone the best man in the world was hardly worth a man
and a half. There was no room for brilliance, only for steadiness.
One stood and killed, or was killed.

The greatest torture was thirst; there was no water at all in the
Vallone. The Westerners had access to stores of it as they fell
back, but the Goths were unable to bring sufficient water carts
through the miles of the carnage. There was a dead heat hanging
over the gulch all that day at the end of the terrible summer. All
knew that, even for this place, the heat was unnatural—that it
must soon come to a breaking point in one of the violent storms
of the area. But the heat would hang on all that day and into the
night, and by that time most of the troops of Alaric would be dead.

Alaric used his own skirmishers. They climbed the opposing
heights and went about the business of killing and hunting down
the archers and ballista men and crossbowmen stationed there.
But they could get only a fraction of the thousands there, hidden
in the *doline*. Alaric also brought a few horses and mules up the
heights by the old secret paths to which there were always guides.
Once up the cliff paths, the horses covered the high rocks well,
for the tops of both plateaus were comparatively level though
very rough. The elimination of a part of the snipers lessened the
attrition on the troops below, and for the first time Alaric had
some hope.

Should he break through the whole length of the Vallone—that
terrible ten miles—to the head of the Adriatic, the enemy snipers
on the Carso side would then be isolated; and they would know
it from the trumpet calls, and from their own points of observa-
tion. If by that time, and it would be late afternoon, the numbers
of the snipers had been reduced sufficiently by the skirmishers of
Alaric, they might send emissaries to him and hold their fire. The
snipers on the Doberdo side would not be isolated, but the
Doberdo is not of great extent from east to west. Many more
skirmishers could be put onto its heights; they would not be in
danger of arrows in their backs from the Carso side as they

climbed the cliffs now. The Doberdo could be further invested during the night, and a considerable force might be brought across to its western crest.

Assuming that this should be successful, the Eastern armies could doubly flank the Western at dawn or just before, around the south end of the Doberdo where the Vallone comes out on the narrow sea plain, and down the western face of the Doberdo which, old soldiers said, was not so precipitous as the eastern.

Alaric climbed up among the crags of the east face of that same Doberdo, keeping his thousands of men under his eye and under the command of his voice. There was one who later remembered that the voice of Alaric seemed to come out of the clouds or out of the sky, and always from directly overhead, wherever in the length of the Vallone one heard it. The clouds of that day are mentioned by several as peculiar.

The clouds would come in low and sometimes screen off the tops of both plateaus entirely. They were full of red dust or, as one said, brimstone. Lightning played in these low clouds, though the sun could still be seen high in the sky. Ball lightning bounced back and forth. There was unusual electric display and static discharge about the men down in the Vallone. The weather was ominous, and there were still soldiers among the Goths pagan enough to believe in omens. It all presaged a great slaughter, they said.

Alaric knew that there would be a great slaughter, and he thought that the fantastic weather would not have anything to do with it. But in that he was wrong. The fantastic weather would have everything to do with it, and would finally decide the whole affair.

Alaric remained hopeful till late afternoon. He still believed that he could do it—up till the time when he had almost done it. There was a constant concourse of messengers coming and going. Stilicho had sent once to ask whether Alaric wanted relief for his men, whether other troops were desired. "No," Alaric had sent back in answer, "these will make dead men as good as any." The answer of Stilicho, reported as coming several hours later, was to ironic effect—"You want to see dead men? On the Sontius I can show you dead men."

But Alaric had already crossed and recrossed the top of the Doberdo, on horseback, and had looked down on the carnage beside the Sontius, between the heights and the river. Whether there were more dead in the main force or in the Gothic detachment—those of the main force were more concentrated and heaped up. The Gothic dead were strung out on a ten-mile course.

Alaric, in the action of that day, killed the first and the second man he ever killed. It is not known whether he ever killed other men in his life. A panegyrist ascribes thousands to him personally, but the form of the account argues against its complete validity.

It was late in the afternoon that Alaric realized he had lost, and he sent word to Stilicho to that effect. He could not have done differently in any case; there had been no other way to carry on the action.

The way of Alaric's men down the Vallone had been made too easy for several hours; it was murderous going, but it was still too easy. It had been a trap to get the Goths to overextend themselves, to go the final miles of the course instead of giving it up as impossible earlier in the day. Alaric could take the Vallone to its very end; but he would not have enough troops left alive to occupy the sea plain effectively, or to turn the corner for a flank attack on the main forces of Arbogast. Alaric had asked Stilicho whether he should begin the withdrawal up the gulch in order, or should wait until further reduction of his forces and the inevitable counterattack of the Arbogastians at darkness should turn the adventure into a rout. The answer from the Master General had not yet come. In the meanwhile Alaric decided, as a point of honor, to fulfill his assignment literally. He would take the Vallone to the very end of it, and then consider his own—and Stilicho's—decision.

It was an hour before sundown that the forces of Arbogast had let the Goths taste green grass and salt sea at the south end of the burning Vallone. Then the Westerners had mounted a su-

preme charge on the thin and overextended Goths. They overwhelmed them with five times their numbers of rested soldiery,
and the Goths had sustained the fearsome heat and thirst of the
Vallone for thirteen hours—since a little before dawn. The object
of the Arbogastians was to harry the Goths back over the ten
miles of stifling hell in the coming dark, to rout them and complete
their annihilation.

It was then that the message came from Stilicho. It stated that,
insofar as human forces and resources were concerned, they were
defeated utterly at all points. Nevertheless, he ordered Alaric not
to withdraw in either an orderly or disorderly manner. They were
to hold the end of the Vallone till there was not one man of them
left. And they were to continue to invest the two heights throughout the night—if they could find men at all for it. "You will find
it as good a graveyard as any," was the final cheerful word of the
Master General.

Alaric told his men to stand and die, and they accepted his
order. There was some bitterness among the Goths, however,
when their own observers on the top of the Doberdo reported
that the central forces of the Emperor Theodosius and his Master
Generals Stilicho and Timasius had themselves withdrawn from
the battlefield between the Sontius and the Doberdo, and had
taken refuge up the defile of the Frigidus and its hills on either
side. They hoped to find better graveyards, or none at all.

Singerich, the cousin of Alaric, came to him and told him that
the situation looked very bright to him. Alaric laughed bitterly
at his cousin's misunderstanding of the simple military situation.
But no, Singerich had not misunderstood the military situation;
he had as good an eye for that as anyone, and it was rather pressing, he admitted. But he had been talking with a number of the
enemies, on the heights and elsewhere, and he had found a deep
dissatisfaction in them. It might not be all over, he said; and Alaric laughed again mordantly.

It gives an idea of the enigmatic young man Singerich, that he
had entered into easy conversation and discussion with various of
the enemy all that day, even when the conflict was at its most bit-

ter. He was a born ambassador and minister and saw no reason for negotiations to cease just because people were killing each other.

The Goths were in red heaps of dying and dead, but Singerich claimed that he also shed blood in the cause. He suffered nosebleed, Hafras reports, from the heat of the day. The other intimate friends were dead, Vargas and Bacurinius and dozens more.

The Goths had lost three-quarters of their troops—more than ten thousand dead—and there was not one man among them not somehow wounded or lamed. They stood in a narrow point of the Vallone, near the end of it, and stopped the heavy assault as night came on.

They heard the movement of troops to their left, going eastward on the sea plain along the south face of the Carso, and they knew that all night the Western troops would be getting to their rear at every point. They heard the movement of troops to their right, and knew that the space between the Sontius and the Doberdo was being occupied in overwhelming numbers—where Stilicho had failed to clean them out in the day-long fight.

Alaric heard from messengers that Bacurius, the commander of the right wing of the Theodosian army, was dead, and that most of the intrepid irregulars were scattered and slaughtered. The Western armies were crossing the Sontius above the Frigidus junction and moving to positions behind the main forces of the Easterners—unless those were continuing in head-long flight through the night.

The Western attackers in the mouth of the Vallone had adopted a massive and disconcerting tactic. They had brought up heavy ballistae, and with these they launched great fireballs above the line of the stubborn Goths. These may have been the first artillery shells ever. Whatever their composition, they exploded with great flashes in the air. The damage was done by a thousand Western archers who let fly, from a hundred yards, at the moment of the flashes; the thousand arrows would whisper down on the numbed Goths in the suddenly following darkness. A man can see and fend an arrow of long course in daylight, but there was no fending these.

It would be a long night. The Arbogastians left off their games of the fireballs, and came in with torchmen and sword and spear to finish the Goths.

The Emperor Theodosius, in a make-shift tent on the Frigidus, was taken by a terrible fever—the same that would kill him four months later; for he would linger and never recover. He had seen the collapse of his Empire and his own coming death. He had seen also, he believed, the collapse of the Christian Church forever; for he, more than others, had appreciated what the victory of Arbogast and Eugenius would mean. Now he saw something else.

This was a dream, he recounted later; and yet it was a standing-up dream, for he left his pallet in the tent and went out in the night air. A fevered man, of course, might see anything in the configuration of the wild lightning that obtained that night; and a man of the vivid imagination of the Emperor might see just what he claimed he saw. Or it may be that the celestial riders actually appeared.

The Emperor Theodosius saw St. John and St. Philip on horseback in the sky. This is their first known appearance in military matters. They appeared to the Roman Emperor and not to his Goths—though, in the next thousand years, it would be to the descendants of those Goths that they would appear countless times in the same aspect, particularly to the Spanish descendants. In the latter appearances, the two Santi would most often be accompanied by St. James.

The Emperor saw the two Saints on horseback in the sky. He pointed them out carefully enough; but no others could see them, and it was believed that the Emperor was delirious.

Yet the Saints were there.

The turning of the fortunes came about midnight. Alaric discovered the trend from a Western soldier whom he took on the top of the Doberdo. The soldier told him that the trend was very widespread and would carry everything with it. Alaric was thought-

ful, and sent to find his cousin Singerich; but the Greek-Goth
had long been out and about the business of facilitating the
switch.

The first and most important of the leaders of the force of Arbogast who came to the Christian side was Saul, himself a pagan.
His importance was in that he, as an old-line pagan in all his ante-
cedents, had been placed by Arbogast in charge of the security
apparatus to discover and prevent defections. But Saul was of the
old rural pagans, not of the new cult paganism that had swept
the West. He had little but name in common with the paganism
of Arbogast and Eugenius.

The motive of Saul in switching to the Theodosian side is not
known. The story that he, like his namesake, saw a Great Light
must be rejected. Saul was still the cheerful pagan when he died
in battle several years later. He was a friend of Theodosius and
Stilicho; but he was also a friend of Arbogast. He was not particularly an opportunist and was known later to refuse prefer-
ment. He was a great soldier, and he came over to the Christian
side during the night; the reason for it cannot now be known.

It was in the same hour that various men began to come in to
Stilicho under the cover of darkness, to Stilicho who held all the
strands in his hands. The distant sowing had finally fruited, and
the late harvest might be ripe by morning. Arbogast had been
suppressing a rumble, and now it would turn into an explosion.
The distant intrigues and projects of Theodosius and Stilicho
hadn't rooted in the great Western leaders, except Saul; but they
had had effect on the medium leaders and on the men.

There was much coming and going through the electric night.
One emissary thundered in, his foam-covered horse crashing dead
at Stilicho's feet—the man leaping clear and giving the word that
a raiding detachment, as intrepid as that of Sarus, had switched.
Fifty more came or sent word, and the pattern formed in Stilicho's
mind. He knew now what hills he owned and what regions he
would own by morning. He knew who it was that was encircled
and trapped.

Stilicho sent what troops he could find to reinforce Alaric, who was still holding out in the south end of the Vallone and whose forces were now almost completely diminished. The holding of the Vallone had been essential to the resurrection of whatever hopes the Easterners might have had; the holding of the narrow way between the Doberdo and the Sontius had not been essential.

Stilicho now sent troops to complete the occupation of that Doberdo, and assembled guides who knew the west face of that height intimately and understood where troops could be brought down that face like torrents.

But Stilicho sent no troops at all to the main Carso shield. He was told, and he had no choice but to accept the information, that the Carso would not be a threat. Instead he drew troops, Western troops who would come over, from the Carso where they had been building up through the night.

Nor had Stilicho worry to spare for his lost right wing—for the dead Bacurius and his broken raiders. Stilicho was told, and again he had no choice but to accept the information, that he would be provided with a new right wing. But he did not let his trust in these things overwhelm him. He sent hundreds of his most loyal men as contacts and reinforcements to his new *fiderati*.

Daylight showed a fearsome panorama, the meaning of which was not immediately apparent to all. The Emperor Theodosius cried out in despair at seeing the armies of Arbogast and Eugenius filling the valley of the Sontius on both sides of the river, at seeing the standards of those Western forces on the peaks behind him, at seeing the pass of the Frigidus behind him black with their numbers, at hearing their trumpets and fifes all through the Carso and the Doberdo and entirely around him in a thirty-mile circle. The sounds of the horns was particularly full and heavy, from a peculiarity of the atmosphere.

There was also a terrifying noise building up like trumpets in the sky. It had been singing over the high Alps through the night. The sun rose blood-colored, and the whole sky and air were red. The Emperor was ready to give his soul to God, but Stilicho comforted him and told him to wait a bit.

Theodosius waved his hand to the thousands of Western troops, now infiltrated to the east of them, and asked in a shaking voice— for he had begun to die that night—how it could have happened; how could the master generals not have known that it was happening?

"They are not theirs. They are ours," Stilicho told the fevered Emperor.

The encircling troops of Arbogast, free of the tight hand of that master, had revolted during the night; and either murdered their commanders or compelled them to swear loyalty to the legitimate Emperor. The commanders of those troops, the old Roman Christians, had been subverted by Arbogast and Eugenius in the two-year indoctrination, and had been solid in their support of the pagan movement. It was the new "barbarian" Christians, the commoners who made up the bulk of the forces, who had gagged at the treason and waited their opportunity. They were barbarian in their ancestry, but they had swung to the Roman Emperor against the barbarian Pretender, Arbogast.

The Master General Stilicho had gathered into his hands, in the six hours before dawn, the divergent strands of that revolt. It was a late harvest but a good one, and from a field not considered. Fate had been compelled, and the draft on Fortune was honored.

The Imperial army, coming from the east, had been defeated in the battle of Frigidus and Aquileia the day before, for an army attacking from the east could not win. They had lost the battle at sundown. But victory was waiting for them in the morning.

But prelude to, and final effector of, the victory was the tempest.

The storm, having become entwined in legend, cannot be appraised as can non-legendary storms. Yet the accounts of it that have come to us may not be too much exaggerated. An English traveler of the nineteenth century describes a tempest in exactly the same locality in even more extravagant terms.

Terrible end-of-the-summer tempests, coming out of the Julian Alps onto the plains that begin in front of Aquileia, had been known for thousands of years. They would follow on a burning heat of two months' duration in their incredible climate.

The tempest of the morning of September fifth (or sixth—the date is disputed) of the year 394 must have been, by any standards, a violent one. It had been building up through the torrid months to the final hellish heat of the day before. There had been dust in the air so heavy that one could taste it, and the sun had risen blood red. It struck in full fury, blowing dead out of the east, down from the heights, shortly after dawn.

The force of it, coming on the Western foot soldiers where they stood, knocked them flat. Supply wagons were tumbled and rolled and blown for long distances high in the air. It blinded the Western army and encompassed them in a solid red cloud.

And out of the tempest struck the Eastern Imperial forces. They had lain flat on their bellies letting the strength of it pass over them. Now they came on its trailing edge, down from the Doberdo heights, around the shoulder of the shielding Mount St. Michael, out of the sea plain from the lower end of the Vallone.

The assault of the Imperial Eastern Army might not have been of effect without the previous terrible assault of the tempest. Many of the Western Christians-turned-pagan saw the tempest, coming at that moment, as the Storm of God, and they became Christians again. Many had been injured—and even killed—by the sudden force of the hurricane, and their confusion was complete.

Arbogast saw, with disbelief, his own left wing turn on his own forces, becoming the new right wing of the armies of Theodosius and Stilicho. They were behind him on the western bank of the Sontius, and behind him all the way to the walls of Aquileia. His most talented forces, which he had sent out in the night to cut off the flight of the Eastern army, had returned as his enemies in the van of those Eastern armies.

The revolt spread like grass fire around the person of Arbogast. Legions and detachments, one after the other, struck their standards and set their heralds to crying out their new, and original, allegiance to the Emperor Theodosius. It was a rout, and it could not be stemmed. Arbogast, the traitor, was betrayed.

For better or for worse, that was the end of the Roman pagan effort, though it was not clearly seen in that light except by the "barbarians" of the Western forces who had spontaneously revolted. Spontaneously—but as the fruit of the two-year counter-intrigue of Theodosius and Stilicho.

It was also, very nearly, the end of the budding Gothic effort—for they had lost ten thousand men, dead, from their finest forces. It is not known to what degree the inscrutable Stilicho had intended this side effect.

The pseudo-Emperor Eugenius was killed where they found him. It is said that he died cravenly, but that is a partisan report. He may have died bravely enough.

Count Arbogast, however, found a horse and cut his solitary way through half a dozen encirclements, wilder than the most daring of the raiders; swam his mount across the Sontius, left it dead in the shallows, and went up a cliff face on the east bank of that river.

Three days later in the mountains, unable to gather followers and hounded tightly, he ended it in the pagan manner—with his own sword.

9. Of the Return of East and West

The Emperor Theodosius died in January of the year 395. He was
the last of the Roman Emperors who led his troops in battle, and
the last who reigned by sheer ability. His son Arcadius was seventeen years old. His other son, Honorius, was eleven years old. He
left the Empire to these two and, in so doing, divided it once more
into East and West. It would remain divided forever.

Theodosius had resurrected a dead Empire, but he had not the
time to bring it to health. It is disputed whether it could ever
have been brought to real life again; but for fifteen years, till the
very end, it had seemed as though it might.

Of the contemporaries of the Emperor Theodosius: Siricius was
Pope in Rome and would die in three years; St. Ambrose of Milan
would be dead in two years, as would be St. Martin of Tours. St.
Ambrose, however, had won his battle; the two great minds of the
opposing parties had been his and that of the pseudo-Emperor
Eugenius.

Augustine, a man of forty, would become Bishop of Hippo
Regius in Africa in the following year. He has been called the first
modern man and may have been the most intelligent observer and
actor in the Empire in all those years. St. Jerome was in Jerusalem
about the business of the great Bible, his translation of the Hebrew
and Greek into the Vulgate Latin which became fixed and remains
the Latin of the Church. It was the case of a man's—a mere trans-
lator's—personal style becoming the style of a universal church
and a civilization.

St. Benedict, the father of monasticism, was unborn; but the institution was in vigorous life before the birth of its father. Gregory of Nazianzen was dead five years, and Gregory of Nyassa died in the same year as Theodosius. St. Cyril of Alexandria was fifteen years old. It has been called the Golden Age of the Greek fathers, but it doesn't take much to make up a Golden Age. Actually, the Early Middle Ages had already begun, unnoticed.

Galla Placidia, the future Empress and wife of a King and an Emperor (not the same person) and mother of an Emperor, was two years old. St. Patrick, the Apostle of Ireland, was the same age; as was Attila the Hun.

There was a shiver went over the world on the death of the Emperor Theodosius—a shock that was felt only by a very peculiar group. There was in the world an ancient brotherhood of kings and emperors—the most exclusive club ever. They might not know each other, even by name; but when one of them died, all the rest of them knew it and felt it as though they had suffered a stroke to their own body. They felt a very heavy stroke now, for the greatest of them was dead.

At that time, Chandragupta Vikramaditya was Emperor in north India, and Upatissa was King in Ceylon. In fragmented China, Toba of the eastern Tsin was King in Ta-tung Fe; Wu Ku was King in Hsi-ping; Kuei ruled the state of Tai in northern Shansi; and there were lesser kinglets in every province. The Empress Jingo was supreme in Japan; Niall was High King in Ireland; Xhusru was Regent in Armenia; and Varahran IV was Pad-Shah in Sassanian Persia. But they were not the world—they were only on the fringes of the world. All of them knew which was *The Empire,* and that it was *The Emperor* himself who was dead; and that the latter days had come to the world.

After the victory of the battle of the River Frigidus and Aquileia, the stricken Theodosius had gone directly to Milan and embraced the Archbishop Ambrose. Rome was the See of the Pope, Ravenna was in the process of becoming the seat of the Western Emperor—though there was no Emperor at the time except Theodosius, the Emperor of both East and West—but it was Milan that was the moral focus of the Empire, due to the presence of Ambrose there. The Archbishop Ambrose had represented the only effective resistance in the West to the paganism of Arbogast and Eugenius. He was the only man who was not broken by their influence; sometimes subtle, sometimes murderous.

It was at Milan that Theodosius received the submission of the rebellious provinces of the West; and it was to Milan that he called his son Honorius from Constantinople, after peace had been established.

This eleven-year-old son was now made Emperor of the West by his father, Theodosius, to be under the guardianship of Stilicho. The machinery for the transfer of power was clearly put into Stilicho's hands. It was given to the Emperor Theodosius to know the day and the hour of his death in advance and while he was still ambulant and clear in his mind. This is sometimes spoken of as a divine favor to him; but many persons would be willing to forego such a favor.

There was great public rejoicing at the exaltation of the boy Honorius to be Emperor; which turned to sudden sorrow on the death of Theodosius the following night. The condition of the Emperor had not been known to the people.

Theodosius had been a sincere man, but a chilly man without the common touch. Yet he was mourned by the common people as had been no Emperor since Philip the Arab one hundred and forty-six years before. Philip had owed the people a grand death, and given it to them, following his celebration of the *ludi saecularea* for the one thousandth birthday of the city of Rome. Theodosius hadn't quite such a spectacle as background to his death; but he did crown his son and then die—as if the moment were of his own choosing.

Theodosius had made a sound choice for the Western Empire—in providing an Emperor of the blood line, and in establishing a very strong guardian over him. The young Emperor Honorius was to remain for the rest of his life as he was then—with the mind of a bright eleven-year-old boy. It is not known why he did not develop, but both Stilicho and Theodosius must have suspected that he would not. With the Master General Stilicho as guardian, the West was in good hands—in spite of the life-long immaturity of the Emperor.

The solution in the East was not so happy a one. The boy Arcadius, seventeen years old, had been given the crown privately before his father left on the campaign against Arbogast, before he knew how that event would turn. The Emperor Arcadius had neither the bodily health nor the good humor of his younger brother; but he was already a man in mind, though he would be a man of weak will. He was intelligent, but not intelligent enough to rule an Empire; and there would come times when he would insist on ruling. It was too much to expect that the extraordinary abilities of Theodosius would be transmitted; and it was too much to expect that an ordinary man would be able to rule half the world.

It was said that Arcadius had been born as an old man. New-born babies do sometimes look like caricatures of old men, but in the case of Arcadius this appearance was so pronounced as to be considered a prodigy. Nor did he ever lose that look entirely. All through his boyhood and early manhood he had a little of the look of an old man. And he did age prematurely and die at an early age.

The guardian of the young Emperor Arcadius of the East was the Master of Offices, Rufinus. Theodosius had not made as good a choice here as in the West—but there was only one Stilicho.

Rufinus was born in Gaul, in what is now Gascony. He has had rough handling in history; and has been painted in colors so black that one looks for the reason without finding it. If he was ambitious and avaricious and unscrupulous—so have been most of the men who came to the top. He barely failed in all his major undertakings. A final success—and it was near—would have marked him as one of the great geniuses of history—an early wizard in government and affairs.

Rufinus was an orator and a lawyer, a master of civil administration and agenda. It was because of him that the Eastern Empire—Byzantium—became a bureaucracy for a thousand years; and lived on because its administration had become too intricate to die—

though there are those who say that its death was concealed in a sea of paper for that one thousand years. The heritage of Rufinus was the first and longest-enduring paper Empire.

It is not accidental that in the tenure of Rufinus as Master of Offices, the duplication of written copies was first brought about. This was not on the order of carbon paper used at the instant of writing; it was wet-process copies made from a finished piece. The process is a detail, however; in the true sense Rufinus was the inventor of carbon copies. Shorthand was then five hundred years old, but Rufinus was the inventor of an improved form of shorthand.

It is believed that certain clerks of his appointing are still shuffling papers at the same desks. The paper world he set up was self-perpetuating.

Rufinus ruled by palace intrigue—a much narrower device than that used by Stilicho. Rufinus was without military understanding; and his problem was to find a master general strong enough to defend the Eastern Empire, and weak enough to be ruled by himself in the name of the very weak boy Emperor. This left the possibility that a strong master general, whether or not he bore the title, would by-pass the master of offices, seize effective power, and then legalize it. There were several who would see this possibility, or have it presented to them.

There was another element. The young Emperor Arcadius resented Rufinus, his guardian, though he knew that he himself was not yet mature enough to rule by his own power. Arcadius began to play factions; and continued that game, to the peril of his affairs, throughout his reign. Part of the explanation of the Gothic revolt is that Arcadius himself had a finger in it. He was raising up the third of the factions, the military one, and he intended to use it as counterweight. The second of the factions of the East was that headed by the eunuch Eutropius.

The young Emperor Arcadius had a close acquaintance with Alaric the Boy Giant of the Goths, who was only a year older than himself. He was under the personal spell of Alaric, and remained under it all his life. The resentment of Arcadius against older authority did not extend to this fellow teen-ager. Arcadius was shopping for his own master general, and he certainly considered Alaric. He intended to put in a general as one of the three factions he would play off against each other; and he was Prince enough to know that three is the minimum.

Did the Emperor Arcadius himself support the Gothic revolt against himself?

On the surface of it such an idea is insane; yet there is some evidence and much supposition to support the theory that the Gothic revolt against himself—which bewildered his generals and drove his ministers frantic—was to some degree *instigated by himself,* or at least had his tacit approval. There is no rational explanation for some of the phases of that revolt and the curious reactions to it. The support of Arcadius, however, may be the most feasible of the irrational explanations of it. It was the case of the young Emperor himself being in revolt against authority, and the revolt of such a boy may take a strange form.

Arcadius was seventeen years old. Alaric was his close personal friend, and Rufinus was his resented guardian. Arcadius had grown up in the shadow of his great father, had felt his own inadequacy before that authority, and had experienced a natural revolt against constituted authority even after that authority was represented in himself. He was an unstable teen-ager, of vivid intelligence but no particular moral fiber. Curiously, he felt that he was not himself a prince born; that he was base-born, and his younger brother nobly born. He came to resent this difference that no one else understood. Arcadius had been born in Spain while his father was still an adventurer-general in exile. His brother Honorius was born in Constantinople after the father had become Emperor. They were full brothers, however.

Arcadius—and this has nothing to do with our account except for the sidelight it throws on the character of the young Emperor—was much given to fetish, to touchings and returnings. He was not superstitious or irrational; the fetish in him was a nervous thing that he was unable to conquer. He had once ridden back more than two hundred miles with a royal party, for the sole reason that he had passed a certain tree on the left side instead of the right. He had waked in a panic at night, and feared that the line of his life had become tangled. They had to journey back, making four days of it in either direction, so that Arcadius could ride around the tree and untangle his invisible line of destiny. Yet it remained tangled, for all that.

Eutropius, the Imperial eunuch, the second factor of the Eastern power complex, was looking for more troubled waters to fish in. He had served very great men for many years, and he had himself begun to develop the appetite for greatness. Eutropius realized that Alaric would still be a power in the world after Rufinus had been taken, by any of the dozen traps that waited for him. Alaric would rise. Rufinus would fall. Eutropius would prosper by both the rise and the fall.

Many of the ideas that Arcadius believed to be his own had actually been insinuated into his mind by Eutropius; and Eutropius was the master of Rufinus at palace intrigue. If Rufinus was the father of bureaucracy, Eutropius was the ancestor of the unofficial cabinet.

The Gothic revolt was but one of a half dozen stirrings in the Empire following the death of Theodosius, but it is the one we are following out. There were troubles in the West, and Stilicho dealt with them. There were other troubles in the East that were variously handled; but they served as diversions, and permitted the limited success of the Gothic adventure.

Rufinus, however, had also begun to cultivate the Goths, just before the outbreak. He was in their camps in Moesia, where many of them had long been and where the remnant of the Aquileian adventure now gathered, and is said to have imitated the Gothic dress and ways. Rufinus, like Arcadius, was shopping for a master general; and he did make some sort of bargain with Alaric. The estates of Rufinus were carefully spared in the early Gothic ravaging of the countryside. Indeed, one of the most peculiar aspects of the Gothic raids, first in the north and then in Greece, was the selectivity of them. It was as though they followed two master lists: such a group of estates and holdings to be spared entirely; such an intermingled group to be ruined irrevocably. There were politics in depth involved, and a simpleminded age such as our own cannot comprehend it.

Eutropius did not cultivate the Goths to the ridiculous extent that Rufinus did, nor was he ever inclined to imitate the manners of warriors or outlanders. However, he did tighten his friendship with Alaric, which had been close both at the Imperial Academy and at the Court. There was mutual respect between Eutropius and the Goths. Though the Goths had an abhorrence for the state of Eutropius, they realized that he was personally more of a man than was Rufinus.

The details of the relationship between Eutropius and Rufinus themselves are not known. Both understood that one of them must die to make room for the other, but that was not an impediment to their co-operation in side matters: the exiling and death of the General Promotus; the overthrow and execution of the praefects of the East and of Constantinople, Tatian and Proculus, father and son; the murder of Lucian; and certain venal affairs—both before and after the death of Theodosius.

The Eastern intrigue, from its very inception, took the form of a *tetraphaleron*—a Greek magic-line puzzle of four foci. The foci of the puzzle were the teen-age Emperor Arcadius; Rufinus the red-handed lawyer; Alaric with his incipient Gothic nation; and the eunuch Eutropius who played men like marionettes. Each factor believed that he could play the other three against each other; and none, for the present, wished to destroy any of the others utterly, or to upset the balance of power completely.

Stilicho handled more weighty matters in the West, and worried about the East. He regarded the plotting there as perversely childish, and it must have been fairly transparent to him.

Stilicho was also, by the pledge he had given Emperor Theodosius, the over-guardian of the East. But he did not interfere there immediately or directly; not till he gave the order that one of the four factors should die.

Arcadius precipitated the Gothic revolt by reducing the amount of the yearly subsidy that his father, Theodosius, had paid to the

Goths—a retainer paid them on the condition that they be arms-ready on short notice. The Goths loudly announced their rebellion and started south under arms. But here there arises the question of identity.

The Goths were an alien nation risen in arms within the Roman Empire. But there was also a federated Gothic army detachment of that same Roman Empire, still acting under orders—often several sets of contradictory orders. The men composing the two groups were the same men.

The Gothic detachment of the Roman army was under orders to secure the peace of the disputed Province of Illyricum. And the Gothic Nation, in its fighting men identical to the Gothic Detachment, was the main threat to the security of Illyricum. But a fiction was maintained that they were not the same.

Just what was the Gothic nation? Was it a real nation with an established territory and a capital? It was very near to being a real nation; it had a partly established territory that it hoped to enlarge, and sometimes it had a capital city. There is needless mystery about this giant capital city of the Goths.

The question whether such a capital city existed or not becomes of no meaning; sometimes it existed, and sometimes it did not. Wherever the Goths assembled, there was a city, and a large one. They could set up a wagon city of one hundred thousand persons in three days, put up large timber buildings, lay out streets, and provide water supply and sanitation. What the Romans could do for a legion and its auxiliaries—twenty thousand men—in one night, the Goths could do for five times that number in three nights. They could make this a strongly fortified place, well provisioned, and able to withstand siege.

And they could strike that same city in three days, sweep it of every stick, and leave nothing but stamped ground and the droppings of tens of thousands of horses.

The Goths were a special sort of nation. They could melt away onto the farms and hamlets of Macedonia and Thrace, of Moesia and Little Moesia, of Dardania and Dalmatia, of Greater Dacia beyond the Danube. They could melt away to these scattered places, and leave nothing assembled but the legitimate army detachment that had served Rome so faithfully, and had recently sacrificed ten thousand lives to the cause of a united Rome.

Who was to say that there had ever been such a national Gothic assembly? That it had revolted? That it had decided to move into and devastate the Grecian regions? That it had set itself up against Rome itself? Was there anything more than rumor to the movement?

No. Nothing more than rumor that was a certainty. Nothing but the sure report of Roman-Goths who had taken part in it, in one of their manifestations, and given the account of it to the Court in another.

Alaric, in the early spring of the year 395, moved southward at the head of a large body of Gothic fighting men. They were the few thousand survivors of the battle of the River Frigidus and Aquileia; new levies of young men; great numbers of older and more seasoned Goths who had disdained to be embroiled in the Roman adventure; and un-Romanized Goths who had crossed the frozen Danube in the weeks immediately preceding. Alaric moved as a Roman general in command of federated Roman troops, charged with finding out and punishing the instigators of a rumored Gothic rebellion—the same that had just chosen him leader. There was unreality in several layers about the situation, but he had his orders direct from the young Emperor Arcadius.

The Gothic forces had assembled in deep Thrace, somewhere in the neighborhood of the city of Philippi. For a period of a week or so they may themselves have set up a much larger city. Then the women and the children, the older men and the reserves, the followers of every sort melted back into the Gothic farms and villages. And the armed Gothic force that marched south and east now showed only one of its two faces—that of a detachment of federated Roman troops under a Roman general.

Alaric came up to the walls of Constantinople with this army. He himself and his immediate retinue had entree to the city. He entered and held discussions with the young Emperor Arcadius, with the Master of Offices Rufinus, with Eutropius the palace

eunuch, and with a fellow-Goth Gainas who was in command of
the defenses of the Imperial city.

It is written again and again that of course Alaric would not
have been able to take Constantinople, and that he wisely by-passed
it after a show of force. But the idea that Constantinople was impregnable is false. It had never been such a fortress as Ravenna,
for instance. It is true that, commanding the sea with a large force,
it would not easily be starved out; that its walls were so formidable
that they could hardly be breached by any engines that the Goths
might bring up; that its garrison was large and adequately armed
and made up of professionals who would respond to command;
and that a serious attempt to take it would have brought aid from
the entire Empire, from Stilicho in the west, from Africa, from
Asia.

But Alaric could have taken Constantinople in a dozen different
ways. No aid to the city could have been timely enough. The walls
are always spoken of as very strong, but they were not yet the
great walls of Constantinople. Those—the triple walls—would be
built by the son of Arcadius, Theodosius II, not yet born. But if
the walls had been impregnable, the gates might have been opened
by negotiation. The garrison of the city, composed though it was
of excellent soldiery, was mostly Gothic; and the commander of
the city, Gainas, was himself a Goth, though of a tribe different
from Alaric's. "New Rome which is Constantinople," like Old
Rome, had seven hills and twelve gates, but it had never really
been tested. Every previous assault or threat had been resolved by
the payment of money.

Alaric could have taken the city. For several weeks he pointed
out to the Emperor and his several notables just how easily the
city might be taken. They, in turn, reminded him how much better the pickings might be elsewhere. Alaric even made recommendations to improve the defense of the city.

Alaric did not take the town, because in taking it, he would have
destroyed his double role and would have become an outright
rebel against the Empire. He also feared retribution from Stilicho.
The Goths withdrew from Constantinople in consideration of

having received a sum of money. This sum was probably identical to the amount by which the subsidy of the Goths had been reduced. In effect, it was the second installment of that yearly payment given them when the main body of their troops had by-passed the city. Alaric parted from Arcadius in friendship. He carried with him orders from that Emperor the contents of which have never been revealed. He now turned south and continued his selective raiding and harrying.

We do not possess exact chronology of the events of that year, 395. Stilicho, immediately on the death of the Emperor Theodosius, had paid a series of lightning-like and powerful visitations to the various western frontiers. He had crossed the Alps in the savage cold of the most severe winter in decades, traversed the Rhine marches, checked on the garrisons of the whole west-European frontier, and returned to Milan. Stilicho was known on sight to a quarter of a million troops on the frontiers, and he changed guards and escorts as he went. He sometimes rode completely alone and arrived unannounced at minor garrisons. These were all garrisons that, till only a few months before, had sworn allegiance to the rebel Arbogast, and many expected large forces to come against them in reprisal. Stilicho came alone and tongue-lashed them and checked on their readiness. He executed but a dozen men on his entire sweep, and these with his own hands.

The garrisons would now remain faithful to the legitimate Emperors forever; Stilicho decreed it to them; to this order there could never be an exception. There were men of the garrisons who later said that they would rather be lashed with a whip than by the tongue of Stilicho. But the Master General satisfied himself that those of the garrisons were good men who had been misled and would not be misled again—not while he lived.

The Western frontiers were solid. Stilicho tapped them with his mallet-like hands and assured himself that there was no real rot in them.

There remained Africa—with the incipient revolt of Gildo, and the east. Stilicho sent a man secretly to Africa to kill Gildo. Then he himself started east, out of Italy and along the Adriatic. He led certain Western Roman troops and certain Eastern Roman levies. He was returning the Eastern troops, left over from the battle of Aquileia, to the east; he wanted them in Italy less than anywhere. He skimmed the cream off them, retaining a few thousand of the finest for his own use.

Near Thessalonika, Stilicho and his forces encountered Alaric with his Gothic detachment, which had just by-passed Constantinople and was raiding south. This was a strange situation.

Alaric was still subject to the orders of Stilicho—the guardian of the entire Empire and the over-general of all the troops. Alaric was also subject to the orders of Rufinus, the Master of Offices of the East; and to Arcadius the young Emperor of the East. Alaric was, moreover, playing a dual role: that of a minor Roman general, and that of the uncrowned (for two years yet) King of the Goths.

Stilicho sat down and talked it over with Alaric for a week or so, and there came others to join in the conversation.

An important man who came and joined the discussion was Gainas, the Gothic commander of the forces of Constantinople. He had been following several days behind Alaric on his ravaging; it isn't known with what sort of force Gainas had followed, nor under what orders.

But Gainas did bring definite orders from the Emperor Arcadius that Stilicho was to advance no further towards Constantinople; that any closer advance would constitute a hostile act. The Emperor ordered Stilicho to turn over the Eastern detachment accompanying him to Gainas; he ordered Stilicho to return to the affairs of the Western Empire—particularly to the African affairs which pertained to the West.

That part was agreeable to Stilicho. He did not wish to precipitate a civil war. His own thought was for the stability of the Empire. He had wanted the Eastern forces returned to the East, and it was for that reason that he had escorted them on the long way. And he was quite willing that Gainas should be the man in charge of them. Gainas was Stilicho's man privately.

Stilicho had come east for one other reason—to kill a man whom he believed to be a malign influence on the Empire. Stilicho reached concord with Gainas on this point also. Gainas agreed to kill the man for him.

Stilicho also came to agreement with Alaric on several matters, or believed that he had. There should be no invasion of Greece, Stilicho insisted. If it were true that Alaric carried orders from the Emperor Arcadius that he should check on the towns and garrisons and general well-being of Greece, then he might check on them. But if, as had been rumored, Alaric intended to loot and devastate the country and set himself up as its master, such an adventure would cost him his life. Stilicho would come and take him and hang him. That was a promise subject to no conditions.

But Stilicho proposed that Alaric should become a different kind of master of a different province—Illyricum.

The division of the Empire into East and West, following the pattern of most previous divisions, gave to the Eastern Ruler, Arcadius, the provinces of Thrace, Greece, Asia (that is, Asia Minor), Syria, Armenia as far as the Persian frontier, and Egypt.

To the Western Ruler, Honorius, of whom Stilicho was direct guardian, went Italy, Africa (which was Africa west of Egypt, Egypt not being considered a part of Africa), Gaul, Spain, and Britain; Raetia also (approximately modern Switzerland), and such territory beyond the Rhine as was held by the Imperial armies at any time. This left the giant, and somewhat unsettled, province of Illyricum (the greater part of modern Jugoslavia), the division of which had never followed a pattern.

In general, the portions of Noricum, Pannonia, and Dalmatia (itself of indefinite area, to add to the confusion) were thought of as belonging to the West; and the portions of Dacia (Lesser Dacia, the part south of the Danube), and Macedonia (also of vague extent) were thought of as belonging to the East.

Stilicho believed that all Illyricum should be ruled as one province, in fact if not in name: the whole Adriatic march that he had just traversed, but not including Greece. He believed that it must be under his own control from the West, whatever the appearance should be. He would not, however, allow it to become the object of a civil war.

The proposition of Stilicho was something like this: that Alaric should be appointed Master General of all Illyricum by the Eastern Emperor Arcadius—but that Alaric must bring about the appointment himself by his own influence and suits, though he would be supported by the secret connivance of Stilicho in ways still to be revealed. And that Stilicho, at the same time, acting in his own name and that of the Western Emperor Honorius, would recognize Alaric as the Master General for the *West* over the same regions. This latter arrangement, of course, would not be known of openly by the Eastern Court. This is to say that Alaric would hold authority from both the East and the West over the buffer region of the Adriatic province.

Stilicho was offering to adopt Alaric into the overguardianship of the entire Empire, and asking him to lend a hidden hand to that heavy burden. Stilicho insisted that he would expect full and final obedience to himself as guardian of the Empire, his own orders to override any contrary orders that either of the young Emperors should mistakenly give.

They talked about it for several days, and Alaric gazed at the distant sky. He gave Stilicho assurance of many things, and Stilicho believed that he had final assurance of this. It is probable that Stilicho did not understand the strong Gothic feeling in Alaric or realize at all the meaning of the Gothic nation. Stilicho was a Vandal, a German who had become completely Roman. To him a nation was but another word for a province. In underestimating the non-Roman elements in the Gothic movement, Stilicho made one of the few serious mistakes of his life.

The dialogues broke up on a promising note. The three burly Germans, Stilicho and Alaric and Gainas, who believed themselves to be Romans and who handled Roman affairs, went their three ways. Stilicho received a packet while he was camped near Thessalonika; it had come from overseas and then by fast courier. It contained the head of the man whom Stilicho had sent to kill Gildo in Africa.

The man who thrust the packet on Stilicho, in its very high and offensive condition, was a fanatical partisan of Gildo. He stated insolently that he brought greetings from his master, and this gift which his master believed that Stilicho might value. He said also that he was to convey that the *Comes* Gildo hoped that he and Stilicho now understood one another.

Stilicho told the man to return to his master, to tell him that Stilicho had received and understood the gift, and that he Stilicho would soon pay Gildo a visit in person.

So Stilicho would have to leave the affairs of the East in doubtful shape and go to Africa to put down the rebellion.

Gainas, with the Eastern troops returned from the battle of Frigidus and Aquileia, took march to Constantinople. And Alaric started south once more, but very slowly. He resumed his selective raiding, against the absolute orders of Stilicho; but he did defer to Stilicho in one respect. In the raiding of the Goths through Thrace and Greece and Macedonia, the estates of Stilicho himself (and he had extensive ones, gifts of the Emperor Theodosius) were completely spared. Alaric had put Stilicho at the head of one of his two lists.

Alaric moved south through Macedonia and Thessaly without real opposition. Two of the appointees of Rufinus—Antiochus the proconsul of Greece, and Gerontius the commander of the Imperial troops—showed great reluctance to closing with Alaric in battle. They were the weak instruments of a man who had already failed —the man whom Stilicho had decided was a malign influence on the Empire. Alaric moved slowly, for he was waiting for a sound.

It came—the news of the murder of Rufinus by the Imperial troops of Gainas the Goth. Stilicho had given an order, and it had been carried out after he himself was far distant from the scene. Stilicho had failed, temporarily, with Gildo in Africa; but he did not always fail. It may be that he never failed in the final issue. The Master General Stilicho could command any of the generals in any part of the Empire; and he would kill any man who was in any way a threat to that Empire.

Alaric studied this great general and guardian of the Empire, this unusual friend who would as soon have had his life at the battle of the River Frigidus. This was the man who would have set him up as a buffer between the two halves of the Empire; who would have adopted him as his own heir in that onerous guardianship of the Empire, making him sharer in the most responsible office in the world. And he was the man who would have him killed as surely as he had had Rufinus killed, if his death would prosper the Empire; had said that he would kill him under the circumstances that were now about to become fact. Stilicho had gone off to settle Africa, but he would be back.

Alaric considered it all—but not for too long. He gave the order to proceed south to the open attack and looting of Greece. This act was in absolute contradiction to every instruction that Stilicho had given him, and Alaric now knew how deftly Stilicho could kill.

Stilicho had sworn that he would come and hang Alaric, if he should do what he was now doing.

10. Of the Game Named King

Alaric started from Larissa in Thessaly on the Peneus River, and swept south into Greece proper. The vague border of Greece, wherever it may be, has never varied much from here. With his forces he picked his way by ragged roads over mountains. At Thermopylae, the Goths could have been stopped or slowed, but they met hardly token resistance.

Into that early first summer, cold and blustery through June, the Goths were in Boeotia and Attica. Then Alaric put together one of the three-day crash marches that were to make him famous, and took Piraeus, the port of Athens. The speed of the assault was so stunning that there was no warning, no resistance, nothing.

The Goths of Alaric's contingent saw that southern sea itself for the first time at Piraeus. They thawed considerably here, and discovered in themselves a new capacity for ease and luxury.

It has been said that the Goths went wild in Greece, like children in a candy store. There is an aptness in this comparison, for one of the things that the Goths went wild about was candy itself —confections. Honey was the only sweetener in that world that did not yet know cane or beet sugar. And Athens was the honey capital of the world; she was this after she had left off being everything else.

Greece itself was, and has always been, one single field of clover. It is furrowed by mountains and interrupted by arms of the sea; pock-marked by plowed fields and broken by groves; infiltrated by swamps, separated by narrow deserts; but it remains one field of clover. It is grazed by sheep, goats, and bees. It is the true land of milk and honey.

The Goths, like all the northern peoples, had had a craving for sweets for generations. Whatever their advances in other lines of agriculture, they were very backward in apiculture. Their only bees had been wild ones, and their only hives had been bee trees. Even their mead—honey whiskey—had been wild stuff, full of bark and pulp wood. It had been nothing like the real mead of the Greeks—which was another name for nectar.

The Goths went wild, literally, over the Greek confections, and they also tasted peculiar confections in other forms. They lived on the countryside and the resources of the Port City while Alaric treated for the surrender of Athens.

Piraeus was a cosmopolitan sea port, as nothing that is not Greek can really be cosmopolitan; it was an international slave market, the second largest in the entire Empire. The Goths were a vigorous and earthy people, but they were unsophisticated in the ancient and heterodox vices. They tasted new confections in the timeless sin port, and indulged in the abominations that are spoken of by the prophets.

And Alaric came down from the hills of Athens, like an angry prophet, to his Gothic people on the Bay of Phalerum, having heard reports that horrified him. He discovered that the Goths had been worshipping strange kine and tasting of illicit fleshpots.

Alaric was not a tolerant man, in either the good or the evil sense of the word. His anger now was somewhere between that of the infrequent but absolute madnesses of Theodosius and the controlled iciness of Stilicho. He appointed executioners, and had more than one hundred of his own men put to death; for sodomy, for abuse of children and slaves, for pygal perversions, for using narcotics. Alaric was not greatly disturbed over simple drunkenness. He fulminated against such; but it was for the perversions that he killed.

Alaric had taken a bold and direct step in this. Even Stilicho, whatever his strong personal puritan feelings, would not have ordered the execution of his own men for such. The lines were drawn now; there could never be any doubt about what sort of man Alaric was. He would play the part of one of the anointed of God, and he would pass final judgments. Only a chosen leader can act in such a manner, whether chosen by himself or by a group. Alaric had been chosen by both. He is still contemned in history by the peculiar brotherhood which one offends at his peril.

Alaric wrought another sort of execution in Greece, for which he has been widely condemned. This was the destruction of many statues, paintings, reliefs, friezes, temples, statuettes, and artifacts of ceramic, stone, bronze, and silver and gold. He destroyed them as pagan survivals; as offensive to the public morality; and as the work of the Devil.

Alaric, in his own mind, had some justification for this destruction, in the orders he carried from the Emperor Arcadius. The formula of the orders of a master General contained certain standardized phrases: seeing to the defenses of the cities, attending to the problems of commerce, putting down piracy, suppressing insurrection. The formula also had a phrase about maintaining the public morality and fostering religion. Alaric put great stress on this one phrase of his orders.

It is true that he did not otherwise follow out the orders of the Emperor, though he did check on the defenses of the cities in his own way. And he did not accept the further orders that the Emperor sent after him.

The couriers whom the Emperor sent after Alaric, on hearing of his depredations, were unhorsed and hamstrung and left crippled by the Gothic soldiers, who pretended to be unable to understand either Greek or Latin. Even Gothic couriers were unable to reach Alaric. They were beaten as bandits and sent on their way under threat of their lives.

Alaric set himself up as judge of the artifacts—as to what should be demolished, and what should be spared. But it was not only pagan art that he destroyed. He also did away with what he believed was bad Christian art. He swore that all bad workmanship, no matter to whose service it pretended, was the work of the

Devil, but that any thing well done, no matter what name it went under, was wrought under the influence of the Holy Ghost and was to be considered as inspired.

The historian Cassiodorus believed that the selective destruction of Alaric, as regards the Greek monuments, was of good effect. Alaric had some taste and was awed by really great art. The Greeks were only human, and all their work could not have been excellent. But almost all their ancient work that survived the ravages of Alaric was of unsurpassed excellence.

There is abominable and worthless ancient Greek art in Asia Minor, in Constantinople, in Thebes, in Eritrea, in the Cyclades and other islands. There is little or none of this worthless ancient art surviving in the path of the Gothic Greek adventure; not in Athens, or Megara or Corinth or Argos. Sparta does not figure in the account at all; it never had art.

It is said that Alaric destroyed half of the art of Greece. It may have been the worst half. He was a critic of unusual effectiveness. But we have run ahead while Alaric was still dealing with Athens.

With Piraeus, the port of Athens, in the hands of the Goths, Athens itself could easily be starved out. But it was not to come to that. She opened her gates and let the army in. The destruction here was, as always, selective; there were no massacres of the people. Alaric had come to the city for one thing, and he knew it was to be had there. Athens had a fund for just such contingencies; she was not the wealthiest city in the world, but she had always budgeted for this.

Athens ransomed herself from Alaric, as she had from a dozen conquerors. She had a great sea trade and was the center of the olive and wine and honey commerce; she was a great exporter of pottery and woolen cloth, and an importer for a wide area of silk and citrus and Egyptian grain. Her slave commerce alone would have made her wealthy, she having the only superior slave schools in the Empire. She imported the raw commodity, instructed and refined it, and reshipped it at high profit.

The contingent fund for the payment of ransom was one of the fixed charges that Athens had always imposed on her commerce.

The treaty of Alaric's Goths with the city of Athens seems to have been a simple one—coin and ingot payment in exchange for freedom from further molestation. Alaric and his retinue came and went freely for some weeks and enjoyed the luxury of the city, though the bulk of his army was kept encamped in the near countryside. There is no serious bill of particulars drawn against the Goths for their destruction in the city, though for centuries the sources of history were in the hands of those who were the natural enemies of the Goths in thought and temperament. Alaric may have been the most gentle conqueror that Athens ever knew.

But it was not so everywhere. After the Gothic withdrawal from Athens, there was a series of massacres in the countrysides and villages through which they passed, and several well-known cities had a bloody taste of them. In particular there was cruel destruction at Eleusis. The Temple of Demeter was leveled there; we have no way of knowing whether it was artistically worthless or of value. It was the one temple that pagans still took seriously—whose effect at that late date was still a religious one. Alaric destroyed it as though it were a pit of snakes.

The Goths took Megara, and—crossing into the Peloponnesus —occupied Corinth with great damage. They ravaged southward, more bloodily now, taking Argos and Sparta. Sparta was then only a village. What special talents Sparta had possessed in a small way—for warfare and for administration—Rome had possessed in a larger way; and Sparta had been made obsolete.

The Gothic winter camp near Sparta, late in the year 395 and early in 396, was the furthest south penetration of the Goths in Greece.

The practice of pillage and rapine becomes a habit. The Goths maintained the fiction of their dual role, as a legitimate arm of the Roman army, and as a wandering nation in search of new land. They had not been vicious or horrifying in their marches through Boeotia and Attica; had not been arsonist or unnecessarily murderous. In the Peloponnesus their ravages became more deadly, and the black rumor of them reached the Master General of the

West—Stilicho, who had never put the Gothic movement out of his attention.

Stilicho, still the most competent man in the Empire, was more isolated than he had ever been, and more fallible. He was the strongest prop of the Empire, but now his perfect judgment began to slip. He had come onto situations for which there was no perfect judgment. His problems were really without solution, and it is not to be wondered that he lost some of his assurance.

Stilicho had not disposed of the African trouble in person. There had developed half a dozen troubles as pressing, and he had to forego the grand gesture. The African trouble was still festering. He had delegated the matter, after seriously weighing it from every angle. It happened that his delegate finally disposed of it satisfactorily, and removed that one threat; but the sign of the future was that Stilicho had been unsure. With troubles springing up once more on all the frontiers, he was driven to distraction. He had raised armies, and then put them on stand-by. He had assembled fleets and disbanded them and assembled them again.

Now he assembled a great fleet in Ravenna and the other eastern Italian ports, crossed the Adriatic and Ionian Seas with it, entered the Gulf of Corinth, and debarked on the isthmus near the damaged Corinth; near the still-smoking ruins of Corinth, according to one account, but that is unlikely unless the stone town had burned for seven months after Alaric had singed it and left.

But Corinth had received worse treatment than had most of the Greek cities that had played host to Alaric. Stilicho was angry with what he saw and with what he was told of the affair. He determined to bring that Gothic tribe to heel, to force it to play the part he had selected for it.

Stilicho was now unhappy with Britain, with the Rhine frontier, with Rhaetia and the Alps; with the upper, middle, and lower Danube; with the lesser Dacia within the Empire and with the greater Dacia outside; with the Huns in Asia and the possibility that they might make common cause with the Persians; with the Senate and Court at Constantinople; with the Senate at Rome and the Western Court sometimes at Milan and sometimes at Ravenna;

with Egypt, with Africa; with the giant province of Illyricum in confusion between the two halves of the Empire; and in particular Stilicho was unhappy with the Goths who had ravaged Greece, and who had disobeyed both the surface meaning and the hidden meaning of the orders he had given.

Stilicho seemed to be the only man in the Empire who was interested in saving the Empire. The frontiers were crumbling like undermined dikes, and one man could not be everywhere. But Stilicho was one man who could be very nearly everywhere, and so long as he lived the Empire could not fall. He had made his own life identical with that of the Empire, and they had a common bloodstream.

It was in line with his being everywhere at once that Stilicho took up his station on the Isthmus of Corinth, with a fleet on each side of the Isthmus. One portion of it was in the Corinthian Gulf; one portion in the Aegean Sea.

Situated on water passages facing both ways—occupying the narrow neck of land with the rebellious Gothic nation trapped below him on the Peloponnesus; with the effete Court of Constantinople within striking distance by either land or sea to the north; with Egypt, Africa, Numidia, Mauretania, Spain, Italy, Illyricum, Asia, Syria and Coelesyria, Palestine and Arabia all as near as his ships —he was at the effective center of the Empire.

The map will show his location somewhat east of center, but the map is mistaken. Certain areas weigh more than others in their effect; Stilicho was at the effective center of gravity of the Empire.

When the spring (of 396) broke, much more pleasant than the icy spring of the previous year, Stilicho moved southward and gave Alaric and his Goths a lesson in the game of chess. It was a game that Stilicho had learned on his early Persian mission.

The chessboard they played it out on was the region of Arcadia, which has been described as a plainful of mountains.

The Pawns were the men, the foot soldiers. The Knights were the horses, the mounted horsemen. The Castles were literally the castles and the walled cities. The Bishops, however, were not the bishops. The misunderstanding of these pieces is from their shape; they are a little in the form of a bishop's miter, but they were first intended to represent the abutment of two sails of a ship. We know from old Persian sources that these pieces were first called *karadjihi,* the ships; though in modern Persian the piece becomes the *fil,* the elephant. But in the military analogy of the game as invented, the pieces were the ships.

It was with the foot soldiers, the horse soldiers, the castles, the ships, and the queen herself—the Empire—that Stilicho played out the game. But what was the object of the game as played by the Master General Stilicho? Or, to ask the question behind the question, *who was the King?*

The object of the game, of every game as seen by Stilicho, was the defense of the Empire as the supreme thing on earth. It had become a passion to him, but it was not a passion for any temporal thing. The Empire to Stilicho was the Church militant, the collective assembly of the people of God. The King of the game, to be defended at all cost, was Christ. Whether the premise of Stilicho was rational is not here the point. To understand the game he played and the way that he played it, it must be understood what he considered the subject of the game, which was Christ and the world redeemed by Christ.

The word Chess is the same as Check, as Shach, as Shah; which is to say King. It is the King Game, and its literal name is King. When one cries "Check" one cries "King." And "Check Mate" is "Shah Mat"—"The King is Dead."

The object of the immediate phase of the game, to Stilicho, was not the slaughter and annihilation of the Goths. He believed that there was nothing of so little value as a dead Goth. His object was to entice and compel the Goths to settle on the lands of Moesia and Illyricum; to farm that land as free men and to give a free tone to society; to provide an anchor in the mass of drifting people. The Goths were intelligent; they were strong and Christian and moral; they had no serious flaws in their character, outside of a certain arrogance and an overavidity for going to war. They could become a stable people—under a different leader it would now seem; and the Empire required stability.

Stilicho, the German-Vandal convert from paganism, believed that when the Goths had become sufficiently Romanized the problem would be solved. But the real difficulty was that the Goths had become too Romanized.

The nobility of the Goths who, though comprising no more than a thousand persons, dominated the rest, were unwilling to abide as simple farmers doing their own work and enjoying their own fruits as freemen. For this, their scattered holdings in Little Moesia and nearby places would have been enough to contain them. But they had seen how the grand Romans operated, the two hundred families whose holdings covered half of the best land in the Empire. The Gothic nobles desired to become grandees, having seen Romans of less ability than themselves live in that way. They wanted great slave plantations and the fabulous wealth of them. For this, there was not enough land in the whole Empire to contain them.

It had been the desire of the Emperor Theodosius and of his Master General Stilicho to reverse the trend of the Empire, which for four hundred years had been away from the small freeholdings and in the direction of the giant slave estates.

In particular it had been desired to restore the more rotten provinces, such as Moesia and Illyricum, by settlements of free peoples—the Goths and others. The Gothic desire to be large slave-owning proprietors, rather than small freeholding farmers, would have to be corrected.

The one place in which that Stilicho did *not* want the Goths to settle was Greece; for the clear reason that it was already settled. The situation in Greece was not ideal, but it was better than in any other part of the Roman Empire. There were still large numbers of free farmers in Greece—enough of them to give a tone to the society.

Greece had served as the nursery for certain ideals, some of which had never been viable on any other soil, but some of which had been adopted by Rome. The Greek *eleutheria,* the freedom

idea, had been one of the nurses of the Roman Republic, and it
seemed that it might outlive its foster child. Greece still could
serve as a model for a society of rural freeholders, however much
it had been infiltrated by the slave estates. Stilicho wished to trans-
plant the surviving idea to other provinces, and he did *not* want
the scant nursery bed trampled.

As to the matter of the great slave estates, none of the notables
of that day—either of the Romans or of the *Foederati*—had clean
hands. They all owned such estates, even Stilicho.

It is true that he broke up some of them before his death; but it
does not follow that he would have broken them all up if he had
lived longer. There were many good and generous men in that
time who released a part of their holdings; who went so far, and
no farther.

The liquidation of the first estates seemed easy—hardly a depri-
vation at all. The difficulty increased as the estates diminished.
None of the magnanimous men of the day is known to have di-
vested himself of more than one-third of his holdings. They meant
to do so; to release their entire landed estates beyond a modest
freehold for themselves; to free and provide for their slaves; to
settle these same or others on their lands under circumstances and
with the assistance that would enable them to remain free and
solvent.

However, in every single case known, there was something that
stuck in the throat of each of these generous men and prohibited
him from following out fully the admirable program. Whether this
curious impediment was physical or mental or moral we do not
know.

But the game itself was played out on the chessboard of Arcadia
between the brilliant young commander and the more brilliant
older one. The game lasted more than a year; as in every chess
game, there were sometimes long intervals between the moves.
Stilicho, in fact, several times left the scene of action. He returned
to Italy at least twice, went to Africa once, went to Pergamum in
Asia Minor once. This latter visitation was completely in the terri-

tory of the Eastern Empire, and the aid of Stilicho had not been requested in that sector. It could have been interpreted as an unfriendly act, but Stilicho made the voyage and returned from it before Arcadius and his ministers heard the news. There is a theory that Stilicho held rendezvous in Pergamum with representatives of Sassanian Persia, and renewed old contacts.

Stilicho had begun the chess game with Alaric with another grand gesture. He had built a high gibbet in Elis, in sight of the mountain Pholoë somewhere in the rough country north of the River Alpheus. And he had announced without equivocation that he would hang Alaric on that gibbet within one year's time.

Stilicho did not employ crucifixion as a manner of execution—respecting the memory of Christ. Nor was he devoted to decapitation, having a true premonition of his own death in that manner and having an aversion for the axe. He was one of the first hanging generals, and legend has it that he is the inventor of the hangman's knot.

Stilicho was impartial. He had killed a personal enemy, Rufinus. He would kill a personal friend, Alaric. The Empire and its defense came first with him.

The shadow of the high gibbet cast its spell over the action of the following year. Stilicho was an adept in the old game of the containment of the Goths. He had learned it from the master strategist Theodosius, and his associates, Bacurius the Spanish General, Saul and Arbitrio who had switched at Frigidus, Timasius, Arbogast. Stilicho and his fellow generals under Theodosius had won that first game when the Goths had every advantage. Stilicho intended to win it once more; now that every advantage was his, and the Goths were caught in a trap.

Stilicho had Alaric out-Knighted. Alaric's source of horsemen was cut off by Stilicho holding the Isthmus of Corinth. Alaric could not obtain any manner of reinforcements, and he had left a great number of horse soldiers in the occupation of Thessaly and Boeotia and Attica. These excellent horse troops north of the Isthmus had not been captured by Stilicho, and could not be, but they were sealed off and of no immediate use to Alaric.

But Stilicho could land reinforcements at Rhium, at Corinth, at Pellene and Sicyon, at Elis and Olympia, at Pylos, at any port near the point of conflict. He could land cavalry, Roman, Gallic, Spanish, or his own Gothic. He could land sufficient cavalry in the rear of Alaric, wherever the Goths might make a stand.

For it was in ships that Stilicho had complete supremacy, Alaric having none at all. Even Alaric's small Gothic River and Pontus boats had been scattered by the regular navy of Stilicho.

Stilicho had Alaric out-Castled. All the fortified places were loyal to the Empire and to Stilicho; and they would not open their gates, now that help was known always to be near at hand. Alaric would be unable to take any walled town at all.

And Stilicho had Alaric out-Queened. The feeling for Empire would work everywhere for Stilicho and against Alaric.

But it is not at all certain that Stilicho had Alaric out-manned, if the thing should ever come to conflict in the open field. Stilicho could have superiority in numbers wherever he chose to assemble them; but in a face-on fight, it is probable that Alaric could have defeated him. Stilicho chose not to put it to the test. He would be careful to drive the Goths into no corner, until the last one.

The Emperor Theodosius had won the battle of containment over the Goths while losing nearly every battle. Stilicho believed that he could do even better. He believed that he could defeat the Goths in every place and in every detail; that he could herd them where he wanted them to go; that he could rout them utterly when they were ripe for the rout; and that he could do it *without fighting them at all*. And Stilicho accomplished exactly that, while the shadow of the gibbet fell across the play board of Arcadia.

There followed one year of frustration for the Gothic forces. From the time that Stilicho first landed near Corinth, the Goths were not able to take any fortified place, nor to exact any tribute in money, food, or goods. Relief was always at hand for whatever place they besieged. The gates would open to the Romans and close to the Goths. Strong places would be reinforced by the sea, or by the short sea roads. Alaric, land-bound, was always at a greater distance from every objective than were the forces of

Stilicho. The Romans outflanked the Goths repeatedly, for the wings of their forces were seaborne.

The Goths believed that they could defeat any army in the world in fair field; and in anything like comparable numbers they could have done so. But in Arcadia they could not find an army to fight.

They found redoubtable fortresses risen specter-like where there should have been nothing but wattled villages; and sudden fleets standing in forgotten bays that did not see a dozen fishing skiffs a year. They found bridges destroyed, and countrysides driven clean, so that there could not be taken even one lamb in a day's march. They found themselves on high wind-swept wastelands in the most bitter cold, where there was not a stick of wood or scrap of dung for burning. And in the heat of the summer they found themselves trapped in dry gulches that had not known running water for a generation. They arrived in grain-rich countrysides and found that the harvest had been reaped early and stored in walled towns. They came too late or too early for the olives and figs and grapes and barley.

The Goths had to give the Romans the advantage of two hours on the end of every day. For the Romans had the use of the walled towns; but the Goths must raise and fortify and circumvallate their camps at every stop. The stragglers of the Goths, once cut off from them, were lost to them forever. The Gothic numbers diminished. There was a certain amount of treason to the Gothic cause, or remembered loyalty to the Roman; and there were promises from Stilicho of rich rewards to the men who should anticipate the turning of events. There was, at any rate, the transfer of large numbers of men from the forces of Alaric to those of Stilicho.

There was real hunger and eroding hardship among the Goths. Their army must always travel in large groups to prevent their being cut off and taken by the omnipresent Romans; and large groups were unable to forage properly. The Romans had access to granaries and magazines and established industries; they had the cisterns and the lakes and the streams. Towns and cities are always built at the confluence of the waters, and the Romans controlled all the towns and cities.

The Goths felt acute hunger; in themselves, in their animals, in their equipment. It was often a hunger for trivial things for which normally they would have traded without considering. They could not get salt, and they could not get iron. For lack of the one, themselves and their horses sickened; for lack of the other, their equipment broke down, and their smithies could perform no maintenance.

Seldom could the Goths get meat in the land where even the gods are sheep-footed and goat-footed. Such cattle as they had brought died of epidemic disease—this one of the Gothic afflictions was not of Stilicho's working—and the Goths died from eating the carcasses. They had brought no sheep or goats, depending on the Greek countryside for these, but these animals were herded into the new-walled villages at every approach of the Goths.

The meadows were burned before them, bridges destroyed, pools poisoned. They knew epidemics in the swamps, while the Romans were well in the towns. They were subject to a country-wide blockade.

Alaric attempted the strong towns of Megalopolis, Mantinea, Tegea, Tripolis, Messene, Olympia, Filiatra—one after the other. He took none of them. He left several thousand dead around their walls. Every town had either a sea entrance or a short sea road by which the Romans could reinforce. The Goths had the feeling that Stilicho was reading their minds and predicting their moves. The Goths would come, after sudden decision, by forced marches to one of the walled towns and see the ships riding high and empty —already unloaded; and see Roman soldiers with the Greek militia on the walls.

Alaric met Greek fire from the walls, and Roman ballistae from within. He had started his campaign from too narrow a base, and had not anticipated the absolute investure by Stilicho of all elements. Stilicho could obtain numerical superiority wherever he desired it. He could personally leave the Grecian field for other affairs, putting competent generals in charge; and he could return when he wished. The Goths would keep; they weren't going anywhere.

The gibbet stood on the high place all that late winter and spring and summer. The Goths had not seen it, but they had heard rumor of it. Now they seemed to move at random north through Arcadia, but they did not actually move at random. They were being herded carefully by Stilicho. Alaric was harried over the playing board, put in check on play after play, and forced to withdraw—sometimes for lack of water, sometimes for lack of grass and grain. He was compelled always into rougher country for what food could still be found; and the Goths would have starved but for the wild game and wild fruit.

Often there was but one possible move for Alaric. Stilicho planned astute combinations, for he was a master at this play. Alaric found his freedom of motion abridged, and he could not understand it. His will was not his own; there was another will anticipating his will. The moves of Alaric were to his own harm and to Stilicho's gain.

In late autumn the Goths were far north in Arcadia, where the three sub-provinces of Arcadia and Elis and Achaea come together. The Goths began to climb, and the foothills below them were invested as they left them. The Gothic army was trapped on the mountain or high plateau of Pholoë. They had insufficient food and water, and a deadly winter—nearly as severe as that two years before—came on them.

All through the tail-end of the winter before, through the spring and summer and autumn and into the new winter, it had been true that the Goths could defeat in fair field any army brought against them. But there came a day, after their wasting away on Pholoë, when this was no longer true. Alaric had a fine instinct for this. He knew to the day, almost to the minute, when his forces had diminished to the point where they would no longer be supreme.

It was not only in Castles and Knights and Ships and Queens that Stilicho had the advantage over him now. Stilicho could now, or would soon be able to, defeat him with foot soldiers on any field, at any time. But it should not be on any field or at any time; Stilicho had selected the site of it and the day it would be, one year before. Today the Roman Master General could beat the Goths flat before the sun was down. Within a week he would be able to rout them within an hour, so rapidly were they weakening.

It was at this time that Alaric, hounded with his men to the furthest extent of Pholoë, looked across the miles and saw, for the first time, the gibbet that Stilicho had built for him—standing black against the new snow.

Alaric had been driven in a series of a hundred interlocked and inevitable moves to the farthest wasteland of rocky Arcadia. He had arrived there by a string of choices and decisions, and now realized that not a single one of his choices had been his own. Stilicho had seen every move of the game from the beginning, and there had been no moment when Alaric could have acted in any other manner or made a different choice or move.

Alaric had lost the game on his first move of the game. He had ravaged Greece against the orders of the Master General. Stilicho called "check" on him for the last time. Alaric moved in starvation and desperation to the furthest extreme of Pholoë. Stilicho called "mate" and there was no move left for Alaric.

The game was over, and the gibbet stood waiting.

11. Of Kings in the Day of Their Blessing

The first King who played the game of King, of chess, was the Persian Pad-Shah Shapur II, who was taught it by his wazir who had invented it. The wazir was the better chess player, but the King was always the winner of the game.

The King attained victory by the ingenious device of overturning the chessboard at a crucial point of the game and declaring himself winner. This showed an imagination of the sort that the wazir did not have; and it was for this reason that Shapur was the King, and the wazir would never be anything but wazir.

The larger view, the seeing that a problem need not be confined to one narrow framework, is useful in many fields. It comes into the solution of certain puzzles and riddles where a narrow framework, implied but not stated, limits the ordinary mind and prevents the solution by such. But the breaking out of the framework gives the answer to a mind with more scope.

The Master General Stilicho had a mind that was nearly perfect in its own way, but it worked by patterns and within a definite framework. The mind of Alaric, not nearly so profound, was nevertheless wider and was not given to setting any limits on itself. It was for this reason that Stilicho did not hang Alaric on the gibbet he had prepared for him.

On a night in the early part of the year of 397, when mountain winter had numbed the Goths in their absolute darkness, and when the Romans slept warm in their encircling fortifications with their rings of fires in the foothills—when the Goths had been beaten without recourse in the last move of the year-long game—Alaric suddenly overturned the chessboard and declared himself winner.

Without fire or light or signal, possibly on sudden inspiration or possibly according to preset plan, Alaric with a few hundred of his Goths mounted on their giant chargers—now lean and savage from the hard winter, both horse and man—charged down the snowy slopes in muffled silence.

They transfixed sentries and guards on their long lances, carrying them along so by the impetuosity of their charge. They rived men open with axe and heavy sword and broke them down with hand mace. They bruted their way out of encirclements of the doughtiest troops in the world, having to go completely through the Roman camp.

It was not a case of overwhelming surprise. The Romans *were never surprised* by attack of day or night. There had been trumpets howling the alarm from the time the first Roman sentry was transfixed on the first Goth lance. The Romans had ten times the numbers of the small Gothic band in arms and alert, on horse and foot, but still the Goths bulled through.

And when the Goths were trapped irrevocably, they hurdled thirty-foot embanked trenches—impossible for horse within the framework of the mind of Stilicho—and lunged their way to the clear. Two-thirds of the Gothic band were loose, leaving the screams of dying horses and the jarring moans of dying men behind them. They had charged clear out of the framework.

No man in the Empire but Alaric—with the possible exception of his cousin, the Roman-sworn daredevil Sarus—could have led such a charge. And no other man at all could have carried through the second and third stages of it.

This was not the main Gothic force. It was an élite group of maddened riders; no more than four or five hundred, and the Romans could set at least five thousand horsemen in their immediate pursuit. And Alaric and his crazy-horse Goths were still entrapped in a double prison. They were thirty miles from water passage, north to the Corinth Gulf at its nearest point; and the Romans controlled all the inlets and seas and had a main fleet in the Gulf of Corinth. There was no way the Goths could arrive at the Gulf, and no way they could cross it if they should arrive.

The Romans had horses as large as those of the Goths, and in much better shape than those starved animals. They also had animals, smaller but superb, and incomparably swifter. And they had the device of the relay. They could change horses at stations that would be open to them and closed to the Goths.

The Romans could send picked riders ahead, on special mounts that were one-third swifter than those of the Goths, to alert interceptor garrisons. They could signal with beacons or with trumpet; and already the trumpet codes were being passed along from hilltop to hilltop. But actually their signals would not be needed. The Romans practiced the discipline of the perpetual alert, and every road and path could be blocked effectively at all times of day or night.

The Goths, even in their breaking out of the framework of Roman procedure, had to use the roads and paths to a great extent. One does not ride roughshod over icy mountains in the night without making use of the elemental trails at least.

The Goths rode through nine encirclements of numerically superior troops, leaving too many dead at every encounter. They rode their horses to death and arrived, impossibly, in sight of the Gulf of Corinth with not thirty horses still standing, and with possibly one hundred Goths on foot. There was a blizzard, and they floundered through heavy snow.

The alert was ahead of them by at least an hour, and hostile horsemen lined the shore. The Roman boats would be waiting for them at the only point narrow enough even to consider as a crossing—a spot between Rhium and Antirrhium. Even at this point, which they now broke down to, there was an expanse of three miles of impossibly cold water whipped to frenzy by the high wind. And the Goths swam badly; most of them not at all. They were so tired that they blew a bloody foam from their mouths and it froze on them.

But the Roman boats were not waiting for them to kill them there.

Several years before, on the cemetery island in the middle of the Danube River, the ghostly Gothic "Father" of Alaric had raised his hand to heaven and called down lightning as a sign.

Alaric now at this moment of supreme crisis, coming down to the rough shore and seeing the howling waves, raised his hand to heaven and called out that the Gulf of Corinth should freeze!

It froze!

And the Goths, shattering the last scrim of Roman interceptors, abandoned their horses and crossed the ice on foot!

That is the story of it. The exact details were later brought into doubt, but not in the lifetime or presence of any of the Goths who were there.

The salt-water Gulf of Corinth has frozen only five times in two thousand years, and it had not frozen during that more severe winter two years before. But, whether or not it was by divine intervention and resulting from the Heaven-compelling cry of Alaric, the Gulf of Corinth *had frozen,* partially at least in its narrow portion between Rhium and Antirrhium, on that winter night early in the year 397. It had frozen in that limited interval, and the alerted Roman boats could not come to the area from either side. The Goths crossed on foot, and the Roman horsemen, pursuing closely, broke through the ice and could not follow.

The Goths crossed, and they were in Epirus.

Their remnant—it has been numbered variously between thirty and seventy men, and was certainly less than one hundred—was immediately surrounded by a large patrol. This was composed, not of Romans, but of Gothic irregulars loyal to Alaric. They were joined, before morning, by some thousands of the troops that Alaric had left in the occupation of Greece north of the Peloponnesus.

"Hos successes alit," wrote Virgil, and *"Possunt, quia posse videntur*—To those successes was good, and the semblance of

power gave power indeed." Or, more modernly "Nothing succeeds at last like success," but perhaps it should be rendered
"Nothing succeeds like last success." Alaric had the last success,
and who should remember the failures that had gone before?

And also Alaric had the sense of the dramatic climax that Stilicho lacked. Alaric cashed in on his grand gesture with forensic
negotiations. His cousin Singerich either was already at the Court
of Constantinople, or was sent there now. He had been mentioned
nowhere as a part of the Grecian adventure; but he was very much
a part of the following negotiations.

Alaric had dutifully abandoned Greece as he had been ordered
—so was his case presented—and he had now undertaken the onerous task of settling and clearing wild and forbidding Epirus.
The real threat to the Eastern Empire—so ran the bill of particulars
of Singerich—was the Master General Stilicho in unauthorized
possession of the Peloponnesus.

The men of the Eastern Court, whatever their weaknesses, had
a fine touch of the comic. And Stilicho, whatever his strength,
had no humor at all. Yet he realized that he was the butt of a joke
that was peculiarly Grecian. The colossal joke that Alaric had
played on Stilicho was appreciated in the East, and the empty
gibbet became a byword.

When some years later, in a time of their friendship, Stilicho
referred to the incident of the overturned chessboard, Alaric did
not understand him; nor had he ever heard of the game. But he
had taught the Master General a new ending to it.

The young Emperor Arcadius had no trace of gratitude to the
Master General. He had cried out for Stilicho every time he was
in real trouble, and had dismissed him every time the trouble
had been cleared. "After thy visitation we forget that we have
wept," as St. Augustine wrote about another matter.

Though Arcadius may have given tacit approval for the initial
Grecian occupation, he had quickly seen the enormity of his error.
Those who ruled him now, his new wife Eudoxia and his eunuch
Eutropius, were happy that Alaric was finally out of Greece and

in Epirus. But they would be much happier when Stilicho had returned to Italy.

With the arrogance that total weakness sometimes shows to total strength, they sent the orders that Stilicho should withdraw at once from the area. His further remaining in an Eastern province would be interpreted as a hostile act, they indicated. Stilicho remaining, after his momentary usefulness had passed, was always interpreted as a hostile act by the Eastern Court.

The Goths of Alaric still remaining in the corner of Arcadia, so ordered the Emperor Arcadius, were to be permitted to leave Greece by the Corinthian Isthmus and to rejoin their master in Epirus.

It was all done. Stilicho accepted his dismissal. He had no personal feelings where the Empire was concerned, and by his word to the Emperor Theodosius he still considered himself the silent guardian of the Eastern Empire. He would not turn against that division in arms. He would return again when he was once more needed; and again he would accept rude dismissal when the need for him was ended.

And Stilicho was nearly satisfied with the way events had fallen. Alaric was out of Greece and in Epirus—if only he would stay there, and work at the restoring of that sub-province and the greater province of Illyricum.

Stilicho was even happy that he had not had to use the gibbet, though it galled him that he had to eat his oath. Men of the ability of Alaric are difficult to discover, and it is still more difficult to nurture them to the point of real usefulness; and Alaric had shown, by his fantastic escape, a greater ability than Stilicho had suspected. The man had earned his life with an exhibition of real talent. Stilicho had the master general's appreciation for the master trick that Alaric had played.

Thereafter they each of them, Stilicho and Alaric, maintained a Gothic leader at the Court of Constantinople. Alaric had his cousin and future brother-in-law, Singerich, who had become a real adept at palace politics. Singerich would have great influence with Arcadius and with his Empress Eudoxia. Privately they were of great friendship, a three-against-the-world group, all of them just coming out of their teens. They were all of them brilliant, even Arcadius under the stimulation of Eudoxia and Singerich, and they fancied themselves as powers and not puppets. Singerich was the only close personal friend Emperor Arcadius ever had. Singerich did not—as has sometimes been indicated—despise the weak Emperor. There was never duplicity in the friendships of Singerich. Singerich also worked closely with Eutropius; and while Singerich was in the ascendancy, Alaric could do no wrong in the eyes of that unstable Eastern Court.

But Stilicho had a Goth of even more effect, Gainas who had killed Rufinus for him, and who was Master of Arms for the city of Constantinople. Actually, the vacillations of that Court had no real meaning, and the rude dismissals of Stilicho were no more than words. Stilicho had his own men in military control of every province of the East; and with Gainas controlling the city of Constantinople secretly in his name, the Eastern Court was of no moment.

On one word from Stilicho, Gainas would have killed the Emperor Arcadius and his whole clutch of favorites. It was a toy Court that obtained there. Gainas was one of the Goths who was completely loyal to the idea of Empire, and to Stilicho as custodian of that Empire. But the person and the word of the Emperor must be considered as sacred, however the effect was modified privately.

One other such Empire Goth as Gainas was Sarus, the cousin of Alaric. Sarus, joining Stilicho by sea in Epirus, was a partner in a private move that Stilicho now made—as daring in its own way as Alaric's breaking out of the Peloponnesus.

Stilicho sent his Grecian army to Italy and Africa by his fleets, after his dismissal by Arcadius. Stilicho then had himself and a very small party set ashore in Epirus. He then rode with only one man through thousands of armed Goths—including those he had lately hounded to the last extremity—to confront the man for whom he had built the gibbet.

The man who accompanied Stilicho was the intrepid Sarus, and the Goths fell back aghast and white-faced from his anger as he rode. The Goths loved Alaric, but they feared Sarus, who was likewise their blood prince.

The intrepid Sarus! *Intrepidus*—the adjective always clings to him like a reiterated Homeric device. Sarus' bold feats of horsemanship in leading small bands at the battle of the River Frigidus had won him the name of the most foolhardy horseman in the Empire; and he was the man most feared in personal combat. He was the Lion. His peculiar reputation was one that not Alaric, nor any other, could ever approach. He was not to be a great general, nor even a good general; but as leader of mad-dog cavalry charges he would never be equaled.

Sarus seems to have exercised a boyhood dominance over Alaric, and he was the only one of the kindred who never acknowledged Alaric's mastery—not at the cadet's school, not after Alaric was King, not ever. By many he was considered a better and more fiery man than Alaric, and he certainly never feared the Boy Giant. He was not ordinarily on bad terms with Alaric, except for disagreeing with him on one basic subject.

At their present confrontation, however, Sarus was the enraged lion. He offered to take Alaric and hang him there himself with his own hands, and he swore that not one of the thousands of Goths would dare interfere. Should Stilicho give the word, Sarus was ready; and Alaric and Sarus shook with passion as they faced off. Had Stilicho given the word, the issue would have been interesting.

But Stilicho did not want Alaric dead now; nor was he given to grand gestures after the fact. Had he wanted him dead, he would have killed him before this. Stilicho had his own sworn men everywhere, even in Alaric's retinue.

Instead, Stilicho talked to Alaric like a Roman uncle. He needed this young man who had so much still the matter with him. He had employed far weaker reeds in the Empire business; the Roman fasces, which he employed as principle, was a collection of weak reeds made into a bundle of great strength. And Alaric might become quite a stout stick in that fasces.

Stilicho told Alaric once more just what the Roman Empire should mean to all men, whether Old Roman or Vandal or Goth. He gave Alaric a title without a title, letting him know that henceforth he would be considered as Master General of all Illyricum, for such a time as he filled that post with honor. The formal title must be given by the Eastern Emperor Arcadius, but Stilicho had intelligence that it was forthcoming. Stilicho let it be known that he himself would be the real master—there could be no doubt on that point—and that Alaric should move wherever he was ordered by Stilicho, even against the forces of his technical master, the Emperor Arcadius, should unlikely necessity ever require it. All that Stilicho told Alaric is not known, but he talked to him for two days. Hafras, who was secretary to Alaric and unofficial Master of Offices of the Gothic contingent, was present for part of the talks, but not all.

The intrepid Sarus, his anger cooled a little, also lectured Alaric in a manner so direct and severe as to be explicable only by their kinship. In particular, Sarus warned his fellow-Goth against the Goths. Sarus understood, much better than Stilicho did, the tide that was rising in the Goths. Sarus warned Alaric once more against Athaulf, his own brother beyond the Danube, calling him a wild beast, and saying that he was Cain. In this one matter Sarus was prescient; Sarus would, in fact, be murdered by his brother Athaulf.

The object of their visitation accomplished, Stilicho and Sarus left Alaric, but not before Sarus, in parting, also warned Alaric against the influence of Stairnon, Sarus' own sister.

Stilicho and Sarus rode away through the thousands of still-amazed Goths, cowering that multitude by their very presence. The two men had "face" in the Roman sense; *confrontatio,* confrontation. There was none who could stand up to the power of their personalities.

Sarus has been described in later historical accounts—written from the Gothic viewpoint—as a traitor to the Gothic cause and as a traitor to Alaric. He was killed as such by his brother and enemy, Athaulf. But no man was ever less a traitor; and no man had ever let it be known so clearly just where he stood. Sarus was an Empire Goth to the point of fanaticism. In loyalty to the Empire, it might almost be said that he took up where Stilicho left off. He remained loyal to the Empire and to the incompetent Western Emperor Honorius, even after the execution of Stilicho by that unworthy. Sarus was loyal to the fetish and the name, even when the idea of Empire went underground, and no one could say what was the Empire. He was one Goth who was truly more Roman than the Romans.

The Balthi family had had in them the ability to found one of the great dynasties of history. The explosion of sheer power in the kindred of that generation is almost without parallel; Alaric, Stairnon, Singerich, Sarus, Athaulf—all out of one nest. Unfortunately, they came still unripe into a disappearing world, and they dissipated their energies in the confusion. Their survival was less than it would have been in almost any other age. It is true that the Visigoth kingdoms of South France and of Spain in the following centuries were their heritage. And the Balthi continued as the Lords of Baux, a corruption of their name, in France for thirteen centuries. There are men in South France today who can trace their descent to the Balthi.

The flood gates were opened now, and honors flowed to Alaric. Actually, there was a power vacuum. A strong man was needed, and he had arisen opportunely. But it did not happen spontaneously; a man is never chosen for high honors of any sort by a spontaneous movement. There is not, and has never been in the world, a really spontaneous movement of this sort. It required a detailed apparatus and an enormous amount of staff work—however it was called. Alaric had used the same surety in making a dozen bonds, and he had given pledges of an absolutely contradictory character to various groups. Often it was sword politics; but it was politics.

Sometime in the year 397, Alaric received two honors, obliging himself by accepting them to follow two opposite courses, to work for two irreconcilable goals, to maintain two contradicting loyalties, and to live in two mutually exclusive worlds.

A decree was published in Constantinople by the authority of the Emperor Arcadius making Alaric the Master General of Illyricum. And in the same year Alaric was raised to the Kingship of the Gothic nation; in addition to which, he was joined in marriage to that Gothic nation in the person of his cousin Stairnon.

For the first honor, Alaric had worked deviously through a multitude of contacts; for, at intrigue, Alaric was a Stilicho in the egg. He worked through the friendships of his fellow cadets from the old School for Generals, and through their fathers and families—some of them very powerful since they were of the tight aristocracy of the nations within the Empire. He worked through the brazen-voiced soldiers in the ranks—Roman, Gothic, Gaul, Scythian—setting them to chanting his name at assemblies—Emperors have been raised by this device alone. He built up a nucleus of vociferous soldier supporters by means of quiet favor and loose gold. He worked through the other Gothic enclaves in the Imperial service, through his own personal friendship with the Emperor Arcadius, and through the influence of his cousin Singerich.

Where Alaric could not manipulate full support, he employed half support: that of Gainas the Gothic Master of Arms of Constantinople, who added a cautious modification to Stilicho's support of Alaric, and who had begun a dream of his own; that of the eunuch Eutropius, who more than any other man of moment in the Empire at that time always knew which way the wind was blowing, and which man would rise and which would not.

The policy of Eutropius had always been to give conspicuous aid to those who do not really need it; who have, without it, just achieved that accumulation of power that makes their rise inevitable. There will be the moment when the rising man himself may not know that he has already achieved this accumulation of power, but a dedicated student of such affairs will always observe it of him. Eutropius, the eunuch, the master of palace politics, threw his support to Alaric; seeming to be, though he was not, a decisive factor in that appointment.

So Alaric was Master General. He had joined the select circle of men, living and dead, who had held such title, and who had been of a remarkably high level of ability. Alaric was Master General of the Empire, and had pledged his life to the support of that Empire in all manner of ways.

But the second honor, received by Alaric in the same year, was a contradiction of the first. For this second honor, that of King of the Goths, Alaric had begun to campaign before he was born— through the pretensions of his family. Alaric was born a prince of princes and was now the ruddy, handsome giant of the outstanding family of the West Goth nobility. He had the presence and the voice and the sense of timing and event by which the image of a hero is created.

If Alaric had been a total Goth, he could not have carried the Goths along with him as he did. But none of the Gothic nobility were total Goths. Alaric, sharing this special status, was able to understand his Goths both from the inside and the outside. He was able to sweep them along with him, to panic them and work them into an hysteria; he was almost able to hypnotize them.

This power in Alaric puzzled many; among them Singerich. This Goth turned Greek has left the opinion that Alaric was not a great orator, though he was a loud one; that he often stumbled and sputtered over his words, perhaps purposely; that the content of his orations and exhortations was often childish, and yet of just the right note to appeal to the Goths. Singerich believed that even an ox could give a more lucid speech; but even a talking ox could not have caught the interest of the Goths as did Alaric.

Singerich, the Goth turned Greek, regarded Alaric as something of a bumpkin and as obscenely full of the old animal juices. But Alaric had, at all times, the total loyalty of Singerich.

Sarus, the Goth turned Roman, still believed Alaric to be a backward boy who needed instruction—possibly with the flat side of a sword.

Athaulf, the Goth who remained a Goth, regarded Alaric as the face behind which he himself must rule; as the mask he would wear and the puppet he would control. Yet, when in the presence of Alaric, the intellectually superior Athaulf became like an enthralled boy. The friendship of Alaric and Athaulf was so close that it could transcend every difference of character and regard. Athaulf was Cain to his own brother, but he was not so to Alaric.

Stairnon, the woman of the Goths who invented the Goths and was the personification of their nation, regarded Alaric as brother, son, cousin, husband, lover; yet she never regarded him as having a mind independent of her own. She felt that he was her own creation; and, to an extent, he was.

Alaric might have been a prophet without honor among his cousins, but none of them—except Stairnon, and she was a talented haranguer—could impel a crowd or send a sudden emotion like earth-shock or thunder through a whole countryside of people.

Sarus could face down ten thousand sullen soldiers and stride through them like a knife, leaving them white-faced and shaken in his wake. But they wouldn't have followed him barefoot through the snow; nor could he, like Alaric, have walked on the water of the Gulf of Corinth. Singerich might entangle two Empires in his palace politics, but the soldiers of his own nation would not know who he was when they saw him. Athaulf could mastermind the whole Gothic program and look down on the entire Empire from his aerie beyond the Danube; but the hand and the mind that brought the world to an end would be Alaric's, and not his.

Alaric was crowned King of the Visigoths and adopted their program. In doing so, he pledged his life to the destruction of the Empire in all manner of ways. From one world viewpoint or the other it became clear that he was a traitor.

The Goths, or the Gothic Party that was in the ascendancy and whose program Alaric had adopted, had their own ideas about the Roman Empire. They believed that it had been created and developed by Divine Providence for the special use of the Goths— the true chosen people; that they, the Goths, were the heirs; and that scurvy Romans and all lesser peoples should be turned out of it like cuckoos from the nests of honest birds.

What Alaric himself then believed is not known. He could not have been sincere in accepting both titles, but he seemed to be.

During the following thirteen years, Alaric changed his basic belief at least twice, and must often have been unsettled in his own mind. As a Goth he was a better horseman than the Romans; but not even a superb Goth can continue to play the Roman Rider when the horses gallop off in contrary directions.

Alaric was crowned King of the Visigoths in the year 397, the first Christian King, not Emperor, ever crowned anywhere. We do not possess the ritual of this first Christian Visigothic Coronation, though subsequent Visigothic Coronations in Spain and elsewhere became the models for all European Coronations down to the present day.

It is certain that there were Gothic, Hebrew, Roman, and Christian elements in that crowning. We haven't the full ritual, but we have a few anecdotes, from Hafras and others, that pick out the high and low places of it.

Alaric refused to don the *Paludamentum,* the purple chlamys or cloak. He said it was a gown for women. He was a Goth in trousers, not a Roman in skirts.

Unction was used. The Biblical words "anoint thee with the oil of gladness" were employed. And the Sign of the Cross was made with chrism on the head of the new King.

A crown was given, the ancient crown of the Goths which was a wooden one. They had not even come as far as the iron crown of St. Stephen. The Roman Emperors were crowned with gold; but wood was sacred to the old Germans, and metals were not.

It is not known whether Mass was celebrated in conjunction with the Coronation, or whether Holy Communion was given from the Reserved Sacrament; but Alaric did communicate. The Mass for subsequent Gothic Coronations was to bear the name *Missa pro Regibus in Die Benedictionis ejus*—The Mass of Kings in the Day of their Blessing. The Lesson was to be Leviticus 26:6-9 and the Gospel Matthew 22:15 seq. The relevancy of neither text to the Coronations is clear.

After this Holy Coronation, from the tents and stockades and open air, Alaric was elevated on a shield by the Gothic soldiery in the original rite.

And again after this, and on the same day, Alaric was married to Stairnon, the Gothic Woman of Legend. Alaric had rejoined the nation of the Goths. The Goths had found their Messias in Alaric. The lines were drawn, and a wise man could count the years till the end of the world.

12. Of Res Romana

In the same season in which Alaric was created both Master General of Illyricum and King of the Goths, he heard in Epirus an oracular voice cry out to him from a sacred grove. There is an anomaly in these voices crying out; they are unnatural and uncanny, yet they always give their predictions in the most polished and involved manner—silky riddles intricately made.

The oracular voice that cried out to Alaric did so in Latin verse that was somewhat in the style of Claudian:

> Rumpe omnes, Alarice mores, hoc impiger anno
> Alpibus Italiae ruptis penetrabis ad Urbem.

"Break off all delays, Alaric. This very year thou shalt force the alpine barriers of Italy. Thou shalt penetrate to the City."

These oracles do not speak as clearly as they might, for surely there is more than one city, even in Italy. But there is a tradition to be followed in interpreting the oracles. The device known as "boxing the verse," for instance, will often give up the key to the meaning. In the case of a prophetic couplet such as this, one takes the first letter of the first line, then the last letter of the first line, then the last letter of the second line, and, finally, the first letter of the second line; in the present instance, spells out *Roma*.

Rome is the city to which the weird oracle referred. However, the oracle anticipated by more than a decade; the event would not come about for thirteen years. It is believed by some that the oracular voice was a Gothic one, for even unnatural voices have their nationality. The purpose of the voice may have been to plant a seed, to foist a legend, or to animate a reluctant hero.

It has also been proposed that the voice that cried out of the grove to Alaric—who often walked in the woods alone when trying to compose his mind—cried out to his inner ear only; and that Alaric himself had the message set in verse form by some talented friend so that it might go more neatly in the record. It does not matter. It is in the record now, and is part of the Gothic story.

The very groves had cried out that Alaric should take Rome.

If the two of them, Alaric and Rome, were preordained as adversaries, it will be of profit to examine the second adversary, Rome. This should indicate what sort of struggle it might be and what should be the odds on the outcome.

The odds will be long, but not unreasonable. What the man should attempt was no more incredible than what the City had done. It was impossible that one man should conquer the City; but it had also been impossible that one City should conquer the world—and it had, nevertheless, been done.

Of the various titles of Rome, the name the New Jerusalem best gives its position as a peculiar local place, and as a universal city. Rome was the City that became the World, but it was disrupted as a city in the process.

Of the two cities, it is always Rome that is mentioned as being built on seven hills, as though it were a high city; and such aspect is never mentioned of Jerusalem. But the impression given by this is the opposite of the truth. Jerusalem is built on the top of a mountain; Rome is built in the bottom of a pit.

One always comes on Rome suddenly, from whatever direction or way it is approached. There is no such thing as seeing it from a distance, except by looking down into it from one of the hill towns around. There is a recurring phrase in writings about the arrivals to the City, "Going down into Rome." The hills of Rome do not rise up. They are the sides of a pit gaping down.

There are more than seven hills of Rome; but those of the canon—all on the east bank of the Tiber—are seven: six of them in a ring or rampart, Capitoline (from which every capitol and capital is named), Quirinal, Viminal, Esquiline, Caelian, and Aventine; and one hill entirely within the rampart, the Palatine (from which every palace is named). These hills, on their outer side, fall off from the level of the surrounding plain; but on the inner side of the rampart they make an abrupt descent to the river level. The City is built on the bottom and sides of a pit and gives the feeling of being a subterranean city. Beyond the City, on every side, the rolling plains are two hundred feet higher than the City of Hills.

Indeed, there is the feeling that the City goes down very deep and below its apparent floor. Under every house and building there were older houses and buildings. The town is underlaid with caves and pits and chasms. The catacombs of Rome were *not* vast excavations or tunnels cut out of the rock. They were natural caves, dressed and widened and shored up a little here and there. The *cloaca maxima,* the great sewer of Rome, was called by the historian Merivale greater than the pyramids of Egypt. An official of the City, after overseeing a cleansing of the drain, once launched a trireme boat on it and was rowed and steered through its miles into the Tiber. But it was a natural gulch and cavern, for all that, and the engineering consisted of facing portions of it with dressed stone. The *cloaca* itself was not dug by men, and the execution of it was not greater than that of the pyramids.

The persistent story of fires burning beneath the City in ancient times was true. There was coal, peat, lignite, and igneous earth burning continuously under the City. These fires, whether lit by man or nature, burned, in some of the air-accessible caverns, for centuries.

The crumbling floor of the City of Rome, the feel of chasms underneath and of old dead cities beneath the living city, and more than anything else the underground fires burning, contributed to Roman and Christian idea of Hell. The Jewish Hell was not necessarily under our feet, nor was the Hell of the New Testament and of the Apostolic Fathers. But the Hell of the earliest Romans, and of the later Christians of Rome, was popularly set below, under the City of the World, and down in the middle of the earth.

Rome was built from the materials at hand, of which it had unequaled supply. This may have been the deciding factor in building the great City in that location. The hills of Rome, on the east bank of the Tiber, are of tufa—igneous or volcanic stone, and from this stone both ancient and modern Rome have been built. From this stone, Rome is a pearl-gray or silver city; just as Jerusalem, from the sandstone blocks of which it is built, is a golden city. But Rome also had another, and even better, building material.

The Vatican slope, and the whole complex of hills on the western bank of the Tiber, are of argillaceous substance. More bricks have been made from the clay of these hills than from any comparable area in the world. These, when baked and cemented with the native sand and lime, have proved even more durable than the stones themselves. Rome, from the second century B.C., was a city of brick and concrete, though having the appearance of stone and often faced with stone. Rome was a quarry and brickyard before it was a city, just as it was a series of mines before it was a city.

Just before the beginning of historical time, the area of Rome was a lake with one narrow outlet. The natural dam of it was somehow riven, and the lake drained out the fifteen miles to the sea, leaving the old pit.

There were towns on all the hills before there was one united town. The Tarpeian Hill, not one of the canonical seven, bore a town named Saturnia. The Janiculus, across the river, had its town. The Quirinal had a Sabine town on it; the Latins had a town on the Aventine; a colony of Arcadians had a town on the Palatine. The Romans built a wall around them all—establishing a policy of union and leagues until they had built a wall around the world.

And just who were these Roman people who did this? Who consolidated and assimilated it all till they themselves disappeared in the assimilation? And who are you yourself, Quaesitor?

You're a son of them, or a collateral of theirs, in some line and to some degree, whoever you are.

For, by the time of the Late Empire—just before the world ended—the citizenry of Rome embraced every sort; from Nubian Negroes, by way of Egypt as artisans, to Chinese tradesmen who had arrived with the Huns. There were East Indians and Irish and deep Slavs who were Roman citizens. But what the Romans *had been* was an utterly strange, though homogenous, people.

The Romans were an Asiatic people who had arrived as strangers. There are twenty legends as to their origin, but every one of them brings them from Asia. They were Asian in a way that the Greeks and the Carians of Asia Minor and the Syrians were not. The Romans spoke an Arian language *that was not their own,* and behind their handling of it was a thought pattern entirely strange to us—even though we may call them our fathers. With the Old Romans we come to a wall, as we do not with the Old Greeks or even the Old Egyptians. There is no word of theirs, and no thought behind the word, that is completely translatable to us. One can take their simplest word, as *res,* a thing, as in *Res Romana,* the Roman Affair or Thing, that titles this chapter. But *res* may mean an affair, a fact, a condition, a property, a profit, an advantage; a suit at law, an affirmation, a matter; the commonwealth, the world, the universe; a cause, a result. The closest meaning of it is "concept," but it is not quite such a concept as we are able to conceive. We use, mostly, the same words the Romans did, but we never mean quite the same thing by any of them. In a dozen histories we come on the confession of this wall that blocks off the Romans, the strangeness of the thought pattern.

The Romans were a serious people; it can be seen on their coins and medallions and reliefs, and the broken-nosed faces of their statues. They took themselves seriously, and there was no chink at all in their attitude.

The devil-gods of the Phoenicians were capable of a grin, for all their evil. In Greek verse or statuary we can never be sure that there is not an element of burlesque, or even that it is not all burlesque. Hittite serpents turn and bite themselves, and Egyptian mummies are buried with their childhood toys. There are Eastern minarets built in the form of a pun, and the most philosophical of all folks had a frog-faced deity. Chinese temple roofs turn up like cowlicks, and wooden Indians have been seen to wink. Only the old potato-faced Romans took themselves completely seriously.

It is true that the Romans of the Late Empire, of whom we are treating, had become a generation of mockers. They had humor, high and low, and little else. But by that time there were few Romans left in the population of Rome.

The Old Romans have given the names to all the virtues; loyalty, honor, duty, fidelity, courage, perseverance—to the solemn virtues, that is, and they were peculiarly Roman. But they did not mean to the Romans what they mean to us, and when we see the reverse sides of those coins we are justifiably horrified.

The Roman patriotism was the most serious thing of this serious people, and was felt by strangers as well. It was not transmittable, and when taken over by outlanders, it became a disease. We become entangled in trying to abstract patterns, in attempting to set up a type or class when there is no class. Some things in the world have happened but *once*. Patriotism is one of these things that is meaningless in the plural. Patriotism is *not* the love of one's fatherland. It is the name of one thing only, the love of the *Patria*. There was only one *Patria,* and it was Roman. The *Patria* was the *Res Romana,* the Roman Thing; it was the Republic, it was the Empire; it was, perhaps, one interpretation of Christendom and Europe. But it was always one thing. Whatever the love of one's land should be, it is not patriotism. There was no *Patria* but the Roman, and patriotism was of single occurrence.

But all that is what Rome should have been, and intended to be. It never resembled such except in idea, and by the Late Empire it was quite different.

The City itself, at that time, had about a million and a half persons—about the same population it had had for four hundred years and about the same that it has today. In the low Middle Ages it was to decline to less than one-tenth of that; but this is its natural population, and it will generally maintain itself.

The City had been deathly sick for five hundred years: since the failure of the part of the reforms of the Gracchi, and the more damaging success of the others—as the temporary grain dole.

Rome knew that it was sick. In its more intelligent groups of citizenry it had consulted thousands of doctors, and had employed nearly every nostrum known. It had, however, watched the deaths of many healthy cities and communities, and had come to take sardonic satisfaction in its continuing state.

The City of a million and a half persons had become involved in the Empire of seventy-five million persons, somewhere between one-third and two-thirds of them slaves. The thinking men of the day knew that the per cent of slaves was too high. For corporate health there must never be more than one slave to every two free men, and it had been announced several centuries before that this balance had been violated.

The Empire had become too unwieldy. It had been broken in two for better administration, but it was still too unwieldy. In the time of the Late Empire it had only been ruled as a unit, briefly, by such strong Emperors as Constantine and Theodosius; and once more divided at their deaths.

Rome was not, actually, the head of even the Western Empire any longer. The Western Emperors had taken up residence at Milan, and then at Ravenna. But Rome was the seat of the Senate and the See of the Pope. It was the most populous city in the Empire—Alexandria and Antioch had each populations of about a million, Constantinople about three-quarters of a million— it was the City to which Councils and Senates could be summoned, and to which the Emperor himself could be summoned. It was still the head and the heart of the Empire.

In physical establishment, Rome was at its greatest in this Late Empire time. There has been great admiration for Augustan Rome, but this later Rome contained everything of the Augustan that had not been replaced by something better; and four hundred years of outstanding building had been added to that former excellence.

But classical Rome was not classical in its building, except for the few and early Greek imitations. For the rest it was as baroque— in the grotesque sense as it is today—baroque from the beginning.

There were twelve thousand millionaires—in sesterces—in the City. To be a millionaire in sesterces would be to have about seventy thousand dollars in modern coinage; but this was to be quite rich when the range of consumer goods was narrower.

Ostia, the port of Rome, was the richest port in the Empire; but in the traffic of the port it is difficult to distinguish legitimate trade from tribute. For the two largest imports, grain and slaves, there was no corresponding export. This very favorable trade balance was the main cause of the sickness of the City.

Coinage was peculiar and late. The Carthaginians, the greatest of old trading nations, had not cared for coinage as such. When they handled the coin of lesser trading nations, Lydia and Greece, they handled it as they would any other commodity, by assay and weight.

The Romans never had an enduring standard coinage. The names of more than a hundred different coins are a jungle, unrewarding to try to cut through. The weight equivalent of copper to silver was 112–1 in value, and of silver to gold 12–1. The more frequent of the coins were the golden *aureus,* the silver *sestertius,* and the copper *denarius,* the biblical penny which had also been silver in its history and had varied in modern value from more than five dollars to less than five cents.

Constantine established the gold *solidus,* seventy-two of them to a pound weight; however, he debased the coin before he left the room, as it were. Ingot and bar metal was used in all larger financial transactions, and credit was based on this ingot metal, by assay and weight. The financial center of Old Rome was the Via Sacra.

Coinage was private, public, or military; but it was mainly in the hands of the generals. It bore their names, and was used primarily in the payment of troops. The generals operated both mines and mints, and the soldiers' money was the nearest to a standard. The generals, and this does not exclude the honorable generals such as Stilicho, were guilty of debasing their own coinage, which was the reason for many troop revolts. There seems never to have been a period when even the greenest of the barbarian troops did not have the technique to assay correctly the various metals of the coinage.

Roman shipping seems primitive when we find that the basic three officers of the naval vessel were the Captain, the helmsman, and the flutist who gave the rhythm to the rowers. But the merchantmen had sail and oar of larger size and combination than had already been around Africa and China, and their size (up to a thousand tons) and number sufficed for the Mediterranean. The effect of piracy brought some improvement, in maneuverability. Pirates could sail into the wind before honest men could. They could tack sharper and turn closer, and could make use of shallower harbors for large ships for which they had methods of beaching also. The Roman merchants borrowed from them, and the marine was continuously improving.

The Empire was breaking up. There was no question of that. But was it a natural process that was inevitable? Or could the trend be reversed by a firm stand? The Master General Stilicho believed that natural processes are only the names of mistakes that could have been prevented; that the Empire was too fine a thing to be allowed to die; and that it could be preserved if enough sincere men could be found to defend it. But enough sincere men could not be found, and many of the sincere men did not see the problem in the same light as Stilicho.

Does the mosaic method work? Does any picture at all of that involved Rome emerge? We will add a few more pieces.

Rome had the first apartments or tenements. A law of Augustus forbade these to be more than seventy-five feet high. But with the low ceilings, this could be twelve stories, and the limit had not been observed in the following centuries.

Men played a game with stone balls on balked tables. It seems to have been more like boys' marbles than like pool, however.

Dice were thrown in threes, not in pairs, and loaded dice survive from the era.

The blocks of houses and apartments faced inward to a space in the center, not outward onto the street. Every block became one internal neighborhood, and there were many who never left it at all.

Rome was a city of pushcarts. From them were peddled sausage and cheese and wine and meat pies; also copper and brass ornaments and cloth and carded wool.

The Romans had sidewalk cafés, and flute girls to play for the customers. The pubs served wine, cider, perry, honey mead—whiskey, and contrived strong wine. The alcoholic, as distinguished from the simple glutton, was not common.

The red-light district was across the Tiber on the Via Avrelia, and red lanterns were used by the establishments for their signs.

An over-sweet sort of popular art ran parallel to the more worthy productions; and Cupids more cloying than anything of later centuries survive.

Men wept openly when taken by emotion, but women might only do so privately.

The Romans had the first underworld, and it was literally under the ground. The criminals of the city lived below the surface in the caves and passages. Nobody considered it unusual that they should live down there as a caste, that they should come up and rob, and then return. Raids were made on them when they were too obstreperous, but there was never a concerted attempt to clear them out. It was assumed that they had been there forever and that they were in the natural order of things. There were even thieves' markets set up on certain days where people could go for bargains.

Vice was practiced till revulsion set in—or with other sorts it was not practiced at all—but it was never restricted by material fears. The social diseases had not yet appeared, and the law had nothing to do with private lives. The only deterrents were the Christian religion, the old Roman hearth religion, and some groups of the pagan stoicism which held above such things.

There were no cats at all in Rome. And what has that to do with these great events? Who can say how one piece of the mosaic will contribute to the final picture? There had been cats in earlier Egypt, there would be cats in later Europe; but there were no cats in Rome. Weasels and their kindred were kept as mouse and rat-killers, but they were not kept as pets. Watchdogs were employed, but the dog as a pet would have been inconceivable; the best dog was the bad dog. The Romans made pets of lambs and kids, and *pecora* were still kept within the city itself; but they would never have made pets of a savage species like the dog.

The streets of the City were well lit, but privately. Lanterns hung at all house and shop entrances. The Romans got their lanterns from factories in Capua, which town was devoted to that one indus-try. There were many such one-industry towns. House lamps were made of clay or terracotta, burned olive oil, and had wicks of linen or moss. Salt was shaken into the lamp flame in the belief that it made it burn brighter. It did not, or it does not now; but the prac-tice was uniform with the Romans. The salt was shaken from leather containers.

White was the color of mourning. Glass windows were rare, though glass was used for vases and ornaments. Most windows were of vellum, leather dressed so thin that it would let light through, but might not be seen through. The Baths were the lodges or clubs. They had walks, gardens, libraries, taverns, cafés, swim-ming pools, even theatres. The emphasis on the baths of the Baths is of seventeenth-century rediscovery, not of the original order of importance. Latrines were furnished with jugs of water and sponges.

Rome has its name, not from Romulus, but from the Tiber whose original name was Rumo. Where the Tiber had that name is not of concern here; this is not a history of rivers.

The Jewish quarter was in the Trastevere section and was very ancient; as old as the City itself, from one account. This was not the same location as the later medieval ghetto.

But the most striking aspect of Rome of this period is that the Romans, whoever they were, had disappeared from it. It was like a whirlpool, or a fountain of which Rome was so full. The original water had long since gone, but other water had taken its place and the apparent configuration remained. The Roman people had disappeared, but newer peoples had taken their places and were playing their parts.

The Emperor of the West had been born in Constantinople of a Spanish father. The guardian of the Emperor was a Pannonian Vandal, whose own bodyguard was made up of Huns. The chancellor of the Western Empire was a Greek. The workers of the Empire were Asiatic and African and Northern European slaves. The senators were mostly from the great provincial families of Lusitania, Lugdunensis, Mauretania, Gaul, or Sicily. The tribunes might be Cyrenaicans or Dalmatians; the consuls African or Acquitanian. The generals were Lombards and Britons, Spanish and Gaul, Macedonian and Goth—more and more of them Gothic in the last days.

Was there nowhere any man remaining of the old lineage, even for a symbol? Is there not one of them, known to us in detail enough for appraisal and of sufficient moment to matter, who might indicate to us the thing that had once been in the thing that remained? Was all the surviving Roman blood to be found in the quarter-breeds on the grain dole of the City? There must have been known men in the City who were of the original line.

It is supposed that there were many, but they can seldom be distinguished. They no longer took particular pride in ancestry, and most of them seemed to live quietly. But there is one at least whom we may consider: Siricius, the Pope. Siricius was a native of Rome and of the old Roman line, a *Quinquagesimus*—one of fifty generations; and for that reason we can hardly understand him. The mind of Siricius was completely orthodox, but it arrived backwards at every one of its orthodox conclusions. In studying him, we come up against the old wall.

We can be glad that the old Romans were gone; they would be strangers to us forever. The new peoples of Rome, at the end of the fourth century, we can understand; they are something like ourselves, with all their vices and aberrations. We are well delivered from the earlier Romans and their horrifying virtues.

We missed it. And we intended to catch it by some device or other. The image of the City of that time cannot be conveyed. You will have to take it on faith that Rome was a large and intricate city, and that it had an incandescent spirit of its own. It was all of one body and blood, however much it had changed from its former state. Those end-of-the-world Romans were a vivid and discrete people, and no inhabitant of an area even within ten miles of the walls could ever be mistaken for one of them.

One final try to make the picture emerge. The gladiatorial games had last been presented in the city of Rome more than a generation before this time. An end was put to the games because the Romans had turned from them in final disgust. The Romans, when they had become alien and decadent, rejected the cruelty they had loved in the prime of their virtues. Remember that of them, at least.

So this was the set of it, when the plot begins to spin out for the last days of the World. In Constantinople, one old spider had just about come to the end of his silk. But in Rome and Ravenna, the Greek Chancellor of the Western Empire—the peculiar defamer, fresh come from that damage in the East—had begun to spin a net that would destroy the strongest man remaining, and leave the Empire a widow.

One of the prime antagonists, Alaric, was in Epirus, and was wedded to the Gothic nation in the person of Stairnon.

The other antagonist was Rome and her Empire, who had for spouse naught but a one-eyed old soldier. Plutarch writes that the most war-like commanders, Philip, Antiogonus, Hannibal, and Sertorius had all had but one eye. Had Plutarch lived later, he would have added Stilicho to his list.

Stilicho, in his last years, was glare-blind in one eye from a wound. He may also have suffered brain damage. He had an amazing mind that could handle detail more than any others of his time, but he came now to strange hesitations and indecisions. The mighty Vandal was to age quite suddenly at the last; and when he was gone there would be nobody else. There is room in the study of Stilicho for an analysis by a doctor with an interest in history.

Stilicho once said that he had thirteen pieces of metal broken off and lodged in his body. But the fourteenth, which would take his life, would not lodge. It would sweep cleanly through.

13. Of the Goth in the Mirror

There is one other color in the unbalanced spectrum of the city of Rome. It is seldom seen directly, but seems ever just on the edge of vision. It is most often sensed just at sundown—that added tincture to the silver-gray stone and brick color of Rome. It is the faint tracery of red everywhere.

The mortar, the plaster, the *tectorium* that binds the stones and the bricks of Rome, had been mixed for centuries with a certain amount of blood. The blood makes good mortar. It binds well; and that which is built with it will endure forever.

Part of it is very ancient. Another part is from the Ten Persecutions of the Christians, which always add up to twelve or thirteen when tabulated: that of Nero; that of Domitian; of Trajan; of Hadrian; of Marcus Aurelius, the kindly, two-faced philosopher who shed ten times more blood than Nero; of Antoninus Pius; of Septimus Severus; of Caracalla, but he persecuted for only two years and then made an end to it; that of Maximinus the Thracian; that of Decius; that of Valerian; that of Diocletian, the bloodiest slaughter of Christians ever, excepting only King Dunaan in sixth-century Yemen; and the First Elizabeth of England.

There was the blood of slaves in the mortar, and this was particularly rich and various. There was that of the victims of the wars —most of them killed far from the City. But it was Roman blood, and it found its way into the mortar of Rome. There were the three Punic wars, the four Macedonian wars, the Syrian wars, the Jugurthine war, the three Mithridatic wars, the Gaulic wars, the Britain wars, the four—more or less—Parthian wars, the three Servile wars.

It was then, after those earlier periods, that all the wars became civil wars. All possible enemies were already in the Empire, or they were Foederati or allies of the Empire. All the Gothic wars, all the Vandal and Lombard and African wars are civil wars. All the peoples had become intrinsic parts of the Empire.

The binding, the mortar of the bricks and stones of Rome became still stronger in those last centuries. No other city or Empire had ever had such a rich binding, and it was no wonder that men said it would last forever. The red of it, always there and just beyond the edge of vision, was deep and storied; and no other city had ever had it to such an extent.

The Goths of Alaric were growing fat and glossy in their Epirus freehold. With their leader, the King of the Goths and Megaskyr of Greece and Master General for two different Empires of Illyricum, they grew and matured. They had wedged open the frontiers of the Empire and the gates of the Danube, and countless other Goths joined them from the north every year. These more than made up for the losses of their previous campaigns. Younger Goths were coming up to fighting age every year, and the people would soon be unresistable.

Yet they needed those several years to grow strong. Goths are slower in this than are other people.

It was then believed, and was written down by Romans of scientific bent, that the Goths had a gestation period of one year. This was longer than that of the Romans and other peoples. It was for this reason, according to those Roman writers of natural history, that the Goths were a larger and stronger people than the Romans. We have seen this disputed in print, modernly by men of the writing sort; have seen it set down as impossible. But these skeptics were not there, no more than we were; and there is now no way of verifying the gestation period of the Goths of the end of the fourth century.

But, in a larger sense, the Goths did have a longer gestation period than did other peoples, and they required long intervals of ease both before and after violent actions. They took one such interlude between the years 397 and 401. A multitude of things happened to the Empire and to the other peoples in it during those years, but nothing at all happened to the Goths of Alaric. They grew like grass in Epirus, and waited for their time.

There are no details of the married life of Alaric and Stairnon in those their first years; nor can it be known how it is for a man to be wedded to such a Valkyrie. These two became objects of a popular Gothic cult, and their legend overflowed even to the Romans. The legend of great Gothic virility and passion was mostly a Roman legend. The Romans were themselves a very passionate people, the proof of it being that their own legends were so exclusively concerned with this. The Romans likely exaggerated the Gothic prowess; and the Goths may have been very like other people.

Sometime in this period Alaric did penance for forty days in reparation for his murderous raids in Greece. He was subject to remorse, for which reason he cannot be ranked among the great military leaders of the world. And in this period also, the Goths became un-Gothed to a great extent. They caught the Greek fever and discovered sudden new talents in themselves. They borrowed stringed instruments from the Greeks—they had had only horns and bull-roarers before—and went music crazy. It has been mentioned that rhyme in verse and song appeared at the turn of that century for the first time ever in the world. Nobody knew where it came from, but all the peoples took it up at the same time. The Goths made ballads in rhyme, in their own language and in Low Latin; and these became almost the signature of that rural Gothic springtime in Epirus that lasted four years.

When the impulse seized the Goths next, after martial interludes of more than five hundred years, they would be the troubadours of Languedoc in South France.

In the meantime, until the Goths of Alaric are ready to move, we will consider another Goth—the mirror image of Alaric—who imitated in advance Alaric's incredible feat, and failed in it. He tried it, not with Rome, but with the Empire that was the mirror image of Rome. We will consider also that old spider in Constantinople who was coming to the end of his silk, while another spider in Rome and Milan and Ravenna would soon begin to spin.

About the Eastern Roman Empire, which became the Byzantium Empire, there is always a feeling of unreality. The feeling is real; the Empire is not. It was only a reflection that men believed they saw. Constantinople, the New Rome, was the mirror image of Old Rome; and the Eastern Empire was such an image of the Western, just as the Greek Sign of the Cross is the mirror image of the Latin.

The image, the Eastern Empire, endured for a thousand years longer than the Western; but it remained only a conjecture, a translucent reflection. The whole Byzantine Thing was a distortion on an alternate time track. It was not something that happened.

The Goth who imitated Alaric in advance was Gainas the Master of Arms of the city of Constantinople. He conquered that city that was the capital of a world, and so brought that world to an end. But, as it happened, it was not a real city or a real world; it was Constantinople, and the Eastern world. Nor was the conquest by Gainas an enduring one. By morning, as it were, it had passed away; and nobody remembered for long that it had happened.

The talented Goth Gainas and the devious spider Eutropius were brought down nearly together, and in the same frustrating net.

Eutropius the eunuch, the Great Spider of the East—we use here the language of his enemies—has possibly been painted blacker than any man in history. There is suspicion about such total depiction. Even the Devil is not solid black; he has some handsome scarlets and ghastly oranges mixed in, every color of fire as well as ashes. We may as well add some confusion to the unrelieved picture of Eutropius that has come down to us. We believe that he was a man in high relief, if not in the round. And he was certainly not a simple man.

We will consider the proposition that he was not one man, but two men in history—one of them in his own history. There was a historian named Eutropius of whom very little is known. There was a court eunuch named Eutropius of whom much is known that seems unlikely. We believe that the two were the same man; and, so far, we are the only ones who believe it.

Of the historian Eutropius, we know little more than that he wrote the *Breviarum Historiae Romanae* [Summary of the History of Rome]; that he dedicated it to the Emperor Valens; and that he, the historian Eutropius, took part in the Persian adventure of the Emperor Julian (in 363), and that he wrote his History sometime between 367 and 378. The dedication had to be after Valens' first expedition against the Goths, for Eutropius gives it a Gothic reference, as to *Domino Valenti Gothico Maximo Perpetuo Augusto*. And the dedication of the History was to Valens living; therefore before 378, the year of the death of that Emperor.

This first Eutropius, when referred to at all by his contemporaries, is treated as a notable of assured position and as the intimate of generals and emperors. There are indications that he took part in more military campaigns than the Persian one; and that once, at least, he was grievously wounded in action. It is known that this Eutropius was an advisor of the Emperor Valens.

Of the *History* it need only be said that it is a very good history. The man who wrote it was completely educated and of an outstanding and penetrating mind. There was excellent perspective in all the handling, and the appraisal of events given in its text has since been followed. There were a multitude of incidents given in all previous histories of Rome as facts, those in the *History* of Eutropius are relegated to legend; and they have been considered as legend ever since. He treated certain Roman pretensions with quiet humor, and showed deepest appreciation of other claims. He translates the old and middle Romans to us, but he does not write out of the mind of an old Roman. It seems fairly sure that he was a Greek, as his name would indicate, who had studied the Roman Thing thoroughly.

It is not believed that the contemporary detractors of the

eunuch Eutropius knew of the *History* written by a man named
Eutropius. The History seems to have been written solely for the
instruction of the Emperor Valens. It goes from the legendary times
of Romulus to the appearance of the same Valens. It is non-
partisan—capable of interpreting various viewpoints—and is suf-
fused with a quality that will have to be called wisdom. Eutropius
was a man who, apparently, served the Emperor Valens in an
executive capacity and wrote out a clear account of past times for
his guidance. And this is all that we can put together, for certain,
of the historian Eutropius.

On the accession of the Emperor Theodosius, immediately after
the death of the Emperor Valens, there is a eunuch named Eutropius serving the new Emperor in an executive and advisory capacity. He seems to have served him well, and Theodosius was
not one who tolerated either incompetence or maleficence in his
men. This eunuch Eutropius was part of the bureaucratic heritage
that Theodosius left to his son Arcadius.

From the beginning of the reign of Arcadius the character of
Eutropius begins to blacken. It is not known how much of this,
or any of it, represented a change in the man; and how much of it
is defamation intruded back into history. But Stilicho had dealt
with Eutropius, and accepted him. Stilicho gave the order for the
murder of Rufinus, knowing that Eutropius would succeed him
in power. There were various understandings between Stilicho and
Eutropius—broken several times, and several times restored. Eutropius may have been as devoted to the rather narrow concept
of the Eastern Empire as Stilicho was to the broader concept of
the entire Empire.

It is not known whether Stilicho had any part in the final down-
fall of Eutropius, though he may have permitted the first phase of
the Eastern Gothic revolt which partly brought him down. Actually, the eunuch Eutropius was destroyed by the defamation of a
she-spider, the Empress Eudoxia, whom Eutropius had himself
arranged to be the bride of the Emperor Arcadius.

The new pedigree of the eunuch Eutropius, put forward at the
time of his defamation and death, was this: He was a native of

either Assyria or Armenia; these were the two lands of evil repute in the social legends of the day. He was the slave of a slave, a boy eunuch given over to the use of one Ptolemy, a groom of the imperial stables. He was a deformed, black-faced, feeble-minded, dwarfish boy eunuch, given over in derision to be catamite to the grossest slave of the Court.

It is odd that Eutropius should have become a black-face in his own lifetime, in spite of the evidence of their own eyes of his detractors. Neither Armenia nor Assyria were lands of the Negroes, however much they were symbols of the black-hearted. But still more odd is it that these reports should have been given credence to the present day, instead of being recognized for what they were: conventions of caricature, a vicious formula of detraction that was practiced as prelude to assassination. It was a weird game that was coming into fashion, introduced partly by one Olympius who would later play it against Stilicho.

From this low state, according to the bill of particulars of the defamation, the deformed, black-faced, dwarfish, feeble-minded boy-slave-eunuch, who had an impediment of speech as well as mind and who had unspeakably filthy habits, rose—with no explanation at all—to be Master of the Court, and then (in the last year of the fourth century) to be Consul of the Roman Empire; this, though he was without sponsors and was hated by all. It was surely an odd event, if the defamations were taken at face value.

However Eutropius had been raised to his high offices, it was now decided to bring him down. The Empress Eudoxia discovered in herself a real talent for detraction which she turned against the Imperial eunuch who was somehow out of her favor. In bringing down the Consul-Chancellor, she herself became the actual ruler of the Eastern Empire, increasingly dominating the Emperor, her husband. And for expert assistant in her project of overthrowing, she had Olympius, who was a real genius in this his chosen field. He will be met later in another context.

In the defamatory version of Eutropius, the riddle of his age is unsatisfactorily solved. He had been a boy prostitute given over to the grossest slave of the Court, who was still a young man.

And yet the Eutropius before their eyes was an elderly man, and probably of great age. Claudian states, in an amazing explanation of this, that with eunuchs there is hardly any interval between youth and extreme old age. But Claudian is mistaken; it was not the case in after centuries, and it could not have been the case then. Our inquiry among those few of our acquaintances who know everything brings the answer that it is nonsense. A little reading in Ottoman and other history brings the same answer. Eunuchs age but only as do other men.

There had been, in the age of the Emperor Valens, a man named Eutropius who wrote a very good history of Rome, apparently on commission of that Emperor; who had accompanied an earlier Emperor Julian on his Persian war; who had been wounded gravely in battle, "To the very man of him," which may have had a special meaning; who was plainly a man of the superior sort, and was most certainly a man of exceptional mind.

Immediately after this, in the age of the Emperor Theodosius, there had been a eunuch who served that Emperor in responsible capacities; who commanded the respect of such men as Stilicho; and who was an able, though not perfect, administrator. This eunuch was also named Eutropius.

And immediately after this, in the age of the Emperor Arcadius, this same eunuch, with the Master of Offices Rufinus, assumed the regency of that Eastern Empire. He committed, it is true, certain cruelties in collaboration with that Rufinus, but not yet the blackest cruelties ever committed. He survived the engineered murder of Rufinus, and was then, for some years, accepted by all as the effective ruler of the Eastern Empire. He ruled well; and the previous cruelties, whatever part he may have had in them, did not reoccur. There is no doubt that the Eutropius who served the Emperor Theodosius is the same who served his son Arcadius.

And then there is the change. Eutropius is no longer the most adroit man of the East, the educated Empire Greek, the trusted administrator of competent Emperors, and the guardian of a less competent one. He becomes either an Assyrian or an Armenian, yet curiously negroid, as were neither of those peoples. He becomes a deformed, dwarfish, dim-witted, stammering slave boy-eunuch. As such they killed him, but the corpse was that of quite an old man.

Reference works list the historian and the eunuch as two different men; and do not make it clear how the despised moronic slave rose to be Consul of the Roman Empire. We believe that the historian and the eunuch were the same man; that he was a most outstanding man; and that the distortion is completely that.

Eutropius was as sincere a restorer of the commonwealth as was Stilicho. In their outlook they differed only in this: Eutropius believed that there were two Empires; Stilicho believed that there was only one.

Enough, for the moment, of the boy-slave who was at the same time the Old Spider of Constantinople. We come to the Goth who was the left-handed or mirror image of Alaric, and who momentarily achieved a left-handed version of Alaric's conquest of the world.

This was the Goth Gainas, who was Stilicho's man, but became his own man also. The fall of Gainas was entwined with that of Eutropius. They were friends, though very unlike men.

A generation before this, in the midst of his trouble with the Visigoths in the whole Balkan region, Theodosius had settled a large force of Ostrogoths in Phrygia in Asia Minor. The behavior of those East Goths in Asia had, for that generation, paralleled that of the West Goths in Europe. They were among the finest soldiers of the Empire—when they were not attacking the Empire. They had not attacked it for a decade and a half until that last year of the fourth century. Alaric of the West Goths was an unwitting cause of that attack when it came.

The fame of Alaric, like that of all destined men, had traveled early and to great distances. Before Alaric had conquered anything at all, except, temporarily, parts of Greece and Epirus, it was known from Ireland to Parthia that he would conquer the world. And it was firmly believed that he had already conquered a great part of it. There is suspicion of organized Gothic propaganda on a very wide scale involved here. There is suspicion that this propaganda was spread by the feral Goth Athaulf outside the Empire, for he had very wide relations with all the exterior peoples; and by his sister and Alaric's wife, Stairnon, who maintained her own connections with all Goths everywhere. But even without organization, the news of a destined man will spread, and the accounts of his achievements will be common knowledge even before they have happened.

Tribigild, an Ostrogoth in Phrygia in Asia Minor, had become jealous of the feats of Alaric and had resolved to emulate him; though, apparently, without being very clear as to just what those feats were. He rose in rebellion in the year 399. Tribigild had recently been to Constantinople and believed that he had not been given proper honors. He had other grievances, and he was an important man of the East Goths.

One thing is clear: Stilicho did not have anything to do with this first rebellion, before Gainas joined up with it, and may have had very slow intelligence of it. He did not stir it up as a diversion or to counteract Arcadius' stirring up Gildo to revolt against the Western Empire in Africa.

Stilicho may have had a hand in it later, after the revolt was taken over by Gainas. If so, this was Stilicho's first serious blunder: not that he supported the rebellion, but that, having done so, he did not make sure it succeeded and survived.

Gainas was Stilicho's Goth in the East, and he was as good a general as might be found anywhere. Likely he was better than Alaric; and better now than Stilicho, who had begun to flounder. But Gainas, possibly the finest military genius among the Goths, was not such a man as would be able to rule the world; and he attempted to do just that.

The revolt of Tribigild began to move like a whirlwind. It isn't an empty phrase. The revolt generated great activity and power at its center, but for a while it remained in one place. Then it began to walk slowly and uncertainly across the land, the while it maintained a great rate of rotation and turbulence at its heart.

The revolt suffered repeated defeats, which changed its direction but did not diminish its force. Tribigild, having wandered three hundred miles south, was defeated in Pamphylia by local forces. He was defeated again at Selgae, trying to turn the corner of the Tarus Mountains. He was knocked in various directions by random encounters. But still his force grew by accretions of dissatisfied elements. It seemed sometimes that he would break down into Syria, or to the sea, or back north to the Hellespont and against Greece. Possibly he was waiting to see what would be sent against him.

Eutropius, in his person of Master of Empire, sent two generals against Tribigild: one Leo; and Gainas the Goth. Gainas had the command of Thrace and the Hellespont, and the defense of the City itself. Leo was given the command of the army of Asia, and so came first against the rebellious Tribigild.

Leo failed miserably, a great number of his troops deserting to Tribigild, and the rest being easily scattered. Tribigild had been in trouble from the opposition of local forces. The arrival of Leo with an Imperial army, instead of putting further pressure on him, brought him relief. The desertions from the Imperial army to the rebel forces were the making of it.

Gainas was then sent by Eutropius across the Hellespont—almost the last command and act of the Imperial eunuch. The sending of Gainas raised serious suspicions in the minds of the people of Constantinople. There was a connection of family or marriage between Gainas and Tribigild. The entire Gothic nobility, now settled in various lands, was closely intermarried.

Eutropius had held back Gainas from these very considerations; but perhaps he would have done better to send him first. Gainas had been alienated by the selection of Leo over himself. He might have acted in loyalty had he been first choice, as he should have been from his rank and his known ability. Eutropius had been in error, and his first mistake gave birth to the second. He had sent the Roman Leo in command of Empire troops, mainly Gothic, in the belief that he would be counterbalance to them and would be able to guarantee their loyalty. But the troops were resentful at the demotion of their leader Gainas, and they caught the Gothic fever on contact with the forces of Tribigild.

It was then necessary to send Gainas, as the only man capable of coping with the situation that had now gotten out of hand. But Gainas, having first been affronted by being held back, now caught his own brand of fever; and the campaign against Tribigild was a very strange one.

The defamation of Eutropius had reached a high pitch while he was still Consul and Master of Empire. The Empress Eudoxia and her creatures had been seeking the occasion for his ruin. They now used these military setbacks.

The ridiculous military failure of the incompetent General Leo reflected against Eutropius, who had sent him; although Leo had been raised to the generalship by Eudoxia and Arcadius, who gave to him a reputation which he did not deserve. The deliberate military delays of the very competent Gainas, the General sent by Eutropius, completed the fiasco. The revolt still remained unpunished, and someone must be held responsible.

Eutropius, on the planning of Olympius, was taken and murdered in a suburb of Chalcedon by an official named Aurelian. And this man, Aurelian, again on the connivance of Olympius, was raised to be Master of Empire.

Olympius, the instigator, was a sort of liaison between the two halves of the Empire—a connection outside and opposed to the apparatus of Stilicho. He was a Greek who spent much time in Rome and Milan and Ravenna, as well as in Constantinople. He had been sent several times as emissary from the Emperor Arcadius to his brother the Emperor Honorius. He had formed a link between the often quarreling brothers; but he had now become the instrument of the Empress Eudoxia, more than of her husband Arcadius.

Olympius had carried through to perfection the project of the defamation and death of Eutropius, and he was now rewarded in having a man of his own sort and party, Aurelian, elevated to Master of Empire. Olympius had his own world aspirations, and to him this was only one step.

But the usurpation seemed a disaster to everybody concerned. Aurelian was not such a man as should be allowed to rule, nor Olympius one who should be permitted such influence.

Stilicho may have sent orders of some sort to his Goth Gainas. Or Gainas may have acted on his own without receiving his orders. Gainas had not opposed his fellow Goth with arms. He had, instead, camped by him and sat down with him for some weeks of parley, apparently friendly. It may be that Gainas was still loyal to the Empire and believed that he could persuade his kinsman to give up the revolt without bloodshed.

Now, on the word of Eutropius' murder—proclaimed an execution in the interest of the state after the fact—and Aurelian's accession to power, two things happened simultaneously.

Gainas sent word that he refused to accept Aurelian as Master of Empire. And he proclaimed himself Master of Empire. This was the official line he took, and he followed it to the last. It may have been Gainas in the person of Stilicho's Goth who made this proclamation, or he may have done it of himself. Stilicho would not have been against setting all the East under a strong military guardianship loyal to himself; letting the shadow Court of Constantinople become even more of a shadow. But he had not intended that Gainas should get out of hand.

What actually happened is that Gainas joined the revolt of Tribigild in Asia, put himself at the head of the rebellious Goths, added them to his Imperial force, and returned with them to the conquest of Constantinople.

And the other thing happening simultaneously to Gainas' seizing power, was the formation in Constantinople, by the new Consul Aurelian, of what might be called the Roman Supremacy Party. This had popular support. The Roman remnant in the city had long been uneasy under the effective Gothic domination. It was a civilian movement, and it attained great proportions while the Gothic men were off soldiering in Asia. There was some killing and looting, and a few Gothic blocks of the city were burned out. Others formed themselves into enclaves, blocking streets and resisting.

The Gothic population of Constantinople was not large, probably not more than one-tenth, and consisted largely of the families of soldiers in the Imperial service. The Goths had not intruded greatly into trade; many of them were artisans, but they had not set up large establishments or factories; a few were in politics, but they were not really strong there. The Romans had no real reason to be jealous of the Goths of the city, and it was certainly imprudent for them to turn to such butchery when the army, composed mainly of Gothic soldiery, was approaching the city.

There was a perverse mind behind Aurelian and his instigated riots, and it would appear later on a grander scale elsewhere. But the riots of Constantinople were not of great moment. The populace had shown great enthusiasm for the Roman Supremacy oratory, but it turned away from the killing; the murders and burnings were of official instigation, and not popular. And the old Greek population of the city, at least equal to the Romans in number, was first neutral; and then sheltered the Gothic families.

There were surely some second thoughts about the thing, as Gainas and his forces came near. Olympius left Constantinople for Italy, glutted with satisfaction of the thing he had done and lucky to escape the consequences. The Emperor Arcadius professed very late knowledge of the riots and disclaimed any official sanction of them. And his own Empress Eudoxia was silent as a cat after a feast, and licked the blood from her lips.

The Gothic Imperial armies returned, under Gainas and Tribigild, to the Hellespont, and there was no effective force to oppose them. Gainas, calling himself the Master of Empire, summoned the Emperor to meet him.

The Emperor Arcadius called out Singerich and other of his Goths who had gone under cover during the weeks of the Roman Supremacy reign. He set the matter in their hands, and went out with them to hold parley with Gainas. The meeting with Gainas was near Chalcedon, in the same Church of Euphemia where was later held the general Church Council of Chalcedon.

Gainas was justifiably demanding. The families of his soldiers— loyal Romans all, he insisted—had been slaughtered; and some of his own near kindred had been killed. The rightful Master of Empire, Eutropius, had been murdered, and a reprehensible man had been put into his place. Gainas, in his claim to be the new and rightful Master of Empire, insisted on absolute rights of entry and occupation. The Emperor Arcadius, on the advice of his own Court Goths, consented. He proclaimed Gainas Master of Empire on the spot and agreed to turn the city over to his mercy.

Gainas demanded a bonus: the heads of Aurelian and Saturninus, the two highest in command; and the two, now that Olympius had vanished, most forward in the anti-Gothic moves.

The Emperor agreed that Gainas should have the two heads. And Gainas entered and occupied Constantinople in his new role of Master of Empire. But it was quickly made clear that his occupation was in an entirely different role; he set out to rule, from the first hour, as the head of a Gothic nation.

Gainas assumed another title, Autocrat of the East. He struck swiftly at the remnant of the Roman Supremacy Party and had more of its heads than two. He filled all offices with Goths. He replaced the Roman Empire with a Gothic Empire.

The world, at least the Eastern part of it, had come to an end. What the partisans of Alaric were dreaming that he should do in the West, the Goth Gainas had done completely in the East. The Empire that was destined to endure forever had ended. The triumph of Gainas and his Goths was so complete, the suppression of the Roman affair so total, that it becomes incredible that it should all be no more than a night's dream, forgotten by morning.

The conquest by Gainas was a seven-day wonder, and we are tempted to state that it lasted but seven days. Actually it endured a little more than two weeks. Gainas was brought down by what moderns consider a minor detail, and which was so considered by himself.

Stilicho would have known better. Alaric would have known better. Even if he had acted in the same way, he would have known and anticipated the reaction. But Gainas was impolitic. It isn't known how a student of Stilicho could have made such a stupid mistake, but Gainas was competent only in military matters. The new and forced stability of the East was scattered like a mist. The queer little Roman party, that had been stamped dead, now rose with new allies and devoured the iron heels of the suppressors.

Gainas demanded a church where his Arians might worship. It was pointed out that the Arians already had a church commensurate with their numbers, as only a small number of the Gothic nobility was still Arian. The church was not commensurate with their dignity, Gainas replied.

Gainas seized the leading church, the Church of the Apostles. It may be that he did not even hear the low gasp of the people at this act. He turned out the Archbishop, and installed Arian trustees. He let it be known that he was considering whether he should declare the Empire Arian. And once more it seems that he did not hear the gasp of the people, the furious low intake of breath before the explosion.

Gainas rode out of the city with a part of his force, to attend to certain disorders in the countryside. He had been in control of Constantinople for twelve days, and had effected such complete changes in the city that he left it with contempt and a feeling of complete safety.

The people shut the gates of Constantinople and rose in arms. They were not only the Roman Supremacy Party; they were also the Greek Party, the Catholic Party, the Empire Party; and oddly enough, the Gothic Party. The city Goths, except for certain of their high nobility, had become Catholic in the generation just past; and it was as such that they rejected Gainas who had scandalized them. They discovered that they were still loyal to the Emperor, however weak a man he might be.

But there was another element. If Gainas had not made a stupid mistake on a religious matter, he would have made it on another matter. He was not the man to play the part of the tyrant, though he had developed a strong inclination towards tyranny. He outraged the dramatic sensibilities of the Romans of the city, who had now become Greek in mind. Gainas had the appearance of an inept strutter; he could not play the role. The people might have accepted a tyrant who looked the part of a tyrant, but they would not accept one who looked the buffoon. They howled him down in an explosion of fury; and they killed his men.

It was mostly the Asian Goths of Tribigild who suffered in this second series of riots, such of them as had been left in the garrisons of the city. The original Gothic soldiery of Constantinople became Roman once more, as easily as changing their coats.

The fighting was finished within one day and night in the city, and within six months it was finished everywhere. It was all a short incredible incident, and perhaps there cannot be a real explanation for it. The man had overreached himself. He conquered his world; and was suddenly seen to be a pretentious fool in his days of triumph. The people turned on him in furious outrage, but behind that they were laughing at him.

People are curiously contrived, and nobody can say how they will react. But a man who cannot look the part will do well not to attempt the world in a single grab.

Gainas died beyond the Danube, caught between the pursuit of his fellow-Goth Fravitta and the obstruction of the young Hunnish King Uldin. It is said that—Arcadius having offered its weight in gold for the head of Gainas—King Uldin drew out the brains of Gainas and poured in molten lead to win a better bargain with his prize. This part of the story has been doubted, and for no better reason than that it had been told five hundred years earlier of the head of Gaius Gracchus—as though a good trick might not be pulled more than once.

So the conquest by Gainas had been unreal, as that Eastern world itself was unreal.

After this, the Eastern Empire fell back into chaos and the woman's rule of the Empress Eudoxia. From then on it was an Empire of whim, of chaos, and of women's rule for more than one thousand years.

The Western Empire, supported generation after generation by half a hundred of the strongest and most remarkable men in history, from Stilicho to Charlemagne, died and disintegrated and left off being the Empire.

The Eastern Empire, supported by fools and slaves and fops, and ruled by the worst and most incompetent of men and women, managed to endure and thrive for a thousand years more.

14. Of Pollentia and Verona

The Western Empire, at the end of the fourth century, was absolutely bankrupt in military power. It was out of such insufficiency and frustration that Stilicho saw, in a vision or dream, seven waves rising above the frontiers to engulf the Empire. Each wave was taller and more turbulent than the previous one. He saw the Empire go down under the assaults, and he suffered agonies from such dreams and visions.

Stilicho had already begun to be a little mentally deranged in those years. Though several of his most incredible feats of daring and effectiveness were still in the future, his failures had begun to appear. Some observers have claimed to see the effect of brain injury in the doughty old soldier.

The worst that can be said of him, however, is that he failed to solve certain problems that nobody else even saw. In retrospect, these problems are there clear enough. But the problems were not clear at that time; and the answers are not clear now. Stilicho was the only one who perceived that there were mortal dangers beneath the surface changes.

There were the affairs of soldiers; the affairs of governors; the affairs of Provinces. There were changes of jurisdiction and certain alterations of administration; there were settlements and resettlements; and there were the deaths and resurrections of certain countrysides. Old men were being replaced by new, and the long-time trend towards centralization was being reversed. They were times of change, but only Stilicho realized that the Empire was dying in the changes; and only he cared.

It may not have mattered. It may be that he was wrong to care. It is only guesswork as to what sort of world it would be today if Stilicho had succeeded in his strong endeavors in those critical times. But for a weird combination of circumstances he would have succeeded. In such a case the Empire would not have crashed; not, at least, in that decade and probably not in that century. Naturally, it would not have survived in the same form forever; but enough of it might have survived for a long enough time to have made a great difference.

It might not have been necessary to spend five hundred years just getting onto its feet again. It might not have been necessary to lose certain noble qualities forever. Certain institutions had to be wrought, heated, and variously reshaped. Much of the furniture of the Empire was bad and outmoded. But it is possible that the house could have been cleaned without burning it down.

Nothing is inevitable till it has already happened. There, at the beginning of the fifth century, Stilicho still had a good chance of saving the Empire. For a while it seemed that he would save it, and there was undeniable improvement under his hand. *The World did not have to end then.*

The East had fallen into desuetude as far as service to the Empire was concerned. Stilicho's Goth Gainas was dead. His head had been sent by the Hun Uldin to Constantinople, where it was kept as a trophy. Perhaps it's still kept as such; there are a lot of old mementos around the town.

But Alaric's Goth Singerich, his brother-in-law, was very much alive in Constantinople and was once more riding high in favor. Singerich had saved himself once by becoming very Roman in the time of the anti-Gothic turmoil; once by becoming Gothic again as Gainas approached the city; and a third time by becoming Catholic and declaring himself for the Establishment, when the people had risen after Gainas' seizing the Church of the Apostles. And who is to say he was insincere?

A commoner mistrusts the motives of a king at his peril, and Singerich was destined to be a king for the last seven days of his life. He had learned to come through defamations and riots and occupations; to change coloration and allegiance. The Goth turned Greek had an important part to play in the Gothic program, and in the tangled roles of his two enemy brothers, of his sister Stairnon, and of his brother-in-law Alaric. It was necessary for the events that he should survive them all and be the last one alive. He kept his feet when the world around him was not able to.

But the East, though it came to stability under a triumvirate of Singerich and two others, had become useless to Stilicho at this time; and it would not properly carry its burden of Empire.

Between the East and West, occupying Illyricum and Epirus, was Alaric who could be a support of the Empire and a bridge to the East; or who could be a lance pointed to the heart of the Empire. Alaric had the force to make the difference—if only he would do as he was told. There was some question now as to whether Alaric was Stilicho's man, whether he was the man of the Gothic national movement, or whether he was his own man. Stilicho suspected that he himself ran a poor third in the influence.

Stilicho could roll with, absorb, and counter any blow whatsoever that should come on him and on the Empire singly. He could almost stand up to any combination of blows. Now, however, there was a veritable conspiracy of attacks. The African campaign had been weakening. There was the mad-dog rising of Stilicho's own people, the Vandals, under their King Godigisel. The British legions were going through those curious convolutions that meant they were getting ready to raise up a usurper Emperor; and none raised so many usurpers as the British. There was furious factionalism among the Franks. The Rhine garrisons were attacked from Holland to the high Alps. Decumates and Upper Germany were in complete turmoil. And from the far north there came the cold wind of a real barbarian movement, of an entirely different sort from the movements of the border peoples who had been miscalled barbarians.

In the first year of the new century the threats had risen to an absolute crisis. Stilicho knew that the threats were concerted and centrally directed, but he could not guess by whom. Alaric could, at least, guess that they were directed by the man so close to him in affection and so distant from him in mind; and he could guess that they were partly directed for his benefit.

It appeared to Stilicho as though every form of attack on the Empire would crest at once. Yet, if they could be ridden out, perhaps they would all subside at once. Stilicho could play at any game. Though not knowing whose was the mind behind the turmoils, he was willing to bet his mind against that mind. He took a supreme gamble.

Stilicho had to secure the frontiers. That had become the matter of the immediate survival of the Empire. He had to trust certain forces. He must accept that Alaric would show good faith; that the East, at least, would not hinder; that Britain would forbear an immediate rising; that Spain, which always acted at the wrong time, would not act now; that Africa would remain chastened for at least one year.

Stilicho acted with the greatest secrecy, though knowing that the man who directed the turmoils would have swift intelligence of his moves. Stilicho, trusting all things that normally he would not have trusted and acting from necessity, stripped Italy and the internal Empire of all troops except the Palace Guards. He flung everything at the northern frontiers.

He *must* secure and clear those frontiers now or there would be no later time. He left the interior Empire defenseless, and prayed that God would give him time to repair the crumbling frontiers and to return again before disaster overwhelmed all.

Stilicho gambled and lost. His striking north was a signal, and it was relayed by the master-mind outside the Empire. The word came to Alaric, who had been listening and waiting while another pulled the strings for him.

The Goths of Alaric, wakened from their four-year somnolence, were out of Illyricum like a blizzard—once Stilicho was in the Rhineland. They struck in short days and weeks through the passes before familiar Aquileia; and were into undefended North Italy and many hundreds of miles behind the troops of Stilicho. They isolated the peninsula to be dealt with later; and moved with bewildering speed and assembled power into the valley of the Po and up the high road to Milan to capture the Emperor Honorius, who was in residence there.

For Alaric and his Goths had their own ideas about how the Empire should be saved: by whom, and for whom. To simplify is always to falsify a little, but here we must simplify. The Gothic effort was amazingly complex, and Alaric was but one of the many faces it wore. It is to simplify too much to say that Athaulf was master-minding the whole Gothic movement and the depredations of the frontier peoples from beyond the Danube and beyond the Alps. Yet it was he who incited and gave movement to most of the invasions along the frontier of more than a thousand miles. His influence extended beyond the Gothic peoples. His own system of intelligence was superb. He kept such a turmoil going on all the northern borders that Stilicho had to let himself be drawn there. And he had to weaken the interior Empire to reinforce the frontier. It was an admirable plan that Athaulf executed, but he was not alone in working out the basics of it.

Athaulf was still a young man, a very few years older than Alaric; and the Gothic nation was ruled by the elders. They might loose a young instigator and a young king, but the elders controlled the councils. The Goths were a people of councils and higher councils and doubly distilled councils of the highest sort. When a Gothic plan was finally put into effect it had been completely refined. The plan of the massive tactical enticement and the swift striking behind the lines was a good one, and well carried out.

The Empire forces of Stilicho were diverted, over-extended, outflanked, under-cut, and fragmented. They left the Empire wide open and undefended. The Goths moved in force on unprotected Milan to take the Emperor; they had isolated the whole of Italy by the same move, and Stilicho was far away.

Had Stilicho blundered gravely? He had not. Stilicho had a perfect sense of timing, and the greater the danger the more sure were his moves. The Goths coming like a blizzard was metaphor, of course. However rapidly they should come, and they came very swiftly, it would take them at least a month to complete their first objective.

Stilicho had not blundered at all. He had seen the trap and was in and out of it before it could be sprung. He had seen in his visions seven waves rising above the frontiers to engulf the Empire, but he surely would not be so weak as to be destroyed by the first of the waves. In spite of his final failure there is no point in his whole career where it can be said that he blundered. Towards the end he would no longer be able to come up with the impossible solution, but he did play out his lone game to a length that strains credulity.

We digress here, while the Goths are striking swiftly along the high road to Milan, and Stilicho is doing rapidly what he must do.

The closest thing to a blunder that Stilicho had yet committed was the marrying of his daughter Maria to the young Western Emperor Honorius. Stilicho believed that this would give him even firmer control over that retarded young man; but the effect was the opposite. The Emperor Honorius was but fourteen years old at the time of the marriage in the year 398. But it would not have made a difference if he had been older. When Maria died, after ten years of the marriage, she died a virgin. Honorius had no interest in girls, or in wives. He became resentful for the first time of Stilicho, and especially of the new mother-in-law, Serena. The wife of Stilicho was a wonderful woman. She had the finest motives in the world and was gracious in all things. She was a gracious meddler, but she was a meddler. The retarded young Emperor became very perverse in his reactions to his guardians, who had now become a complete family.

It was at this time, or shortly after, that Olympius returned from the Court of Constantinople to the Court of Honorius at Milan. He had been the principal effector of the defamation and death of Eutropius in the East. Now he became a new spider spinning a web of malevolence in Rome and Milan and Ravenna. This was the beginning of the seventh wave, which would crest last of

all, but had its beginnings earlier than most of them; the roots of
the wave were very deep.

Stilicho was occupied; and Olympius was smooth. Here was a
threat, completely ignored, that was farther and more deadly behind the lines than the forces of Alaric.

Olympius had been peddling his poison for two years at the
time when Stilicho was put into his straited military position. And
the poison had begun to have its effect. But was Stilicho a man
who could be brought down by such as that?

Just what was Stilicho who maintained the world almost by himself? A man has to have a face. We know from many sources that
he was a large and powerful man, but what did he look like?

His face is said to be on three coins; actually, two coins and a
medallion. But we have not been able to find illustrations or reproductions of them. We must make do with a painting that is not
quite contemporary with him.

It's in several of the old history books, and apparently dates
from a century or more after the life of Stilicho. The Roman dress
has now become enriched; it is half-way to being that brocaded
effect worn by kings in a deck of playing cards. The decorations
are early medieval, and on an animal-footed chair or throne sits
Stilicho as Governor of Rome. But his face is not a convention—
not at all a period stereotype. Though it must be a copy of a copy,
it is the face of one man only; a face that could not have been
worked twice. It is the genuine face of Stilicho. The face of a striking man always comes true in legend and painting.

Stilicho is a German; let there never be any doubt of that. He is
a kraut-head—shock-haired, blue or gray-eyed (though there is no
color in the reproduction), German in jaw and jowl. He is a rather
good-appearing, serious man, and gives the impression of having
whole worlds in him.

He holds in one hand what appears to be a cucumber; but is
probably a small fasces—the bundle of rods, the symbol of authority. In his other hand he holds a scepter with an eagle in the
laterna part. On top of the scepter is a replica of himself in the
same position, holding the same scepter, on which again is an ex-

pressive smudge which would be a still smaller replica of him holding a still smaller scepter. The box within the box within the box
trick is very old.

Below Stilicho is a forgotten symbolism of animals: an ass or
mule kicks a bear; a lion attacks some species of horned cattle;
other people and animals do things that are not clear. Above the
head of Stilicho is a formula in the form of a series of abbrevia-
tions run together. It reads EXCSACSTABETTMMPORREXCCOR, with
no break between the letters. We are not scholar enough to in-
terpret it, but it is not the moto of Stilicho.

The motto of Stilicho was *Torcular Calcavi Solus*—I have trodden the wine press alone. It's from Isaiah: I have trodden the wine
press alone, and of the Gentiles there is not one man with me.
Stilicho himself, both in body shape and flavor, was like a barrel-
ful of the iron-tasting old wine. He was a big bodied man with a
face to be remembered; and he was now occupied on the frontiers.

The Goths of Alaric had broken out of Illyricum and into Italy,
and were on the high road to Milan. Both the dates and routes are
vague to us. Alaric left Epirus late in the year 401. He reached
Aquileia by way of Haemonia (or Aemonia) and the Birnbaum
Forest (we cannot find out the ancient name of it). The Goths
were completely unopposed on the way into Italy past Aquileia—a
sign of the extent to which the interior Empire had been stripped
of troops.

There was nothing but the palace guard in Milan, in panic; and
no forces at all to oppose Alaric on his road to that capital. The
advice of the ministers to Honorius was to capitulate; to give up
Milan, to give up Italy, to cut and run for it to Arles, an occasional
capital in South France.

To strengthen Milan, Stilicho sent one man only. Even one good
man was more than he could spare from the border warfare. It
would seem that a single man would not be of sufficient effect, but
this was an exceptional man. He was the Goth, Sarus.

This began Sarus' direct service to the Emperor Honorius, which
would become a tangle of frustration and temporizing. There

would come the time when Sarus wished to serve the Empire more than anything, and would not know where or in whom the Empire could be found.

Now, however, he brought very simple orders. He came livid in anger and firm in his insistence that those simple orders be carried out.

The Emperor Honorius must not leave Milan. Nobody would leave Milan. It was the command of Stilicho, and Sarus' own! He would not allow a few thousand guards to contradict him in it! All would stay and stand siege; and Sarus appointed himself captain of the defenses. The palace guard and the citizens must stand siege of whatever forces the Goths might bring against them. This was an order, and was not subject to countermand.

The Emperor must remain in Milan because Milan was the only city in the region with walls sufficient to delay Alaric at all; and the presence of the Emperor would insure that Alaric would come to Milan and not take some unpredictable tangent. The orders of Stilicho, which were now the orders of Sarus, were to hold Milan to the last man. It was essential to delay Alaric and his Goths as long as possible; and to hold them, by involving them in a siege, to one location.

Meanwhile, Stilicho rode along the frontiers to find an army he could employ. He is reported to have traveled with such speed that it is likely an error has crept into the accounts of the thing; but he did not travel in panic.

He was unsparing of himself in the travel, but he did not strip a single garrison that was immediately required. He crossed the Alps in winter. He was along the Rhine for its entire length. He checked and rechecked garrisons and led attacks hundreds of miles beyond that river. He pierced to the heart of every gathering storm and turbulence, hanged leaders, and cowed men. He himself took part in three separate battles in a single week. He crushed all festering centers of opposition; several times taking levies of new troops as tribute from the routed peoples.

He shifted troops from the areas where the immediate threat was diminished and reinforced other sectors that were more critical. He attacked with savagery and a cruelty that was unusual to him, for he had no time to lose.

He stood and surveyed the frontiers; and they were, for the moment, at peace. In many places it was a bloody, mangled, resentful peace, but it would suffice till he could return. And the bulk of the Imperial troops he left on the frontier.

But he did peel off an army of sorts, any excess of troops he could manage, and started them off towards Italy under competent leadership and destined for selected rendezvous points. Though personally moving with all possible speed, he did not do any thing too fast; and did not, in any case, have to backtrack to attend to any thing he had neglected.

Living like a saddle bum and having no care at all for himself, Stilicho now rode three thousand miles in sixty days, changing horse more than one hundred times. He held night-long conferences with his subordinate commanders, after riding all day. Most of the time he rode alone, often forgetting to carry even primary arms.

Stilicho made one more deep excursion beyond the frontier and returned from it with a special detachment, small in numbers but in many respects equal to an army. This was the special group of Huns who traveled with Uldin. These were devoted fighters, and their leader, Uldin, a friend and former student of Stilicho, was another firepot of the sort of Sarus.

Having stabilized the frontiers for a certain time and in a certain manner, Stilicho turned and rode for Italy; gathering up the divisions of the moving army as he went, coming to the relief of the Emperor in Milan.

And it seemed that the timing of Stilicho was perfect; that Milan, inspired by the intrepid Sarus as captain of the defenses, would be able to withstand siege until help should arrive, and that the ambushing Alaric should himself be ambushed. The Goths, for all their sophistication in warfare, were never able to avoid the wide secondary encirclement, when the Romans had the men and the means to make it work. The Romans seemed to have both now, though barely; having bled both the shaking frontiers and the in-

terior Empire for them. And Stilicho had correctly calculated the
term of the affair to the exact day.

But the siege of Milan was raised three days early; three days
before the Goths could have broken down the town with the engines they were constructing; three days before the forces of
Stilicho would arrive. The siege was raised when only the most
advanced skirmishers of the Empire troops had begun to make
contact with the Gothic forces of Alaric.

Every man of Stilicho had serious failings, and the Master General used what he had. Had they been without failings, they would
have been other Stilichos. Sarus may have been the only man in
the Empire who could have inspired Milan to such a stand by his
anger and will alone. But Sarus was not a great general, and he
was no planner at all. His system of intelligence was most rudi-
mentary, and he had no understanding at all of the Court that obtained in Milan. He had eyes for only one thing—the defenses of
the town—when he should have had eyes for everything.

The Emperor Honorius had scutted out of the city like a scared
rabbit, accompanied by no more than a hundred courtier guards;
and he left the defender of the city, Sarus, in ignorance of his escape. The Roman deception left the Goth in the dark. He was
absolutely uncomprehending of the reason for it when Alaric and
his forces wheeled off and left the environs of Milan with precipitous speed. His first thought was that the army of Stilicho had
arrived in full power; but he could catch no sight of it, and he could
not conceive of Alaric leaving a field of action without a fight.

Moreover, it did not appear to Sarus that the Goths were fleeing
from the arriving frontier armies, for the sounds of a flight have
their own tone; these were the sounds of a pursuit. And the angle
of movement was wrong for it to be a retreat: the Goths were going due south, and the border legions would arrive more from the
west—through Gaul, around the southern end of the Alps, and to
Milan from Turin.

Sarus posted the city forces and then rode out following the
Goths fearlessly to the south with quite a small force. He did not

pursue; he followed in bafflement, with not one-twentieth of their numbers. He had ridden out for several hours before his scouts informed him that the frightened Emperor was out in advance, and that it was he whom Alaric pursued.

Alaric did not want the city of Milan. He wanted the person of the Emperor to use for a basis of negotiations.

The way went to Ticinus (which is Pavia); then turned west and a little south to Hasta (which is Asti). The Emperor Honorius slept that night in the little walled town of Asti, and Alaric gnashed his teeth outside because he had not been able to take him during the day.

Whatever else history forgets to recount of the young Emperor Honorius, who would always be a boy in mind, let it not forget to tell this: he was a horseman. Whenever it mentions of his courtier guards that they would not stand and fight, let it also mention that they could ride. The Court of Arcadius, though very unwarlike, had always been hunt-crazy; wolf, fox, boar, and deer hunts were their main occupation. On their light swift horses they were excellent, and they rode like steeplechasers. They escaped Alaric that day as a fox escapes, with a great rush of speed when it was believed that they had been ridden to the ground, and with a sudden veer to the side through thickets and brakes.

Milan had stood siege for a month and would have stood at least three days longer, according to the calculations of Stilicho. Asti would not be able to stand for two days. Alaric would shake the Emperor out of that town like shaking a raccoon out of a tree. But already time was running out for Alaric and for everyone; he now had not even two days to give to it. Outriders of the Empire cavalry were sighted early in the second day of the siege of Asti, and the infantry would be no more than a day behind.

Alaric forgot the small walled town for the moment and prepared for the coming attack. In the meanwhile Sarus was called off and sent back to secure Milan, by advance order of Stilicho. There was the pretext that Sarus, being the brother-in-law of Alaric, might not be trusted to oppose him to the ultimate; but actually the apprehension of Stilicho was quite in the opposite direction.

Though the two brothers-in-law were never personal enemies, yet on finding themselves on the opposite sides of an affair they would have fought to the death. Stilicho did not desire the death of either of them, nor the destruction of any of the forces involved. He had a need for all in his later plans.

Sarus had asked for the command of the oncoming cavalry, and it was refused him. There was a moment when it seemed that Sarus would affect not to comprehend the orders that Stilicho had sent in advance, and would take command of that cavalry as the one who best knew how to use it; and Stilicho himself had not yet arrived. But Sarus obeyed, in spite of his itch for combat. He always obeyed Stilicho, or anyone speaking with the voice of the Empire. Sarus rode back to Milan. And Saul of the Alani captained the cavalry—to his death.

The orders of Stilicho to Saul were to seek for a device to force the surrender of Alaric's contingent with the least possible fighting. Only if no such device could be found, should an all-out assault be ordered; and that only after the infantry was in sight. Alaric had been delayed so long that his hopes of taking the Emperor had failed. He would have to face the forces of Stilicho without any such royal hostage to hold as a club.

On coming onto the scene, Saul believed that he had discovered such a device to force the sudden surrender of the Goths, and he proceeded with it without waiting for the arrival of the infantry. He resolved to surround the Goths as he saw them, assembled in robes in great numbers for the Easter Mass, and apparently believing that the Romans would also respect the Peace of God on that day.

Much has been made of the perfidy of the Empire forces attacking the Gothic encampment on Easter Day (April 6, 402) when the Goths were celebrating the Easter Mass in grand and pious assembly. This seemed especially reprehensible in view of the fact that Stilicho had placed Saul, a pagan general, in command of the attack.

But Saul was one man in whom no perfidy at all could be found. He was a small man physically (he had been called the gad-fly), but he was the commander of auxiliary troops that were incendiary in spirit. He had been a general under Theodosius; even under Valens. Though himself a pagan, he had been the pivot in the turning of the troops from Arbogast to Stilicho and Theodosius at the battle of the River Frigidus. He was a close friend of Alaric, of Stilicho, of Sarus. Nobody who knew him in life has ever spoken or written a disparaging word about him. Now he believed he saw a device to compel the bloodless surrender of a force in revolt against the Empire.

As for the trick itself, it proved to be a two-way business; and it was the ruse of Alaric that won out. The Goths had not left their camp as unguarded as it appeared, nor was their attention so wholly taken up by the celebration of the Easter Mass as they wished observers to believe.

It was also a thing that had never happened before, that all of them—Arian, Catholic, and pagan—should assemble at one Mass, and in the mode of extreme piety. The Arians and the Catholics, in spite of their very similar rites, always held their Masses separately. Probably any force but the pagan Alani of Saul would have suspected such perfect amity among Christians.

Saul surrounded them with his horsemen, the huge assembly packed closely together at worship, and called on them to surrender in the name of the Empire. But the Goths threw off their Easter robes, showing themselves fully armed, and immediately swung into disciplined squares. It was their casque helmets on which they had knelt, and they erupted like a wave under the rearing Alani horses. The Goths themselves had the advantage of the surprise. At close quarters they worked great slaughter on the Alani riders and their back-rearing horses, transfixing them with pikes and chopping them down with sword and axe.

Saul tried to reform his forces and maintain the encirclement, but he could not. In the old cavalry term, he had overridden himself. He had begun his charge too soon and from too great a distance, believing that speed was essential for the surprise and that the Goths were unarmed. He miscalculated and arrived winded in horse and men. The Gothic footmen stood like one great bull,

and tossed the on-coming horsemen on their horns. They broke
the attacking cavalry with the stubbornness of their resistance; and
then swept them clear with their own horsemen coming up capably
from the neighborhood of Alba, where they had been hidden waiting in a woods.

The Alani, probably the noisiest horsemen ever assembled, had
been effective against more barbaric foes. But they had been compelled to carry out their first charge in silence, for the surprise of
it; and thereafter their intimidating tactics availed nothing. The
Goths were unafraid of shouting and noise and incendiary tactics,
figurative or real. The flaming arrow, a favorite of the Alani, is no
more to be feared than any other arrow; and a screaming foe is
sometimes less frightening than a silent one. The Alani horses of
Saul were shattered, and the fiery little general ended his long soldier's life in the action.

By their sudden and complete victory over the advance cavalry,
the Goths had put the Empire forces of Stilicho at a great disad-
vantage. Stilicho, himself coming to the attack an hour after the
defeat of his advance infantry, was also forced to override or over-
march himself—and to bring his troops wearied and staggered onto
the field of battle. There was an intangible here, and Stilicho had
to join battle before the feeling of the Gothic victory had solidified.
The impression of a victory is sometimes as important as the victory itself. That impression had to be challenged before the troops
of Stilicho—most of them German and many of them Gothic German—should entertain the idea of swinging to the victorious German Alaric.

It is impossible to say who won the victory on the field that day.
It went into the Roman annals as a Roman victory, and an ovation
was later proclaimed for it by the Roman Senate. But ovations
were often proclaimed for doubtful actions; and a triumph—a
greater thing than an ovation—was declared for even a minor
victory.

The troops opposed evenly and without breaking till nightfall.
Then they withdrew a little from both sides. The two forces were
still intact and unbroken, and about evenly blooded. However,

there is a feeling, from the extreme modesty of the Roman claims at that time and later, that the Goths had somewhat the better of the day's fighting. And the Gothic hopes for the next day were certainly higher than the Roman.

Stilicho, as he had done several times before, lost a day-long battle—or at least had no better than a doubtful draw; but, as always, he won the battle during the night. The alarmed Goths realized, sometime in the night, that Stilicho had stolen a great advantage over them, and in a way that struck them deep.

Alaric, at Milan and at Asti, had gone after the person of the Emperor, to use him for a point of negotiation. Stilicho now took royal hostages for the same purpose. By his intelligence set-up, even in the midst of Alaric's Goths, Stilicho knew where was the *Waibergroub,* the party of Gothic women. He knew how they were guarded, and how the guard might be subverted.

Stilicho, sometime between midnight and morning and before the Gothic leaders realized it, took about one hundred Gothic women, the wives of the notables, the nobility, and the elders of the Goths. Among these was Stairnon, the wife of Alaric.

What should the Goths do? The old Romans would have advanced resolutely to the attack, and have worried little about the execution of their wives while the weal of the Republic was the question. But the Goths were people; and the old Romans, perhaps, were not. The people of councils held many councils over this, and the decision of most of them was that they must treat with the Romans and agree to withdraw. Alaric, at first, opposed this decision out of stubbornness or out of Gothic national feeling; and his opposition worried the Gothic national leaders for a reason that seemed in contradiction to their program.

But if Alaric should pursue the assault, either through unbending spirit or through strong Gothic feeling, then he might lose Stairnon to the Roman vengeance; and it was through Stairnon that Alaric was bound to the Gothic nation. She was the one hold that the Gothic elders had over Alaric, the one thing that kept him Gothic. Alaric would burn up with fury after Stairnon was

killed, but when the fury was gone something must take its place.
The Gothic elders knew too many Empire Goths of the sort of
Sarus who put the Empire before their own people. Without
Stairnon, Alaric might become like that. He would attack Stilicho
furiously for the moment; but he would later need something to
become the object of his life. The elders wanted Stairnon alive
to maintain their hold over Alaric; they knew that the seeds of
Empire were very strong in him.

At least three times in the following week Alaric started, or in-
timated that he would start, hostile moves against the forces of
Stilicho. Each time he was dissuaded by the council of the Goths.
They were very vulnerable in their wives. They could not, like
the old Romans, put their country ahead of their wives and families; to the Goths, their wives and families *were* their country.

It was the belief of the Gothic councils that they should pay the
ransom demanded by Stilicho: their leaving Italy and giving
pledges that they would settle once more in Illyricum and Epirus
and that they would maintain the Empire there. They would leave
Italy, by the agreement of Stilicho; and after a term of weeks their
wives would be given back to them again.

They could always break their pledges, and return to Italy another year, the Gothic elders reasoned. But should they lose the
conjugal influence of Stairnon over Alaric and he teeter towards
the Empire, they might never have a leader able to mount the
final assault on Rome.

It is not known where all the wives were sent, but Stairnon was
held longer than most of them, for nearly a year. She was sent to
Rome and kept in Stilicho's own house. There she lived with
Serena, the friendly and admirable wife of Stilicho. But also with
Galla Placidia, Stilicho's young ward, the sister of the two young
Emperors.

This was one of those minor circumstances that might have
been of great moment, had it fallen out a little differently. For it
appeared that Stairnon came to the side of the Roman party, as
Stilicho had intended. The friendship and influence of Serena was

very great on Stairnon; and Stairnon left bemused some months later, believing herself of the Roman arrangement, and seeming to realize that all the Gothic turmoil had been nothing but childishness. Stairnon was completely captivated by the goodness and reason of Serena, as were many. Stilicho, a man of excellent judgment, had always said that he had the finest wife in the Empire. From him this was a statement of fact and not of affection.

But the transformation was flawed, though this was not realized till years later. In the household of Stilicho, Stairnon had also lived with the young Galla Placidia, and between them there was total opposition. The young girl, for Placidia was then about nine years old, would taunt Stairnon to fury. There was an implacable enmity between them, and the fate of the world would hinge on it.

Stairnon believed herself completely changed now, and of the Roman party; but there was this opposition. One day she would come to see not Serena, but Galla Placidia as the symbol of Rome; and her hate would return.

The following action is an indeterminate tangle, and it cannot be unraveled. Stilicho split the Goths, treating with several of their leaders behind Alaric's back, giving them their wives and sending them back, under pledge of good behavior, to their home provinces. The force and influence of Alaric dwindled, and he roamed the countryside with what he had left, in strange indecision. Auxiliary Roman forces surrounded the Goths remaining with Alaric and traveled with them like a company of gnats, but did not attack them.

Alaric was still defiant in council. We doubt the actual words that he is reported to have used, however. We are willing to believe that, in Gothic council, he swore angrily that he would not leave off the attack, that he would find in Italy either a kingdom or a grave. But we are not willing to believe that he put his declaration in such a jingle form of Latin verse as has come down to us.

There were other actions in the Gothic-Roman conflict. There is evidence in Bury's great history that there was another battle

near Asti, near to the site of that first battle of Pollentia. This
battle was not of major importance, however, nor was the final
engagement at Verona in June of the year 403.

Alaric is described, after this action, as beaten, deserted by his
troops, dejected, and despairing. He was, to some extent, all these
things except the last. He was too young for despair. He was puzzled and baffled.

He was deserted by his troops because he had sent those he
still held along to their lands in Illyricum and Epirus, unwilling
to hold them any longer against their will. The more important of
the Goths, with their separate retinues, had long since given their
pledges to Stilicho and gone home; intending to break their
pledges later and return. King Alaric was in disrepute with a large
segment of the Goths, and would have to re-establish himself.

There was the day when Alaric sat with his brother-in-law Sarus
on a high rock above Verona, after a skirmish that was no more
than that. He heard from Sarus that Stairnon was now one with
the Roman cause, and that Alaric himself should be. Alaric considered the matter through long hours of discussions with Sarus,
and made his decision.

He gave his word to Sarus to convey to Stilicho that he would
maintain the Empire for the rest of his life; that he would support
it in the middle provinces of Illyricum and Epirus, and would support it in the East and West. He pledged that, as King of the Goths,
he would serve Rome as faithfully as Saul had served it as King
of the Alani, as Uldin was serving it as a King of the Huns.

The Gothic invasion had ended as a family affair. Sarus had
been in command of the last Roman forces harrying the last
Gothic guard, that of Alaric, back towards their own provinces.
He had skirmished with them near Verona. Then, in an interval
of the struggle, he had appeared in the middle of the Gothic Council, and had taken part in it.

This action of Sarus would be the equivalent of a quarterback,
in a modern football game, claiming and exercising the right of
joining in the huddle of his opponents at a crucial moment of

the game. But Sarus claimed the right to enter any Gothic Council anywhere; he claimed this right as a Blood Prince of the Goths. And when Sarus claimed something as his right, nobody had the temerity to stand up against him.

He was in arms against them. He held a Roman commission to enforce their departure. But he demanded and was given entry to their Council. After this turn of events it had become very difficult to keep up the pretense of hostilities. Alaric had sent the remainder of his army home, and had remained for his own Council with his cousin and brother-in-law.

Alaric gave his word to Sarus, and without equivocation, that the Gothic risings were ended forever. He assured his brother-in-law that he had now left off being a boy; that he would reassume his ascendancy over the Goths, that he would rule them as their King, and not be ruled by them. He stated that he would know how to handle the extravagant ideas of his people, as Saul and Uldin had been able to contain the dreams of their own tribes.

Alaric pledged his word absolutely on this. Within a week he received back his wife Stairnon, brought to him by her brother, this same Sarus. Alaric and Sarus parted in friendship. And Alaric and Stairnon followed their troops into Illyricum, there to be faithful props of the Empire.

Here we must make a statement that is directly at variance with an accepted view of history. *Alaric kept his word. He kept it in every way for the remaining seven years of his life.* Subsequent actions that seem to contradict this have been misunderstood and misinterpreted.

Sarus, to whom Alaric had given his word, was one of those who would misunderstand. He believed that Alaric had turned traitor to the Empire, and he was wrong in believing it. Stilicho would have come near to understanding the events, but Stilicho would then be dead.

There will have to be good explanations offered in contradiction to those great historians who wrote the tomes and those small creatures with initials who inhabit the footnotes of them. It's a fearsome essay to contradict established authority and then be called upon to produce the evidence.

We will try.

15. Of the Seven Waves

The seven waves which Stilicho in his dreams had seen rising to engulf the Empire were these:

First was the Gothic revolt in the years 402 and 403 which we have just examined. During this action Stilicho accomplished, for the last time, the old Roman trick of the containment of the Goths. Though the movement was well planned, and was aided by contrived diversions from beyond the Empire, the Master General smothered it completely. By the use of the Gothic wives as hostages; by the infiltration of the Gothic Councils; by appealing to the good faith of those who were in the process of committing acts of bad faith; by the fortunate appearance of maturity in Alaric, the Gothic King; by the assurance of the Gothic Prince Sarus, who was devoted to the Empire; and by singular good fortune in other details, Stilicho brought the Empire up, dripping but unharmed, from the overwash of that first wave.

The second wave was the colossal barbarian invasion led by Radagais and comprising a third of a million warriors—the largest single attacking force in all history up to that time.

The third wave was the series of Vandal risings under King Godigisel and King Respendial. These risings of Stilicho's own people were a continuing affair for several years. This third wave was, in some respects, contemporary with the first, second, fourth, and fifth; but in the main portion of its action it must take its place as the third of the series.

The fourth wave was the rising of the Burgundians and the kindred Lombards, mostly along the German borders, though with considerable penetration to the heart of the Empire. It was closely connected with the third or Vandal wave, for the Vandals were always involved with the Burgundians and Lombards, were nearly of the same family, and sometimes shared the same Kingship.

The fifth wave was out of Britain in the year 407. In this the British legions, intertwined with twice their numbers of auxiliaries, set up a usurper Emperor and crossed to the European continent as invaders. This was the final madness of that series that had afflicted the British legions for more than a century. It was final because, on their leaving the island for the mainland, the British connection was finished; there would never again be Roman rule or legions in Britain. When they left they left forever.

The British legions had raised up a false Emperor Marcus, and then killed him after a matter of days. They had, immediately after this, raised up the false Emperor Gratian, and then killed him after about four months. Somebody then called out that they needed another Constantine. Constantine the Great had been so raised to Emperor by the British legions nearly a hundred years before.

The soldiers of the British legions found a private soldier named Constantine, and they raised him to be Emperor. This man has been called, in verse by Sidonius, the Inconstant Constantine. He was about what could be expected of a seasoned soldier out of an old line legion, raised up for no other qualities than his name; yet out of a milieu that was rich in talent of the practical and administrative sort. There have been worse men come to power in more accepted ways. Constantine showed some ability, and he mounted a heavy attack against the Roman world.

The sixth wave, following closely on the fifth, was a rising of the Celts in both Britain and Gaul, and especially in Armoricae—which is now Brittany. The revolt of the Celts was against both the New Germans and the Old Romans. There is some confusion about the parties of this. The Celtic revolt was first against the usurper Emperor Constantine, who claimed both Britain and Gaul in the first stages of his conquests. But it was a brief from the Emperor Honorius in Ravenna that gave the Celts their independence, which they already had, and was no longer the Emperor's to confer. There was the attempt of a three-cornered compromise in this. By this sixth wave the permanent loss of Britain to Rome was confirmed, and also the loss of a large part of Gaul.

The seventh wave was the one that would take the life of Stilicho in the year 408. It was the only one that he could not correctly put the name to in his dreams, for it was vague to him. It was an amorphous, gray wave that was not from beyond the physical frontiers of the Empire; though actually it was from beyond the frontiers of humanity. In the framework of his mind Stilicho did not understand it, and he died not understanding it.

In locale it was based on Ravenna, to which city Honorius had moved his Court from Milan. At the crest of this seventh wave were two men: Olympius the Greek, the king of the defamers, who had brought down Eutropius and others; and Solinas who, in the service of Arbogast and Eugenius, had worked the Frankish subverters into positions of authority around the Emperor Valentinian until that Emperor was a prisoner in his own Court.

The defamer Olympius and the infiltrator Solinas worked in concert. They had become close to the resentful young Emperor Honorius while Stilicho was occupied with other things. This seventh wave was of a viciousness without parallel, and it rotted from within the Empire that had withstood every assault from without.

It is true that the Empire had suffered from internal rot since the day of its birth out of the Republic. That had been only such rot as is common in all cumbersome institutions, however. It was accompanied, for most of the period, by a compensating new growth; and it did seem as though the Empire would endure forever. This final rot was deeper and more poisonous.

There were these seven waves rising to engulf the Empire. It had been given to Stilicho to see them, as it had been given to the

Emperor Theodosius to know the day and hour of his death. We are past the first of them, the Gothic rising: and are come to the second, the giant barbarian invasion that was headed by Radagais.

There was a wave of absolute terror that went through the cities of the Empire at the news of the coming of the vast hordes of barbarians. It was a form of folk mania, though curiously it was confined to the inhabitants of the great cities. The foul breath from the north sent them into total panic, though the serious assaults of more seasoned hosts had hardly come to their attention. There was prayer and fasting that this wrath of God should pass. The litanies of the Church of the first decade of the fifth century came to contain seven additional petitions:

Ab Impeto Gothorum, Libera nos, Domine!
Ab Procella Barbarorum, Libera nos, Domine!
Ab Rapina Vandalarum, Libera nos, Domine!
Ab Trucidatione Burgondarumque Langobardorum, Libera nos, Domine!
Ab Perfidio Britanorum, Libera nos, Domine!
Ab Irruptione Celticarum, Libera nos, Domine!
Ab Insidiis Diaboli Calumniatoris, Libera nos, Domine!

"Lord deliver us," they prayed variously, "from the Assault of the Goths; from the Tumult—or the Tempest—of the Barbarians; from the Rapine of the Vandals; from the Slaughter of the Burgundians and the Lombards; from the Perfidy of the Britons; from the Eruption of the Celts; from the Snares of the Defaming Devil."

It was the seven waves of the vision of Stilicho all over again, now seen fitfully by the populace of the cities.

In times of turmoil and in the eras of barbarian attacks there are always prodigies seen and heard. This was almost a universal law with the Romans. Instances of such, at this time and earlier, are given by Pliny, by Strabo, by St. Augustine, by Ausonius, by Zosimus, by Appian, by others. Appian, writing at the time of an earlier barbarian threat, has recounted that dogs howled like wolves, that wolves entered the city of Rome, that cattle spoke in human voice, that newly born infants spoke. Statues sweat; some even sweat blood. Groans and dirges came from far underground. Loud voices of men and the tramping of horses was heard where nothing could be seen. Continuous lightning fell and spelled out words on walls and paving stones where it fell. Appian does not tell us what the words said.

At the time of the appearance of the spectral force headed by Radagais there were all these wonders and more. Comets were seen in the evening sky. Stones fell from the moon. There were earthquakes and lava flow. Herds of monocerets (unicorns) came near to the habitations of men, which never occurs in years of good omen. A Roman matron gave birth to rabbits. Monsters were born. Sheep spoke with human voice. It had been cattle at the time of the earlier barbarian appearance.

What was this horde of humanity from the north that so affrighted the cities of the Empire?

A contemporary has written it crudely: "The Doors of the Empire had been left open, and the animals came pouring in." It is stated by another that they were indeed like animals, or demented men. They stared and did not comprehend. They were the poor relations of the border Germans and of the steppe peoples. They were trolls who came up out of the ground in the north.

It was denied by the Goths that these barbarians were Gothic, and by the Vandals that they were Vandal. They were the sweepings of the northern forests and tundras; and were driven, like animals, by famine. There were those who seriously doubted that these new barbarians belonged to the human race; as, two thousand years earlier, the Mycaenean Greeks had doubted that the first Dorian barbarians were of the human race.

It is said that they were Alani; that they were Suevi and Burgundians; that they were Cimbri and Chatti. Perhaps they were, but they were not of the branches of those people who had been in close contact with the Empire peoples for more than five hundred years. They were much as the Goths must have been before they were taken over by their civilized nobility some centuries before and started to fermenting with new life.

The barbarians were out of the northern timelessness, and
could have been from ten thousand years earlier, before the ice
had left. Cassiorodius called them a species of cattle; but they
were wild, spooked cattle, not the well-tended beasts of the Empire. Though most of them had iron, some of them incredibly
had lances tipped with stone. They were from a long way back,
and were the true barbarians.

Here we come to a semantic difficulty. Other peoples who were
of considerable civilization had been referred to as barbarians
for more than a thousand years. Others had been called by the
names of the wolves. When the wolves themselves came, there
was no other name to give them. The Goths, who were kingdom-
founding Christians, had been called barbarians. The Gauls of
ancient lineage had been so called, and the talented Vandals.

Even the Huns had been called barbarians. This is a thing beyond all comprehension, and yet it is not safe to contradict the
idea even today. The Huns were a race of over-civilized kings
traveling with their Courts. In the ordering of military affairs and
in overall organization they had no superiors in the world. They
were skilled diplomats, filled with urbanity and understanding.
All who came into contact with them, Persians, Armenians,
Greeks, Romans, were impressed by the Huns' fairness in dealing
—considering that they were armed invaders; by their restraint
and adaptability; by their judgment of affairs; by their easy luxury.
They brought a new elegance to the Empire peoples; and they
had assimilated a half dozen cultures, including that of China.
But the Huns were not barbarians; no more were any of the other
violent visitors to the Empire heretofore.

The real barbarians who came now, however, may have been
some kindred to these Huns, just as they may have been kindred
to the Goths and the Alani. They were mongrel folks, and as such
could not be spoken of as having race. But they were, the great
horde led by Radagais, the true barbarians. Most of the people
of the Empire did not know, or had forgotten, the difference.
That is why they quaked on their couches and shivered with fear

in the sun. If such a horde of barbarians should come down on them, how might they escape?

But the astute generals, Stilicho, Sarus, Alaric, appreciated the difference instantly. They understood that these new people were in no way what they themselves had been; that this was something as timeless as the rocks—the people who had been before the people. It was because of this understanding that the generals considered the gigantic barbarian invasion in a different light than did the peoples of the Empire, and particularly the peoples of the cities.

The action is generally set in the year 406, but it may have been a year earlier. Chronology, even in the last days of the Empire, is uncertain. A certain number of military adventurers joined the horde as it came into Italy and gave it such direction as it possessed.

The multitude of savages could not take the securely defended Ravenna where the Emperor Honorius had now established his Court. Thousands of them sank out of sight in the quicksands that surrounded the fortress city of Ravenna; and the barbarians could not even come up to the walls of it. Nor could the horde take Ticinum (Pavia) where Stilicho had set up his headquarters. It bogged down in a siege of Florence, but it had swept the countryside of all animals as it went.

Stilicho had an army of about thirty thousand men to oppose a horde estimated at between a third of a million and a half million fighting men, not counting their dependents and families. It is said that even the little boys of the barbarians carried clubs and pig stickers, and spat like animals as they rushed to the attack of any thing in their path. Stilicho could have raised three times as many men as he had—this would give him a third or a quarter as many as the barbarians had—but Stilicho raised no more men. Instead, he disbanded some of those he already had present and under arms, and sent others to the occupation of distant places. And Stilicho sent strict orders to Alaric to stay where he was.

It was not that Stilicho did not trust Alaric. He now trusted him completely. It was for another reason that he did not want him in the conflict. Stilicho put two men in charge of the small forces who were to cope with the barbarians: Sarus the intrepid Goth, and Uldin the Hunnish King.

Stilicho, at this time of terror to the inhabitants of the Empire cities, may have permitted himself a smile. He had little to smile about in that decade, and was not usually a smiling man. But he appreciated the joke of the terrified people.

Stilicho was troubled, of course. He sought to minimize the hardship and slaughter, for which reason he so held down the numbers of Empire troops. He tried to keep the roads clear of all other traffic so that there would be more room to dispose of this thing. Like a Vandal Christ he had compassion on that multitude: what would happen to them; how they would be fed; how should so many corpses be disposed of; how harsh would be the slavery of many of them, and how terrible the wanderings of the remnant. But the idea that he should fear such a horde had never crossed his mind.

A remark attributed to the Goth Sarus has been misunderstood. He had thrown up his hands and cried out that it was all to no use. But the Goth Sarus did not mean that defense was useless. His meaning was entirely the opposite. Sarus, who was afraid of nothing, was always avid for combat with any respectable foe; but he seems to have had no stomach for this slaughter. Sarus had the command of one small force; Uldin the Hun had the command of another. Sarus believed it a foolish waste of effort that both of them should be employed at a task that either of them could have handled alone. Nevertheless, they both of them were sent out to deal with the barbarians.

The Romans and their affiliates surrounded and cut off the head of the horde, and actually this finished the whole matter. The military adventurers, who had given the slight cohesion to the movement in their taking service with the barbarian Radagais as he neared the Empire, were cut off at Faesulae near Florence. Sarus and Huldin executed the few hundreds of them that they caught in one clutch; and there were not enough of them scattered throughout the remainder of the horde to make a difference. The headless body of the barbarian aggregation thrashed about the country, taking a while to die.

The Romans straited the horde, surrounded it with earthworks, herded it into a giant compound, and let it starve for a while. The horde had eaten itself empty in the area. The barbarians had been herding cattle, five thousand of them at a time together, slaughtering them and roasting them whole for a single meal. It took such to feed them, but it had run out; and they starved in their open-top compound prison.

After a week, Sarus and Uldin moved in with a few men and scattered the dismal horde. The great invasion was over with, except for the bitter suffering of the survivors.

Slave dealers came in and took many of the barbarian men, who went willingly with them. Humanitarians came to offer care for others. Large and efficient arrangements by Stilicho, but far short of satisfactory, saved many of the thousands from starvation. And what was left of the multitude staggered north once more; some through Gaul, some through Pannonia, most to die in the hills. The vultures came in such flights that they darkened the sun, and the fields of that region were abandoned for one year; but afterwards were quite fertile.

The peoples of the Empire cities had been terrified by the reports of mere numbers of barbarians—which had not been exaggerated. But Stilicho and his astute generals had known instantly what the real barbarians were. They had understood that primordial men, in whatever numbers they come, can never be even a remote match for civilized men in armed warfare.

It had been the Goths, and then the barbarians, in the first two waves over the Empire. Now, in the years immediately following, there came four further waves of much greater destructiveness than those first two. These were the wave of the Vandals, that of the Burgundians and Lombards, that of the Britons and the British legions, and that of the Celts. The Empire did *not* come up dripping but unharmed from these four waves; it did not come through intact. Very large segments were washed away, and forever, by this series of waves. The world had not yet ended, and perhaps it did not have to end yet; but great chunks of the world were broken off and gone.

Britain was lost forever to the Empire, in the legions leaving it for the continent in a state of revolt, and the vacuum being filled by the Celtic surge. Britain had been the least securely held and the least Romanized of the provinces of the West. A distant issue of this was that, eleven hundred years later, Britain would be the only western province ultimately lost to the Church. She had never been Roman in the sense that France and Spain and Italy and Pannonia (Austria), and High Germany and Illyricum had been. Britain would keep a great lot of what she had received from Rome, but she would reject the central Roman idea. She became once more, and has remained, an Island. But once she had been part of the continent.

Gaul was largely lost to the Empire, and everything north of the Alps. Spain remained vaguely within the Empire, but it seemed as though she had moved a great distance away. Spain was in revolt against the usurper Emperor Constantine, who was in revolt against Rome. The Spanish nephews of Theodosius the Great, four cousins of the Emperors, led the revolt: Didymus, Verenianus, Theodosius, and Logadius. They revolted, however, in the form of a national and divisive movement. They were conquered and crushed by the false Emperor Constantine, but nevertheless they were conquered for the Empire and brought back to the influence of the Empire.

South France was still held, all of the Iberian peninsula under the peculiar conditions given above, Africa, Italy, Norica, and Pannonia; and Illyricum by arrangement with Alaric. Militarily the tide had turned. The Empire was awash to the scuppers from the waves, but she still floated.

The genius of Stilicho, both for the military and the diplomatic, had never been shown in such manner as in his surviving these four last military waves. As difficult as the maneuver of the containment of the Goths is the diversion of the Vandals, the fragmentation of the Burgundians, the occlusion of the Lombards; but Stilicho was master of all ways of handling the nations.

The treating of the legions of the usurper Constantine and the rise of the Celts was more difficult. The Celts, now between the British legions and the German frontier, were given their independence (which they had already seized) by brief of the Emperor Honorius at the insistence of Stilicho. But at the same time they swore themselves as fiefs and associates of the Empire. It was the first such medieval association, and the Celtic nation acknowledged the Roman Empire as overlord.

Sarus and others were in the field against the usurper Emperor Constantine, and had put him on the defensive. But negotiations were at all times carried on between Stilicho and Constantine during all the time of their intermittent warfare. Stilicho had known Constantine personally through the years, as no other Master General would be likely to have known a single private soldier out of the several hundred thousands of the Empire who had been raised to power by chance.

Stilicho, using all his connections, refused to consider Constantine and his legions as an outside force. These were Roman legions, returned from distant service; they were a part of the Empire, even though led by a pseudo-Emperor. Stilicho believed that he could yet bring Constantine to his side, as he had brought Alaric around; and the man showed an ability for action that was too rare. He was of the diminishing stock of which generals are made, and Stilicho was resolved to find a use for him.

The external threat had temporarily burned itself out. Doubtful allies had begun to return to Stilicho. The Celts, who were militarily competent and were in the ascendant, would serve as guard of the German frontiers under their new feudal arrangement. They would hold Britain in fief, as they themselves were held in fief by the Empire. There might be time allowed to restore the bodily health of the Empire in its restricted sphere of influence.

There had been many movements beneath the surface, and most of them of good influence. Stilicho, for ten years, had been seizing slaves for the service of his armies; and turning them out as free men after their period of service. They were established on freeholds on the vacant land, and many of them had adapted.

Certain reforms had been accomplished, unnoticed, and out of necessity. There was a new ferment working.

The Late Roman Empire is often represented as very effete and in the last stages of senility. It was anything but that; actually, it was bursting with new vigor. The ineptitude of the Empire in many things was a sign of awkward adolescence, and not of advanced old age. The unprecedented mixing of the races for the last hundred years, and particularly for the last fifty, had begun to pay off in a burst of energy. The Roman world of the first decade of the fifth century was much younger than it had been one hundred years before.

The direction that the new energy took was not the direction that it had to take. It worked for the total destruction of the Empire, and the long and painful birth of the new world. But there was a time when it still might have restored the Empire from within. We don't know what we missed by taking the other alternate. We only know what we have now.

Stilicho had brought the Empire through six towering waves, and there was the promise of peace and renewed health ahead. But the seventh wave, meager and mean-minded, killed it.

Meanwhile, the Eastern Empire was enjoying comparative peace. This was due, to a large extent, to the efforts of Alaric, from the time in the year 403, when he returned to his own provinces with the pledge to support the Empire, till the moment (early in the year 408) when he once more stood with his armies on the border of Italy.

Alaric occupied a position unparalleled in history. The two brother Emperors, Arcadius and Honorius, had now become violent enemies. Alaric held the giant province of Illyricum between the two halves of the Empire. He held it in the name of both Emperors, and with the title of Master General from both. And, strangely, neither knew of his arrangement with the other.

This was possible because of the unsettled condition of the times, and because neither of the Emperors was the effective ruler of his own realm. Alaric held the anomalous position because of the great guardians of the Empires, Stilicho in the West, a triumvirate in the East—men of intelligence, and devotion to the crumbling Empire.

Stilicho worked with one out-of-the-Empire ally, the Persian Emperor Jezdegerd himself, a close personal friend from the early years. And he worked with the triumvirate of the Eastern Court. This was made up of Singerich, Fravitta, and Anthemius.

Singerich, the brother-in-law of Alaric, was no longer Alaric's own Goth at the Eastern Court. Both Alaric and Singerich realized their subordinate places in the Empire. Singerich was tied to Stilicho through Sarus.

Sarus was a very busy man in those years. One season he would be in the field against the usurper Emperor Constantine in Gaul. Another he would be in Illyricum with his sister, Stairnon, and her husband, Alaric. He would then be in Constantinople at the Eastern Court with his brother Singerich. Sarus had become, for a period, the most powerful of the three brothers.

With Singerich in the triumvirate that ruled the East was Fravitta, the Goth who had prevailed over Gainas. Fravitta was a military genius of the line of that Gainas, and Sarus and Alaric and Athaulf. The Goths of that generation had a special talent for generalship, and Fravitta was one of the best. He knew his limitations and did not meddle in matters other than military. His loyalty was unquestioned, and it was also given to the idea of the one Empire. The third man of the triumvirate was Anthemius.

Anthemius, who would be the grandfather of an Emperor not yet born, had been made Consul and Praefect of the East in the year 405, after completing a successful mission to the Persian Empire that was reminiscent of the early mission of Stilicho. On that mission Anthemius had not only carried official credentials from the Emperor Arcadius, but also private patents from Stilicho to his friend the Emperor Jezdegerd. It is not realized how much of the peace enjoyed by Constantinople was on sufferance of the Persian monarch Jezdegerd whose land had become quite powerful and prosperous. In the exclusive lodge of the high rulers of the world, Jezdegerd had always considered his friend Stilicho as the true ruler of the Roman Empire.

Anthemius was something more than one-third of a man. He was a clean, careful man; and, when his time came, he died naturally in bed—something that can be said of very few men of that day. He was an able Consul, and he realized to what extent he must rely on more powerful men: on Fravitta his associate; on Alaric in Illyricum; on Stilicho in Rome and Milan; even on Jezdegerd in Persia. He ruled on the sufferance of other men, but he ruled well. And Singerich was once more in ascendance over Arcadius and Eudoxia and was able to persuade them, for a time, to refrain from meddling in the politics of the Empire. It was a workable arrangement.

But the Eastern Empire also prospered on the sufferance of one other powerful man, Athaulf the brother of Singerich. It was greatly on his account that the powerful whirlwinds of humanity came against the Western Empire, and not the Eastern. Athaulf was now unofficial lord of the whole north, and was of great influence in a dozen nations outside the Empire. This feral Goth was poised like an eagle over the high Alps, and the destruction of Rome had always been his fixed objective. He never gave up his campaign to wear down the West, and he had had a finger into the elbow in every one of the towering waves that had shook the Empire. He believed that Alaric would yet serve as his instrument, and he would wait his time.

It was in these same years, in Illyricum, that their children were born to Alaric and Stairnon. These two have become people of legend, and as such can have no private lives. They were the characters of the Eddas and the Nibelungenlied, reappearing like lightning in the mythology of the north whence their people had come. They were the boy giant hero and his valkyrie bride. Yet they were a private people, managing their own estates and farms and serving both an Empire and a Kingdom. Alaric deserves all adjectives, both as Master General and King. And Stairnon was a perfect Queen, slightly larger than life.

But of Stairnon a doubt creeps in, doubt of even her nonpareil beauty. This doubt is engendered in us by that goblin-child Galla Placidia. That slight, dark, Spanish-Greek, mud-homely nereid, in the household of Stilicho with her salty-tongued comment, had made Stairnon feel like an ungainly cow. Stairnon would never forgive it, but we cannot forget it. What if Placidia was right? The superb Gothic style, to Mediterranean eyes, is a little over-done.

There is a tendency to force speculation and look for tie-ins to earlier history when anything rises as suddenly, powerfully, and apparently rootless as did the Gothic effort.

Remember the closely-knit and talented Gothic nobility or élite was not entirely of the same race as the Gothic commoners; that much is plain from every hint and evidence. They were a taller and less bulky people; brunette and red-headed, while the commoners were tow-blond. The difference in type was always recognized on sight by the Romans and others. Slaves might, on occasion, be taken from among the commoners; but they were not taken from among the élite. There was close intermarriage among the high families, particularly the five families that might attain the kingship. There were terms and words used by the élite, but not by the commoners; almost a parallel language. It is a fact that this nobility was born to rule, and they ruled well and were never challenged. There is the further fact that the Gothic nobility practiced circumcision, and the commoners did not. Many primitive peoples practiced circumcision; but not many in the north of Europe, and none others as an affair of one particular class only.

There is persistent legend that the Gothic leaders came from over the sea. This has been interpreted as the Gothic arrival to the mainland of Europe, in the neighborhood of the Vistula, from the Scandinavian peninsula, about the time of the Incarnation; but it probably refers to an earlier arrival of a part of the Goths to Scandinavia by sea.

The Goths, before their becoming Christians, practiced two separate religions: an animistic paganism full of animal totems by the commoners; and an affair of the high lodges of the élite, the content of which is unknown.

There are many vestigial Mediterranean characteristics to be seen in the high Goths; and there is the theory that they were a classical people arriving by sea to that Baltic shore by way of the Atlantic and the Mediterranean.

In the final centuries before the Christian era, there had been dozens of small nations of a higher civilization than Rome that were conquered and absorbed by Rome: In Italy, particularly in Magna Graeca, that early Greek-speaking lower Adriatic coast, and in Tuscany; in Spain around ancient Tarshish; in Punic Africa; in Sicily; in south France where were many old Greek colonies; in Crete; in Rhodes; in nearer Asia. There were many irredentist nobilities that left their own lands and wandered far, unwilling to accept conquest. The first Romans, long before, may have been such an uprooted nobility from Asia. The Gothic nobility, seldom numbering more than a thousand persons out of possibly a half million Goths, were a special clan of high genius and undisputed leadership; and they *did* have a different origin from the commonalty of the Goths.

Rome was, without a doubt, at the center of many of the tales of the northern Goths, in a way that it could not logically be. The high nobility of the Goths, reappearing out of the north after half a millennium, *remembered Rome*. There is the feeling that they remembered her with revenge.

But that is all surmise. So on with the account.

Very early in the year 408 Alaric marshaled his forces and came up to the western extent of his territory, to the gates of Italy. Another force passed him on the way, going east and south. The two forces stopped for consultation, and then parted peacefully. The other force was composed of Uldin and his Huns. Whatever was the agreement between Alaric and Uldin cannot be known, but they seemed to be moving by agreement, and were likely obeying the orders of the same man or group.

The forces of Uldin would set down in Thrace, to the consternation of the Eastern Empire. They did not ravage. They did not forage. They bought what they needed and paid in gold. The Huns always had a store of gold. The Huns camped silently, and a wave of terror went through the peoples of the cities of the East; much like the fright that had seized the cities of the West at the coming of Radagais. Uldin had been assigned to the guarding of part of the giant province of Illyricum. Alaric had been summoned, it is not known by whom, to stand by for other possible need.

This Uldin is usually spoken of as *the* King of the Huns. He was the Hun who moved in and out of the Empire and who was trusted by Stilicho, who, in fact, was a general of the Roman Empire as well as a King of the Huns. But he was only one of a dozen Kings of the Huns. They were not to raise a high King again until Attila should come to that honor, and he was still a small boy.

Alaric is generally represented as coming at this time to threaten Italy once more; to demand, to extort, and then to invade. This view is connected with the organized defamation of the time, and it still prevails. It was necessary to attribute aggressive motives to Alaric in building up the treason charges against Stilicho; to prove that Stilicho had connived with an outlaw for the destruction of the Empire.

But Alaric did not come as an outlaw, though neither did he come at the orders of Stilicho, who was the man entitled to give orders. He did not come into Italy at all, though he did come to the very border of the province of which he was Master General.

He came and waited; and communicated with Stilicho and others.

Alaric came up to the border because he was sent for by a council of the German-Roman generals in the service of the Empire, which summons was secret from Stilicho. Most explicitly Alaric came because he was sent for by his brother-in-law Sarus who was high in the generals' council.

This group advised Alaric that the Empire was in mortal danger, and that they wanted his force near at hand. All was not right with the regency, they advised; and it might be that all was not right with Stilicho. The generals, whose training was military, correctly appraised a non-military threat. They knew that the Empire had never been in such danger as from that amorphous gray seventh wave that now rose and curled.

16. Of the Death of an Oak

Stilicho had stood to the young Emperor Honorius as a rather stern German father; and there is something in the Mediterranean mind that will finally revolt against this dictation even when (as was the case) it is well-intentioned and largely necessary.

Honorius was his ward; Stilicho was guardian. He put the cap on it when he became the boy's father-in-law. He pushed it beyond the breaking point by his insistence that Honorius have offspring for the continuance of the Empire. The boy who never grew up was incapable of having offspring, either physically or out of some malfunction of the spirit. Stilicho believed that *anything* in the world is possible if only one have the will. Honorius, apparently, did not have the will.

The young Empress Maria, the daughter of Stilicho, died right at the beginning of the eventful year 408. She had been married ten years, had married Honorius when he was fourteen years old, and she died a virgin. Stilicho, with the continuance of the Empire always in mind, immediately married his younger daughter, Thermandia, to the Emperor Honorius. The correct military procedure is always to insert a second force into a required position when the initial force, through unforeseen event, has failed. A vulnerable position must be occupied. But even Serena, the wise wife of Stilicho, was against it.

Thermandia was more aggressive than had been her sister Maria, more aware of her duty to the Empire in this respect. The young Emperor was actually terrified of the insistent approaches of his new wife, and he fled Rome permanently; going first to the old military capital of Milan, and then to his new fortress capital of Ravenna. He never lived with his new wife, after that first night when Stilicho had locked him in.

Stilicho understood the workings of the most intricate world, but he did not understand the small people who made up that world. However close to him he had been, Stilicho did not understand the Emperor Honorius who would always have the mind of an eleven-year-old boy—a mind now tortured by its inability to cross the gap. Honorius was easy with most men, and especially with soldiers of the common sort when they themselves were on the simple side. But in the presence of any woman he could hardly speak.

There was one man, however, who did understand Honorius; a peculiar sort of man who understood and used the furtive side of everything. He saw how he might turn the weakness of the Emperor to his own final strength. This man was Olympius.

It was Olympius who had brought down the Imperial eunuch Eutropius at the Eastern Court, in a campaign that was a masterpiece of its kind. And for his assistant in a new but kindred project he now took one Solinas, who had been in the service of the Frankish Count Arbogast and the pretender Emperor Eugenius. Olympius intended, with the help of Solinas and others, to fell the strongest man of them all, and to take his place.

If a man have a special art, he is impelled to express it no matter what the circumstances. Olympius had a special art for defamation and vilification, as had Solinas for infiltration and intrusion. They would have done their work for love of it if nothing had been offered; but what was offered was control of the richest realm in history.

The battle field on which Olympius launched his effort was the mind of the Emperor Honorius, an eleven-year-old mind in a twenty-four-year-old body. Olympius would defame the great Stilicho in that mind and substitute himself as the trusted advisor. He had brought down Eutropius in a shrewd campaign, and he had had to blacken him to an entire Court and a whole Empire. Here, due to the peculiar concentration of invested power that Stilicho had himself set up, Olympius had to blacken Stilicho to only one man, a defective and impressionable man. And this did Olympius, in his new office of Master of the Court, proceed to do.

For his own phase of the campaign Solinas had a little broader field. His talent for infiltration and intrusion was well known. Moreover he had available broken pieces of a machinery that had once before been used. In his service of Arbogast and Eugenius, Solinas had worked groups of Frankish subverters into positions of authority around the Emperor Valentinian. Solinas had the gift for bringing men into his own party, for moving them into positions of importance around his victim, and for pulling the string before the design was even suspected.

Stilicho remained ignorant of the disastrous orientation of the many new men of talent who suddenly came to the fore in the various services. Some of these were Frankish men who had been used before; some of them were dissatisfied Romans. But Solinas did not scatter his shots. He concentrated them in two restricted areas, areas to which Stilicho seldom paid attention.

The city of Rome was ignored by Olympius and Solinas, except for the half dozen men in the Senate whom they had made their own. These were not enough to have important effect on any voting, but the voting of the Senate itself was no longer of real importance. The half dozen men were sufficient to create a diversion, to raise a turmoil wherever desired. It would also happen that several honest men, Lampadius and others, would give unwitting help to the campaign of the subverters through misunderstanding.

But the main area of Solinas' campaign was among the military of two cities. In North Italy, where were always the stand-by legions for the defense of the interior Empire, were three military centers: Ravenna, the new capital and a great fortress; and the two great staging towns now called Pavia and Bologna.

Solinas left Bologna, the central of these three points. It was Stilicho's own base, and it was unassailable to his type of campaign.

Its soldiers were German of their several sorts, and were completely loyal to Stilicho.

But Ravenna and Pavia might be different matters.

The Court City of Ravenna was filled with Imperial Guards, not with campaigning soldiers. In their own way they were superb, and nobody ever thought seriously of attempting the city garrisoned by them. They were a cosmopolitan force, not particularly German. They were from the provinces of Africa and Mauretania, from Tarraconensis and Baetica in Spain, from Aquitania and Lugdunensis in Gaul, from Britain and from Sicily and Italy—as well as from the German groups. Such of the great families of the Empire who still set their sons to soldiering had managed that they be sent to the Imperial Fortress City. Such Germans as were among them were often of the peoples opposed to Stilicho and envious of the Vandals and Goths. They were a mixed and highborn soldiery and subject to factions. And Solinas was a man who knew how to use factions.

Such strong Stilicho adherents as were among them now found themselves the recipients of sudden Imperial promotions which tended to take them *out of Ravenna*. Solinas was a master at kicking a man upstairs. Stilicho's men were sent on high-sounding missions all over the Empire; and into Ravenna came new men who were not close to him.

Stilicho had never concerned himself greatly over Ravenna. He knew that by its location, surrounded by swamps and on the Adriatic, it was hard to come to. He knew that its garrison was militarily competent, and that its masters were possessed of one phase of military knowledge—fortress defense—to a greater degree than himself. Stilicho had settled in his own mind that the Emperor Honorius was absolutely safe in Ravenna from any exterior attack—and so he was. He could not be threatened as he had been threatened by Alaric at Milan. But the very secure Ravenna had passed out of Stilicho's hands without his noticing it.

The soldiers of Pavia were much less German than those of Bologna. They contained the only large concentration of Old Roman soldiers still left in the Empire, and a great number of other non-Germans. It was a lesser center than Bologna, but Stilicho still kept close control of it and had his own strong men strategically placed. It became the business of Solinas to surround those strong men quietly. In the end, however, it would have to be a bloody business. Stilicho would not lose Pavia by default.

A new trend was in the air through the Western Empire, and Olympius and Solinas took advantage of it. The same trend had appeared in Constantinople several years before, in the movement which we have called the Roman Supremacy Party. It had not now coalesced in the Roman West, but there were signs of the feeling.

The curlew senses a change in the wind before any other bird, and cries out sharply at it. Olympius and Solinas were peculiarly sensitive to the cry of the curlews over Italy, and were quick to take advantage of the change in the wind.

There was resentment of the people of Italy against the Germans. It was a thing that came and went, and ordinarily the waves of it passed without serious disturbance. The people felt themselves of no consequence in their own house. But they were unwilling themselves to maintain the onerous burden of Empire, and someone must assume it. In the end they had always resigned themselves and left it to the Germans. The conspirators, however, were resolved that this wave of feeling would not pass without serious disturbance.

It was then that the coming of Alaric gave them a great opportunity.

Alaric had come to the approaches of Italy at the solicitation of his brother-in-law Sarus, and of the other generals. They had informed him that Stilicho himself had shown signs of weakness and indecision, and that the Empire was in danger. Stilicho was not an old man, fifty or slightly above, and he still rode and spoke with his accustomed vigor; but the generals had sensed that something was wrong. They were looking for his possible successor, should something go amiss, and they had tentatively settled on Alaric.

Sarus had taken himself out of consideration. He knew himself and his own failings. He knew that Alaric, who seemed still an unfinished boy to him, was capable of tremendous growth and development; and that he himself was not. There was at this time no thought of setting a general up as Emperor; but rather of selecting a master general who could rule competently through the Emperor, should something happen to Stilicho. It is likely that Stilicho had shown some oddities of conduct that had given the generals unease, but which have not been related down to us.

Alaric came because he was sent for. He also came for his money. This part was a nervous business. Illyricum still held publicly from the Eastern Empire, and was subject to tax to the East. The military recompense to Alaric and his forces should also come from the Eastern Court, for all ordinary military service. So it did; but very modestly, and for very ordinary service.

But the Goths for some years had undertaken military obligations all out of proportion to the wealth of their province. They had served both the Eastern and Western Empires in a variety of actions, and maintained the frontier all the way from Decumates and Raetia in the high Alps to the Black Sea. They had sent detachments to the provinces of Asia and Syria and had undertaken punitive expeditions far beyond the Danube. They had maintained the frontiers so well that while five invasions had broken into the Empire of the West none at all had broken through the frontier assigned to the Goths. The Goths had also sent detachments on loan to the West for service against the usurper Emperor Constantine in Gaul, and against the Celts and Burgundians.

The Goths were not numerous. Less than half a million people among the seventy-five million people of the Empire; but they had been responsible for the defense of one half of that Empire. And many of their actions were unknown to the Court of the East with which they were publicly affiliated.

Some provinces, like Sicily and Africa, produced grain for the Empire. Some, like Greece, produced wine and honey and olive oil. Illyricum of the Goths produced military service.

Alaric sent ambassadors to Stilicho, from Viruum in Noricum, to inform him that it was time to pick up the tab, four thousand pounds of gold. It was not an unreasonable fee for the years of service, and it was probably the fee previously agreed upon. And Rome was gold-rich.

Stilicho sent the word that he would attend to it. And then the outcry arose. Olympius and Solinas got hold of it, and raised a tumult. Their surprise and outrage was feigned. They knew the state of affairs, but the public had not known of it. The Master General Stilicho had effectively ruled both the Eastern and Western Empires without the full knowledge of either of the incompetent Emperors. The populace of neither Rome nor Constantinople knew of this dual role, though the leading men of affairs of both realms would naturally have known of it.

Alaric held concurrent commissions from both the Eastern and Western Empire. His ordinary pay was from Constantinople, but his extraordinary pay must be from Rome. Alaric himself had been out of pocket a tremendous fortune. It takes bribes of gold, as well as a show of great military force, to maintain the restive frontiers; and Alaric had paid off dozens of wandering tribes.

Stilicho, in his management of the Empire, had accounted to no one. But now the outcry was to call him to account. The outcry was, at first, synthetic; and was so understood by all men of moment. The protests made it seem that there was duplicity, even treason, in Stilicho. But he had always acted in the interest of the Empire.

To quiet the protests, and because he felt secure in his position, Stilicho agreed to put the matter to the Senate of Rome. To do this he had to awaken that body from a sleep of nearly four hundred years; for it had handled only minor matters, mostly of the City itself, in all that time. Stilicho caused the Senate to assemble in the old Flavian palace of the Caesars.

But the Senate no longer had any strict organization or leadership. It found its new leadership supplied by the half dozen expert men who had been intruded by Olympius and Solinas into that body; and these began a campaign of great invective against Stilicho and opposed any motion to pay tribute to the barbarian Gothic invader who threatened Italy.

Several honest men of the Senate, misunderstanding the affair, were caught up in the violent opposition. Lampadius, a good man, orated strongly against the "tribute," urging the Romans to reaffirm their old liberty, and to fight rather than be dishonored. The Roman people followed the debates with lively interest, and began to shout death to all the Germans. Stilicho felt his prestige slipping away, and knew that he had suffered a defeat more serious than any he had ever met on a battle field.

At the same time Stilicho suffered a personal treachery out of his own household. Galla Placidia, fifteen years old and perverse as a young shoat, claimed royal privilege—as the sister of the Emperor and the only one of the family in the City—to address the Senate. She discovered that she was a Roman, or affected to; nobody could ever be certain when Placidia was sincere. She had been salty-tongued from the cradle, and she now harangued the Senate with an incendiary, anti-German, all-for-Rome, drive-out-the-barbarians speech. She brought the Senate to its feet and gave it a thrill it would not forget. Placidia was of fantastic talent, and a great actress was lost in her.

This wounded Stilicho deeply. He thought of Galla Placidia as his own child, and she still lived in his house. He believed that he had made of her a strong convert to the cause. In a way he had, for she would be the last Roman of them all; but she had her own way about it. Her humor had always been cruel, but this was shocking to the Master General.

But it had to be carried through, so Stilicho put an end to the show. He took the floor of the Senate; explained all the damaging circumstances in all their ramifications; told the Romans that they were no longer defended by Romans, and in reality had not been in the life times of any of them; stated that the fee was a just one, that it had been so contracted for, and that it must be paid. He pointed out also, and in great anger, that there were individual Senators present with *annual incomes* in excess of the amount of the fee, which was true. He deflated them brutally and said that they were children defended by men; that their affairs were being taken out of their hands as they were not competent to deal with them. He swore that the fee would be paid, or any other fee that

he ordered, and that there would be no more interference or fool-
ishness. He was impolitic, and realized it; but he had suddenly
become weary of the thankless service.

The Senators who had been honestly deceived now saw how
the affair lay, but they saw it with bitterness. Others who had always understood, but who had held their peace till the foolish
storm should have subsided, now came forward and pushed aside
the synthetic leadership. They voted the appropriation for Alaric,
and Stilicho carried the day. But they never forgave the Master
General for the vehemence of his counterattack. The fiction that
they were still the power of the world had been very dear to them.

The four thousand pounds of gold voted to Alaric was never
paid, however, due to intervening circumstances.

Stilicho had won a victory more damaging than any defeat; and
Olympius and Solinas must have rubbed their hands in glee at the
delicious defeat of their own party in this matter. The anti-German
spirit was fueled in earnest. The Romans did not mind being defended and maintained by outlanders so long as they could continue the fiction that they were the masters; they had now been
told too bluntly that they were not.

After this, the award voted but still not delivered, the ambassadors from Alaric met with Stilicho and the Emperor Honorius in
Ravenna. An agreement was reached. It was decided that Alaric
should immediately take his army into Gaul against the usurper
Emperor Constantine. Should he be able to dispose of this pretender, and Alaric had no doubt at all about being able to do so,
the Empire would be almost secure. The Goths would as soon
spend a season in Gaul as anywhere; and they had broken stronger
forces than this Briton-Roman aggregation, and without unduly
advertising the fact. The Goths had been growing stronger by the
year, and now considered themselves invincible.

But once more fate intervened—as it is its business to do. The
Emperor Arcadius of the East, the brother of Emperor Honorius,
died on May Day of the year 408. The disposal of the Eastern
Regency now took the attention of the West.

Olympius took advantage of this unsettling death, and changed the emphasis of his vilification against Stilicho, which was already having effect in the mind of Honorius. Olympius convinced Honorius that Stilicho had had his brother Arcadius murdered. He showed him documents purporting to prove this. It does not matter what Olympius showed him, for Honorius could not read, though he had great respect for the written word. Olympius produced other documents supposed to show the intent of Stilicho to have Honorius himself murdered. Eucherius, the undistinguished son of Stilicho, would then be placed on the throne of the East, and then of the West also. Honorius had always been envious of his contemporary Eucherius, as being a brighter boy and most often in the same household with himself; though Eucherius was a very ordinary young man and something of a disappointment to Stilicho. These suggestions, implanted by Olympius, fermented in the limited mind of the Emperor Honorius.

Honorius, at the instigation of Olympius, announced that he would go to Constantinople and appoint a guardian for his nephew, the seven-year-old Theodosius the Second, the son of the dead Arcadius. Stilicho coolly forbade Honorius to take the trip, stating that he, Stilicho, would take care of everything. Stilicho already had the triumvirate of Singerich, Fravitta, and Anthemius to act as guardians to the new boy Emperor. He now sent dispatches to these three telling them what he expected of them. At the same time he sent word to Alaric to remain in his buffer province to guard against possible disturbances in the East; and to defer the campaign against Constantine to another season.

But it was at that moment, in being forbidden the trip to Constantinople, that Honorius finally slipped away from Stilicho. Olympius had been impressing on Honorius that he was completely without power under the thumb of Stilicho; and that he must assert his rightful power. Stilicho, worried about affairs, had been unnecessarily blunt with the Emperor; though heretofore he had always made a point of being gentle, though firm, with him. Honorius was now a man of twenty-five, and Olympius succeeded in awakening resentment in him. The Emperor also had a fear for his own safety, engendered by the fantastic accusations of Olympius against Stilicho. Now Olympius, understanding his subject, added another note.

Stilicho, Olympius told Honorius, was an irreligious man who intended (as soon as he had murdered him, Honorius) to reinstate paganism and suppress the Church. Honorius was shocked by this. He was a very religious Christian boy, for boy he was in spite of his twenty-five years. He forgot for the moment that it was Stilicho who had brought him up so religiously, and who had instilled in him the Faith. Honorius was in genuine horror that Stilicho should suppress the Church—after killing him, the Emperor. He was shocked that Stilicho had dealt treasonably with the barbarian invader—the General Alaric who had been his own friend—Honorius may not have realized that they were of the same identity. Honorius was completely bewildered by these various charges against his guardian and father-in-law; but the important thing is that he began to believe them.

Olympius had realized early that Honorius was of very short memory, that he always believed the last thing he had been told. And Olympius made a point of telling Honorius a certain series of things many times a day.

Olympius now decided, for the furtherance of his plot, to take the Emperor Honorius on a tour. He decided on this suddenly in the absence of Stilicho. He would take Honorius to the great staging town of Pavia where the anti-German movement had made much progress and where Olympius himself was very strong. This was one city that Stilicho did not want Honorius to visit.

The whereabouts of Stilicho at this particular time is not known. He still made very rapid journeys alone to various parts of the Empire. He may have gone to visit Alaric in Noricum, where Alaric waited at the furthest extent of his own territory. Stilicho still held Alaric in readiness on the borders of Italy; for possible movement to the East should there be trouble in the transition there; for possible movement into Italy should real trouble develop—for Stilicho had also smelled the change in the wind. Or

Stilicho may have gone to Constantinople to see about the transition personally.

The journey of Honorius and Olympius to Pavia was undertaken. They were escorted by a detachment of Roman troops from which every vestige of Stilicho's influence had been purged. At this point there is a slight confusion in the recorded history.

One source states that the Goth Sarus caused a mutiny of the Imperial troops in the fortress city of Ravenna, where he is never mentioned as having being stationed, where his influence would have been less than almost anywhere, and which city Honorius and Olympius would have just left. No outcome of this action is mentioned, and no other source alludes to it at all.

But other sources recount a riot, or at least a disturbance, among the troops at Bologna at this same time, with no leader mentioned. It is probably that the two accounts must be combined to arrive near the truth.

There was certainly a disturbance at Bologna. There is no real evidence of one in the Court City of Ravenna. And the disturbance at Bologna seems to have the hand marks of Sarus all over it, though he is not there mentioned by name.

It was the day before the arrival of the Emperor Honorius and his new and still unofficial minister Olympius, the Greek Master of Court. It was a lightning-like daylight raid carried out by less than fifty men—the sort of raid that Sarus had led several times before and would lead again, one of them the final one that led to his capture and murder.

The less than fifty men and their unidentified leader, who was almost certainly Sarus, struck through thousands of armed men into the center of the staging area where there was a practice assembly for the welcome of the Emperor; swiftly killed a score of men; and rode out again, losing about half their own number dead in the action. One account states that the raiders were masked.

The men killed had all been high men of Olympius, intruded into Bologna by Solinas, except two of them. Two of the men murdered were supposedly key men of Stilicho, very competent and trusted by the great Master General all the way. But these two trusted men had either been subverted and turned against Stilicho, or at least Sarus—if he was the leader of the raid—believed that they had been.

It is disputed whether the move of Sarus, in view of final happenings, was a wise one. Sarus was solidly for Stilicho and the Empire, and he had posted his warning of sudden death for all traitors to the cause. But Bologna could never have been subverted, and the twenty men would not have mattered. This raid was used as a pretext for a counter-massacre, which had likely already been planned, however.

The Emperor Honorius in coming into Bologna the next day did not understand the report of what had happened. Olympius was furious at the murder of his picked men, and yet perhaps secretly pleased. He now had tenuous justification for his coming act, which he had almost certainly planned before the provocation.

The Emperor Honorius was treated with respect and shown every honor by the soldiers of Bologna, who were solidly Stilicho's men after the killing of the few subversives. Honorius was their legitimate Emperor, and no troops were more devoted to the Empire than those of the staging area of Bologna. Olympius, the unofficial new minister, was given a chilly reception, however. The great military men looked through him and not at him; they did not deign to notice him or to answer his direct questions; and they disarmed his Roman bodyguard, stating that they would return their weapons to them when they left the city, but not before. Moreover Olympius was drenched with a bucket of offal from a high place in the town, in an unfortunate accident.

It was for this reason that Olympius and the Emperor Honorius remained in Bologna no more than a day, and may even have left on the day of their arrival. Honorius would have liked to remain a while. There was the promise of fine riding with some of the best horsemen in the world, and riding was one of the few talents of the Emperor. He also liked the company of soldiers, to be around them and their harness; to talk to the common troopers, who abashed him less than did the generals. There were many minds as boyish as Honorius' own among the common soldiers of the predominantly German forces, and they had a liking for the young Emperor.

Olympius would have none of it. In fear of his life he hurried the Emperor along to Pavia. He would not feel safe until he was within the confines of that place with its soldiery more Roman than German, and where Solinas had done his work of intrusion and subversion so well. It is more than a hundred and twenty-five miles between Bologna and Pavia, and the retinue covered the distance within five days.

The Roman troops of the entourage, who could be disarmed and rearmed by the German forces at their pleasure, likewise went in fear of their lives.

On the day after Olympius and the Emperor Honorius had left Bologna, hurrying on towards Pavia, Stilicho himself arrived in Bologna: Stilicho the *Quercus Romae,* the Oak of Rome. He had come to investigate the reports of the raid; knowing what had happened; knowing that he would not be able to get a true report from any of them of what had happened. The men of Bologna were strongly loyal to Stilicho, and there was a tacit understanding in these matters.

But Stilicho did reaffirm that the person of the Emperor Honorius must be considered as inviolate, no matter what should occur. Honorius was their rightful Emperor even though he should fall under tainted influence, and he was to be considered the personification of the Empire itself.

On the day following the arrival of Olympius and Honorius in Pavia there occurred the revenge that had been planned before the act. The predominantly Roman and cosmopolitan troops, with their German minority, were drawn up for Imperial Revue. Suddenly at a signal—some say it was a word from Olympius himself, some that it was the squeal of a fife or the blast of a trumpet—picked Roman soldiers surrounded the prominent men of Stilicho, and struck them dead.

Then the whole army broke ranks and went on a two day orgy of slaughter. Every Goth, Vandal, Lombard or other German was hunted down and killed. Even those Germans who had been sub-

verted to the party of Olympius and Solinas were killed, for the
new minister did not believe in leaving any loose ends.

The Emperor Honorius wandered through the streets and areas
of Pavia for the two days of the slaughter, not understanding what
it was about, begging the soldiers to stop the killing. He was a good
boy, and he disliked bloodshed and cruelty. It illustrates his peculiar position that he was never in personal danger from the soldiers
of either faction. They set him gently aside when he tried to inter-
vene. He was retarded, almost moronic, but he was their Emperor.

Pavia, when the slaughter had finished, was a completely Roman
camp, voided of all Germanic and outlander influence. And it was
entirely the town of Olympius and his faction.

It would seem that Olympius had overreached himself. He had
Pavia; but Stilicho had Bologna, which blocked the roads both to
the Court City of Ravenna, and to the old Imperial City of Rome.
Stilicho had much the more powerful and battle-worthy forces; he
had the routes and resources; he had Italy below him; he had
Alaric on the north-east border of Italy with his control of Illyricum, and his control—with the triumvirate—of the East.

In a civil war, the party of Olympius would not have a chance.
Olympius had only the forces of Pavia itself. He could draw on
nothing. Gaul at his back, and Spain through Gaul, were controlled by the pretender Emperor Constantine.

But Olympius had not overreached himself. He had risen to
power by his complete understanding of one mind, that of the
retarded Emperor Honorius. But he also had a near-perfect understanding of another mind, that of the great Master General
Stilicho. Olympius knew how Stilicho would react to the next move;
but the great soldiers of Stilicho's party did not understand one
aspect of their chief at all. They were ignorant of the extent to
which Stilicho considered the person of the Emperor and the word
of the Emperor sacred, even when the Emperor was his own sorry
creature.

Olympius drafted an order and had the Emperor Honorius sign
it. Honorius was always honored to write his name, for he could

write nothing else. It was a command for Stilicho to report to the Court City of Ravenna at once to answer charges of treason. Olympius also sent secret orders to his own men in control of the city of Ravenna; in particular to Count Heraclian, a powerful man who was no lover of Stilicho; orders instructing the men what was expected of them.

Meanwhile, Stilicho, on hearing of the massacre in Pavia, ordered to assemble in Bologna all the generals of Germanic blood. These came and consulted with him, and waited their decision.

Stilicho ascertained that the massacre had not been against the Emperor; that the person of the Emperor Honorius was safe. To Stilicho, but not to the assembly of generals, this put a different complexion on the affair.

The assembled generals advised Stilicho that there was but one thing to do, or two variants of the one thing. They could march at once against Pavia; take the town; and put to death Olympius and his adherents. They would protect the Emperor Honorius if possible, though knowing that Olympius would use him as a shield.

Or they would immediately declare Stilicho Emperor—a move that they believed was long overdue. When a dynasty is no longer competently represented, they said, then there is nothing but to raise a praetorian Emperor to restore the realm. The need of it had cried out. Even the British legions, in raising Constantine to the purple, had had much right on their side. They felt that a weak Emperor was intolerable.

With Stilicho declared Emperor, then, several of the generals would move in force to settle the business in Pavia, with no particular care now of the deposed Emperor Honorius. And Stilicho could ride with another force to Rome to be confirmed as Emperor by the Senate; and he might then set up Court either in Rome or Milan or Ravenna.

It was clear enough as the generals put it; but Stilicho hesitated. They looked at him in amazement; and he showed no agreement to the one thing that had to be done. Modesty was no part of the generals and no part of Stilicho. His time had come, and there was no call for hesitation.

But Stilicho seemed in a daze. He was in such a state, and from it he would never emerge in his life. Above all, he had a horror of civil war, which he considered a desecration of the Empire. He had, which nobody understood, a mystic devotion to the person and office of the Emperor, though it was his own personal creation that he was devoted to. He would never be able to overcome it; nor to see himself as Emperor. He had devoted his entire life to the defense of the Empire, and in so doing he had become imbued with unalterable ideas.

It is possible that, from this time on, Stilicho was mentally deranged. Sarus and the other generals had seen slight signs of it when they had sent for Alaric. Stilicho was an old soldier who had spent his talents lavishly, and had never spared himself in any way. For many years he had spent eighteen- and twenty-hour days in the field; in the saddle; at his desk. Many have testified to the incredible extent to which he drove himself at work. He suffered from diseases, fatigues of campaign, and fevers; and he had been wounded more than a dozen times. He said once that he had forgotten how to sleep. An old head wound, that which had blinded him in one eye and left a piece of iron lodged in his brain, may have caught up with him; that, and other things.

Stilicho had been depressed and puzzled by the attacks of Olympius on his character that had come to him. Olympius had caused one of his Senators to cry out *"Quare ergo rubrum est indumentum tuum?"*—"Why then is thy apparel Red, and thy garments like them that tread in the wine press?"—the Biblical verses following that from which Stilicho had taken his motto. But the garments of Stilicho were not particularly soaked in blood; and every drop that he had shed was in defense of the Empire.

But Stilicho was a scrupulous man, and he sought whether the reason for his defamation was not in himself.

Stilicho hesitated. There had come to his hand the orders from Olympius, signed by the Emperor Honorius, ordering him to proceed to Ravenna to answer to the charge of treason. Stilicho had not revealed the contents of this message to the generals. Mostly it was because of these shocking orders that he hesitated.

The generals became impatient after several days. They stated
that they would follow him in whatever he would do, but that he
must do something. He must lead, or he must abdicate as leader.

The Goth Sarus became uncontrollable, and swore that they
must declare Stilicho Emperor on the spot.

Stilicho refused.

Sarus stated in white heat that Stilicho must become Emperor,
or he must die. In Gothic practice, an old bull that has been defeated for leadership of the herd is always killed.

Well, then he would die, Stilicho told them out of his daze. And
Sarus took his small force and rode out of Bologna in shaking
fury.

Sarus returned at midnight in one of the most fantastic of all his
raids, once more with no more than fifty men. He rode to the center of the city of soldiers, through the thousands of armed men who
were afraid of him in his madness, and attacked the picked Hunnic bodyguard of Stilicho.

Sarus and his raiders slew the Huns every man, a cool force of
fighting men and three times the number of his own small forces.
Sarus came to the tent of Stilicho to kill him. And the old fox was
gone.

Sarus and his men ran swords through baggage and bedding.
They dragged every rag out of the tent, and Sarus beat the empty
ground with the flat side of his sword in fury. They ran out howling
that they had missed him.

Sarus set the ring of his men around the tent of the Master General, to kill him should he return; and went out alone through the
town, sword in hand, to have the big man.

The thousands of troops turned the town and the camp upside
down looking for Stilicho; some to defend him; some to kill him;
some to reason with him for the last time. They did not find him.

At dawn Stilicho walked out of his empty tent, which has never
been explained, for it was guarded all the while. It was the last trick
of the wiley old fox, and he is entitled to it. He passed Sarus who

stood yet sword in hand. And the weary Sarus, completely lost and his anger now turned to bewilderment, let him go.

Stilicho mounted horse and announced in a listless voice that he was riding to Ravenna to answer in person charges that had been brought against himself. The soldiers turned their backs on him and let him go. They had lost their leader and must find another.

Stilicho rode the sixty miles to Ravenna alone. With one word he could have been Emperor; but he rode slowly to his death. Everywhere on the road the soldiers he passed turned their backs to him, and he slept that night wrapped in his cloak on the ground.

Late on the second day he rode into the fortress city of Ravenna, commending his soul to God.

There was no trial. Instructions for his execution, drafted by Olympius and signed by the Emperor Honorius, had preceded him. Stilicho died, by the axe of Count Heraclian, on August 23 of the year 408, two years and one day before the world ended. One blow took off his head cleanly, for Count Heraclian—of later fame in Africa—was a powerful man.

Stilicho was the greatest Master General Rome ever had, and only once in his life did he ever hesitate.

17. Of the Empire Misplaced

The sullen generals remained in Bologna after receiving the not surprising news of the murder or execution of Stilicho. They sent ambassadors to Alaric in Noricum, and also sent secretly to the more responsible men in Ravenna, though these were not of their party. They sent deputies to their contacts within the city of Rome, and to the triumvirate in the East. They consulted and renewed their contacts; but they did not move.

They were nailed in place by a device that had been contrived by their lost leader Stilicho. The great Master General had arranged it that no group in the Empire, and certainly not his own group, could ever move against the Empire itself. He had taken hostages of all, and had set every group as guard over every other group. The families of the German soldiery, their wives and children, were settled as small isolated enclaves in the Italian cities. And the wealth of these German soldiers, and it was sometimes considerable, was also stored in those Italian cities; that in liquid form banked there, that of a less negotiable form ticketed for them in special depots.

Ordinarily, this had been a good arrangement. The families had been safe in the only province of the Empire not threatened by exterior attack; and the Empire itself had been the guarantor of their wealth. Now, however, the soldiers perceived that they had indeed given hostages.

The grand minister Olympius had them on the hook. The Gothic and German families kept to themselves in tight quarters in the Italian cities, almost no men among them. The women were not nearly so cosmopolitan as the men; they drew to themselves as strangers, collected their allotments, and waited out the years. Their dozens of scattered small groups had no defense at all, in the middle of the large Italian towns, from the attack that now came on them. Should their men move against the Empire, then their women and children would immediately be slaughtered.

Had a praetorian Emperor been raised it would have been a different matter. The Italians would have refrained from apprehension of what might follow. But they would not refrain for a leaderless outlaw move.

It was then that Olympius let the outlanders off the hook in a very ungracious fashion.

Olympius was a great one for comprehending other minds: that of the Emperor Honorius, that of Stilicho, that of the Roman people collectively, and the minds of the generals he had man-trapped. But nobody has ever comprehended the weird mind of Olympius.

What he did now he did of choice. It was the one thing he desired most in the world; and for it he would throw away life and Empire and honor and wealth. He suddenly saw the pearl beyond price, and he traded all that he owned for it. It was a black pearl, and he was impassioned of it.

Olympius threw away the advantage that had kept the opposing generals tied down and unable to move against him. He ordered that the slaughter of the outlander women and children should begin. And such was the temper of the Roman and Italian people, the anti-German wind having been blown to a storm by the agents of Olympius and a low form of propaganda, that the people fell in with the plan. Secret groups in every city set it going, and the people joined it. The evil folks partook of it with great enthusiasm, and the good people made themselves scarce and did nothing. The news came in of the slaughter of the outlander women and children in a dozen cities; and then in a hundred.

Olympius, now back in Ravenna, was beside himself. This was as high as he could get. It was what he had been born for. He had enjoyed the slaughter of the innocents in Constantinople, but it had not been of such an extent as this.

Whatever should happen now, they could never take this away from him. He was heard to cry out that this was greater than Empire. Solinas shared his glee, but nobody could enter into it to such full extent.

This peculiar triumph of Olympius is without parallel. He is one man who attained what he really wanted in life. Everything afterwards would be anticlimax. He had sunk as low as it was possible to sink.

Then the orgasm was finished. Sixty thousand women and children, mostly of the Germanic races, had been murdered. The reaction of the Italians to their own act was curious. Their anti-German feeling had burned itself out in the slaughter, and was as though it had never been. They put it clear out of their minds, forgot it entirely. Once more they were willing to let the Germans protect them and carry the burden of Empire.

But the puzzling aspect was that the Germans did not so quickly put it out of their own minds. The Italian people were genuinely puzzled by the animosity which the German soldiers, ranging through Italy in the next half dozen years, showed against them.

The triumph of Olympius was complete, and essentially his life had been lived. But now he took thought of the morrow. He let it out—which was not the truth—that only a certain portion of the families had been slain, and for a warning. Actually the only ones not killed were a very few thousand who had been hidden by compassionate Italians who had not joined in the madness.

Olympius put out the word that the families of the generals themselves, and those of all the men of the rank of centurion and above, had been spared the slaughter; that they were all gathered together in a secret place; and that by his one word they could all be dead in an hour, now that the generals had seen how he could kill.

The assembled generals did not know what to believe. This drove a bitter wedge between the officers, who preferred to hold off till they could obtain sure word, and their men who wished to ravage Italy in revenge of the murder of their families. Groups of men began, leaderless, to leave Bologna, and to go down into Italy as outlaws.

But Olympius had read the collective mind of the generals, and had gambled on their indecision. The generals now appealed to Alaric, who had not fallen into the trap.

The women and children of Alaric's Goths—not all the Goths of the Empire—were safe on the farms in Illyricum and Epirus, and a minority were with the men in Noricum. Alaric had been singularly deaf to a suggestion of Stilicho, repeated several times, that a token number of these Gothic families should be settled in the cities of Italy to promote further integration of the Romans and the Goths.

Nor had Alaric heeded the prompting that the treasure of the Goths would be safer in the secure Italian towns. The Goths did not have enough treasure to bother about, Alaric had told Stilicho. But Alaric, though his own family and those of his people were not involved, was seized with an anger such as he had never known in his life.

Alaric had been completely broken up by the news of the murder of Stilicho. He discovered, too late, that he had a genuine love of the old dead soldier. It may be that Stilicho was easier to love in death than in life. Stilicho had hunted Alaric out of Greece and out of Italy; he had built a gibbet to hang him on; and had defeated and disgraced him several times in battle. But he had also taught him almost all that he knew about military ways; he had given him the strong idea of Empire; and he had brought him to maturity. Stilicho had dealt with him as a man, after the time was past for dealing with him as a boy. And, as a general, Alaric would never have been able to find anyone to admire so highly as the greatest Master General of them all.

Among the assembled generals in Bologna there was also a swift turning of feeling in favor of Stilicho, too late, after he was dead. The generals and soldiers were ashamed of their treatment of him, realizing that they had turned their backs on him when he was sick and bewildered and at the end of his rope. They were looking for another Stilicho, and they requested Alaric to take the part.

Alaric was horrified at the slaughter of the families in Italy. His own system of intelligence, which was certain but which came by the long way around—from his brother-in-law Singerich in Constantinople—told him that the families of the officers and generals had *not* been spared. But Alaric did not inform them of this yet, to dash their hopes.

Alaric sent word to Bologna that he was entering Italy with his army. He informed those troops that they were not to join him at that time, and that they had better not oppose him.

He sent word to the Senate of Rome that, since they had not yet paid him the four thousand pounds of gold which had been voted to him—for the sending of the payment had been put off several times on the excuse that the roads were unsafe for the transport of such a treasure, or that the weather was too unseasonable, or the times too unsettled—he, Alaric, would save them the trouble and would come in person to collect it.

And Alaric sent word to the Emperor Honorius in Ravenna that from him he wanted only two things; the head of Olympius and the head of Solinas. He wished, he said, to present them to some friends of his on his return journey north.

So he entered Italy.

Olympius, in the name of the Emperor Honorius, ordered the forces in Bologna to take the field against Alaric, on peril of the death of their families. The generals sent word that they could not find the forces of Alaric. The scouts from Bologna silently saluted the Goths of Alaric as they went by, but they could not find them.

Olympius, again in the name of the Emperor Honorius, ordered the Goth Sarus to lead an army of Roman and cosmopolitan soldiers against Alaric. Sarus had made himself a special person in the Empire. He had no wife or children, being wedded to the Empire. He no longer considered himself one of the party of Bologna, since the death of Stilicho. He was loyal to the Empire to death, but—as bewildered as Stilicho in his last days—he no longer knew of what the Empire consisted.

Sarus roamed North Italy with his small band, looking for the Empire; and could not find it. Could he have been secure in his mind that the Empire still resided in the person of the moronic Emperor and his diabolical minister, then he would have served them without question. Could he have persuaded Alaric to declare himself Emperor, *as a Roman,* with the provision that he would outlaw forever Athaulf and the Gothic element represented by him, then Sarus would have served his brother-in-law in the high office in all security of mind.

But Sarus was too single-minded to make a decision, and was tortured by the question. In such a state he had ridden into Ravenna with his small band. He came and went as he wished. There was no man and no city that dared close a gate in his face when he came with half a hundred men.

Olympius repeated the command that had been sent: that Sarus should head a force against Alaric. Could he be trusted, Sarus asked ironically, to lead an army against his own blood kindred? He did not wish to put himself under the temptation of treason, he added.

Sarus had taken the field against Alaric before, Olympius pointed out.

Yes, but by the orders of a greater minister than Olympius, Sarus answered.

Sarus would lead the forces against Alaric, and he would give his oath of loyalty, Olympius insisted. Even the devil Olympius knew that Sarus would abide by an oath if he should give it. Sarus would lead the army, or he would give up his head that day, was the final statement of Olympius. Olympius had thirty thousand men, and Sarus had fifty.

Let him take my head who may, Sarus told the minister. And Sarus rode out of Ravenna with his small force. The soldiers opened a path for him and let him through, in spite of the hysterical orders of the minister Olympius to seize the man and to cut down his force. But Sarus had a sort of hypnotic presence on these queer missions of his, and he was never crossed. He rode out of Ravenna unobstructed.

Sarus knew where to find Alaric, for all that the men of Bologna pretended that they could not. He confronted him on the way, near Modena, and demanded what he intended to do.

Alaric would go to Rome to collect his pay, he told his brother-in-law Sarus. Then he would return by way of Ravenna and pick up two heads. He would present them to certain mutual friends in a town not thirty miles from where they then stood; and he would then return to Noricum, and be for a while longer a bystander.

Sarus told Alaric, as he had told him many times before, that he must never bring Athaulf into the Empire; or that he Sarus would be forced to kill both of them.

He is your brother, Alaric told him.

He is not my brother, he is Cain, said Sarus.

They spoke in Low Latin; for Sarus, as a Roman become, refused to understand or answer even one word of Gothic. Sarus then asked Alaric miserably of what the Empire consisted.

"Perhaps of you and I for want of better," Alaric said. Sarus shook his head, and they went their separate ways: Alaric to collect his pay in his own fashion; and Sarus still to wander distracted through the north of Italy. No man was ever more loyal than the single-minded Goth Sarus; but he was now unable to settle on the object of his loyalty.

Here there enters confusion, in the last fifteen months of the world. There is no unanimity among historians as to the details of Alaric's three sieges of Rome. Certain happenings are placed by some at the time of the first siege, by others at the time of the second. Alaric's ravaging of the Adriatic coast from Rimini on south was almost certainly a preliminary to the second attack; but it is most often attached to the first. And Athaulf's joining of Alaric has to be just before the third and final assault; not before the second. We will sort out the discrepancies as well as we may, knowing that we will be in error on at least a third of the details; but knowing also that, fortunately, the points in historical dispute are not major ones.

In the late spring or early summer of the year 409, Alaric

marched to Rome *as a Roman General,* leading a regular Roman
force—composed, however, of men of Gothic lineage—to collect
the pay which the Roman Senate had voted to him and his men;
and which the Senate had been unable to transmit due to—in the
words of the Senate itself—the inclemency of the weather (for more
than one year) and the danger of the roads. Alaric encountered no
particular danger on the roads, and the weather was serene.

He came slowly to Rome. His force had a penumbra of irregular
soldiers from the north who had abandoned their officers and were
set on revenge on the Italians for the massacres of the soldiers'
families. A dozen towns that had been particularly murderous in
that affair were now ravaged by these irregulars. Alaric curbed
them, but he did not do so swiftly. He usually gave them a few
hours to settle their affairs with the townsmen, and to take the
equivalent of their looted property; for a busy army cannot be moving at a moment's notice to investigate every report of a local disturbance.

Alaric came and surrounded the city of Rome, deploying his
men in a series of leisurely camps that just made a circuit of the
City. He sent in ambassadors to reiterate his simple demands to the
Senate. He had come at great personal inconvenience to collect
the pay that was overdue him, he stated. His request was an honorable one, and the answer to it had been too long delayed.

The Senate refused to deal with him. It branded him a public
enemy and announced that the City would resist. Rome had lavish
promise of aid from the Court City of Ravenna, and there were
reports that loyal Imperial legions were on the way from every
direction to raise the siege.

But aid never arrived, as Alaric knew it would not, and as the
more responsible men inside Rome knew it would not. Alaric surrounded the City completely, blocked all twelve gates, and cut off
both river and road traffic from the port of Ostia. This was the
main move. Rome depended on imports of grain from the provinces
of Sicily and Africa through the port of Ostia for its main sus-
tenance. It could do a while without the beef and pork and fruit
and wine of the Italian countryside, likewise cut off from it; but it

could not live long without the grain from the two overseas provinces. The Romans were bread eaters, and their dole consisted of bread only.

Alaric sat down with his army to wait. The City set up an admirable administration for the distribution of the foodstuffs in the City. The people went on two-thirds rations, and then on half rations. There were inequities, but a general spirit of fairness prevailed as the weeks went by. The City doled out what food it had, and waited for the loyal legions to arrive. The emergency depots were opened and cleaned out, and personal hordes were searched for.

The City went on one-third rations, and the relieving legions were very tardy.

There is a sameness in the accounts of the sufferings of cities under siege. The people were reduced to eating dogs and rats, and the bark of trees. Finally, when relief was still not in sight, and when necrophagy had become widespread in the City, the Senate capitulated.

Alaric gave them surprisingly easy terms.

He was not a public enemy, of course, he explained. The Senate withdrew the proclamation; and Alaric was no longer a public enemy. His pay he must have, he insisted, and a certain interest upon it for the time and trouble. The four thousand pounds of gold was now five thousand pounds; surely the Senate could see the justice of that. The Senate had no choice but to see the justice of it. They paid the sum.

There were other matters, and other expenses. For acting henceforth as special protector of the City—for it was now plain that she had no other protector—Alaric and his Goths would agree to accept a modest fee: thirty thousand pounds of silver. It was indeed, under the unilateral circumstances, a modest fee; and the Senate paid.

And as an afterthought, and as a gesture of friendship from the Roman people, the Goths of Alaric might be prevailed upon to accept the free gift of three thousand pounds weight of pepper. Pepper was then expensive. The city of Rome controlled the importation of pepper into all Europe, and sold it for 2000 per cent profit.

And the Goths liked a little pepper. Rome had pepper and no food to use it on. The Senate agreed to the free gift of the pepper, and Alaric prevailed on his Goths to accept it.

The Romans listened for the list of further demands.

But, to the amazement of the City, Alaric reopened the road and river traffic from Ostia; and even aided with his soldiery in moving the grain to the City. He withdrew from the twelve gates of the town and permitted normal traffic to resume. He sent his army to establish winter quarters in Tuscany; for he had spent some months straiting the City, and it was now autumn. The siege was finished.

The City could not believe that it was so easily delivered. It need not have starved at all. Such losses as these it could easily recoup in a year. It may be that Alaric had no real idea of the great money wealth of the City, or it may be that he was not venal at all. Alaric was still faithfully in his role as Imperial General, not as the Gothic King.

He now set about the business of treating with the Emperor's party at Ravenna. But someone in Ravenna had meanwhile had the wisdom for a move that was to undercut Alaric. The Count Heraclian had sailed out of the Court City to assume the administration of the province of Africa. He was the most competent man of Ravenna, and was loyal to that particular administration. The African grain flow could be controlled at its source; and Alaric in encompassing Rome might himself be encompassed; for they knew in Ravenna that he would be forced to return to the Roman enterprise.

Alaric selected three Roman senators to go to Ravenna to deal for him. He insisted on the heads of Olympius and Solinas. He desired to be recognized as Master General of the entire Western Empire. And he asked three provinces for his people: Dalmatia, Noricum, and Venetia. Much of Dalmatia he already possessed, included in his province of Illyricum. Part of Noricum he had already occupied in the early part of the year 408, the vague boundary between Noricum and Illyricum being a matter of opinion. And if he wished to seize Venetia, there seemed no force able to prevent him.

The Goths would not be great gainers by their shift to these provinces, but they would be given strategic position. From the giant buffer province, they would be partly shifted to the crossroads of the Empire routes. Such position was necessary if they were to become the actual guardians of the Empire.

The most difficult of the demands was the first one. Olympius conducted the negotiations in the name of the Emperor Honorius; he might have been willing to give up the head of Solinas, but he was totally unwilling to give up the head of Olympius.

The three Roman senators were dismissed by Ravenna, but they were not handed over to Alaric's escort. Instead they were given, by subterfuge, to six thousand Imperial troops from Ravenna to accompany them back to Rome, a most foolish move. The vengeful German irregulars ranging through Italy annihilated the escort. It was too small to be an army, and too large to be considered an escort under truce.

Alaric tried again. He selected a larger number of Roman senators, and compelled Pope Innocent to accompany them to Ravenna to present his cause in the most reasonable terms possible. Alaric gave them his statement that he was still a loyal Roman General; that he had no other thought than to restore the stability of the Empire; and that his three demands were the absolute minimum for restoring that stability.

Alaric must have the heads of the two conspirators to heal the breach between the Old Romans and the Empire Germans, and to atone for the massacre.

He must himself be proclaimed Master General, since there was nobody else capable of assuming that onerous task. Alaric was without either modesty or vanity. He saw his own worth clearly, and was puzzled that his position should be misunderstood.

And he must shift the topographical base of his own people to the provinces indicated; for from no other position could they protect the whole Empire. He was right in this last assessment also; though his enemies might have said that the new position would better permit him to control, rather than protect, the Empire.

It was the same refusal. Olympius had tottered, but he had not yet fallen. He steadfastly refused to give up his head. He still kept the negotiations largely in his own hands; and he intercepted, by his good luck, several communications that would have bypassed and undone him.

Alaric and his emissaries could not reach the Emperor or the more nearly responsible men in Ravenna. The senators were dismissed, to the escort of Alaric's troops this time. But Pope Innocent was held in Ravenna, as a prisoner disguised with much honor, and as a pawn in the game that the party of Ravenna might somehow play.

Alaric could not reach the Emperor. He resolved to raise his own Emperor. He returned to the second siege of Rome.

But, by a conspiracy of fate, Alaric left Ravenna too soon. Olympius fell while Alaric was on the way to Rome. The defamer had his ears cropped, and was dismissed. Alaric could have had his head for the taking, had he known about it, and known where to find the creature.

Everything seemed to be working for an event that nobody really wanted to happen, except possibly the extreme party among the Goths. It did not have to happen, as Stilicho had said again and again in his lifetime. The Empire did not have to go down. It could have been saved; it could yet have been saved.

It did not have to happen, but it happened. Every move, conscious or unconscious, of every party involved brought it nearer to its end. Jovius had replaced Olympius as the power in Ravenna. Other men, Eusebius and Allobich, rose and fell. Finally, it was a jungle of divided authority in the fortress Court City, and indecision became the rule.

Alaric returned to the city of Rome, picking up his main force from their quarters in Tuscany. He returned now with a simple request: that the people of Rome give him an Emperor. The City was timorous and shut its gates on him. It had not believed its good fortune before. Rome looked on this visitation as the second phase of the assault, as a cruel jest following the earlier show of gentleness. It was now believed that the Roman people would be massacred. So it had to be starvation all over again before Alaric could make the Romans see the light.

Alaric did not surround the City. He did not shut off the meat and fruits of the countryside. He occupied the port of Ostia and shut off the flow of grain only. The Romans could survive longer under these conditions, but they could not survive forever. They could not live without grain for bread. Alaric hoped that it would not be for long.

He sat with his troops among the granaries of Ostia and waited for the Roman people to capitulate. And soon he became quite anxious that the people capitulate. The grain boats did not arrive from Africa. Alaric understood that the Count Heraclian had shut them off, and that no more would arrive while he maintained his hold of the City.

It had all grown up as a peculiar political-economic arrangement. The province of Africa, by an age-old tribute, was required to furnish the million and a half people of the city of Rome with grain; to a lesser degree the province of Sicily was also required to supply grain to Rome. For this reason, grain-growing had been abandoned in the portion of Italy surrounding Rome, and the land was diverted to raising livestock, fruit, grapes, olives, and vegetables. If the siege continued long enough, the forces of Alaric would themselves feel the pinch. They might have to abandon their occupation of Ostia and travel a hundred miles to a grain belt; or Alaric would have to split his forces and make himself vulnerable, sending considerable numbers to occupy harvest lands and seize the produce.

It was also the fact that the granaries of Ostia were near empty, and the depots inside the city of Rome were bulging full. The possibility of the second investure of Rome had been foreseen.

Fortunately for Alaric, and most fortunate for Rome, the siege was not of long duration. The Roman Senate negotiated with Alaric once more, and found that his request was just as originally stated—with one demand now added. Alaric insisted that all slaves in Rome who could prove themselves of northern "barbarian" lineage should be freed to him. This gave the Romans cause for thought, but they quickly saw a side of the matter that Alaric had not understood; and they agreed to this.

Rome had long been a city on a pension, drawing on the ancient tributes of the Empire. The life on the dole was easy on the citizens, and easy on their slaves. They were a town people, and most of them had never visited or wanted to visit open country. They were born in the pit formed by the hills, and they would live and die there. The slaves were a part of the City; they had no memory of the open life in the north.

They had no desire to take their places as free men at the hard work of farming in the inhospitable north. They would live in the streets of the City, and would work when they were compelled to work. They had no wish to be free men on their own resources, and compelled to work all the time for their livelihood.

Of possibly one hundred thousand slaves who could qualify as to northern barbarian lineage, not ten thousand chose freedom with Alaric and the hard settlement on the land. But Alaric carried his point here, and the best of the slaves did leave the City as freemen.

It was during the early part of the negotiations that Alaric discovered a horrible thing to have happened. The girl Galla Placidia had been raised in the household of Stilicho, the ward of that great Master General and his wife, Serena, who was cousin as well as step-sister and step-mother of Placidia. Galla Placidia, the sister of the Emperor Honorius, had remained in that household in Rome even after the fall of Stilicho; and after Honorius had divorced Thermandia, the daughter of Stilicho and Serena. Eucherius, the son of Stilicho, had been murdered by a mob; and the position of Serena had been precarious. Placidia had been her shield in the intervening period.

But Galla Placidia had now caught the Roman fever, affectedly at first; then earnestly. She now regarded Serena as wedded to the German cause in Stilicho; though Stilicho had been pro-Roman to the point of subduing his own people; and Serena was Spanish and Greek as was Placidia herself.

Galla Placidia, now either sixteen or seventeen years old and already known to the Senate for her flaming eloquence, denounced

Serena to that body. She had denounced her for carrying on correspondence with Alaric outside the walls, with no evidence whatsoever.

Serena was incapable of intrigue. Galla Placidia had either been convinced of these charges by a party of Romans bent on the destruction of every vestige of Stilicho, or she had acted out of sheer perversity. But her impassioned denunciation was the turning point, and Serena had been condemned and executed for treason. And Galla Placidia continued to live in the house of Stilicho, alone.

Galla Placidia, after her death many years later, would be venerated as a near saint; and there would be some justification for the veneration in her long and complex life. It may be that every saint is an early devil. Placidia had considerable of the devil in her when she was young, and she defamed to death the only mother she remembered.

Alaric nearly broke off negotiations on hearing of this happening; and he all but lost faith in Rome. He was persuaded to continue the council by one Basilius a prominent senator, and one John the first tribune of the notaries and a long-standing friend of Alaric; they had become acquainted during certain Empire transactions when Alaric ruled as Master General of Illyricum. Another man who brought pressure on Alaric to continue the talks was Bacurius, the old Spanish General and now a high senator. But was not Bacurius killed at the battle of the River Frigidus? So it was said, so it was reported; but this was the same man, and alive.

These men, with Attalus who had replaced Pompeianus as Praefect of the city of Rome, now took a leading part in the transactions. Alaric repeated once more his one request, the one thing he wanted from them, the thing he had to have. He asked that the city of Rome should give him an Emperor. And he waited. Surely such competent men could not be so dense as to fail to comprehend what he meant.

Attalus the Praefect of Rome had understood from the beginning, but he had a sense of timing. At the proper moment he suggested himself. He was a man after Alaric's own heart in this detail, for Alaric had no patience with reluctance. And Attalus was the

most justifiable choice. As Praefect of Rome he already held the
highest office. He could trace a degree of kinship to several dynasties of Emperors, as could many of the high senators. And he was
reputed to be a clever man.

It was a matter of no more than a week, with all the forms observed and the proper amount of eloquence spilt. The Senate
proclaimed Attalus to be Emperor. Alaric raised the siege and permitted provisions to flow once more into the City. The granaries
of Ostia were not quite empty, nor were the depots of Rome; and
Alaric knew that the Count Heraclian would once more permit the
grain boats to leave Africa, as soon as he Alaric had left the vicinity
of Rome.

Alaric took his new Emperor Attalus, and his army, and started
for Ravenna once more. Alaric was now Master General of the
entire Western Roman Empire by proclamation of the Senate of
Rome. He would settle with the faction at Ravenna, and in all
legality. Perhaps Honorius would be continued as an inactive co-
Emperor.

Alaric also took with him, as prisoner, the wayward girl Galla
Placidia who had caused the murder of her step-mother and
cousin.

18. The Day the World Ended

Alaric came once more to the walls of Ravenna; with his army; with his Emperor; and with his royal prisoner, Galla Placidia, the sister of the Emperor Honorius within Ravenna. Alaric called for negotiations, and he had every hope of success.

Olympius no longer ruled in Ravenna. In the confusion within the city one would be at a loss to say who did rule; but the truculent opposition had melted. Pope Innocent had been, to a great extent, responsible for the more mellow atmosphere. In heavily Catholic Ravenna he was of great influence, and his one desire was for peace. His enemies had often said that he was willing to pay too high a price for peace; but he had not been a persecutor when he had the power to be, and he was not so deeply sworn an enemy of the Arians as his predecessors had been. He was not opposed to Arians holding strictly political office, not even the high office of Master General of the Empire if it should bring peace.

The name Innocent of Popes is sometimes pronounced with irony, as though some of that name had not been innocent; and as though it were the opposite of innocent to vaunt such name as though a brag. But all others used the name from admiration of this Innocent I, and he had it as a family name "Innocentius," which went back to pagan days in their town of Albano. It was his own name; he was born with it.

In the new atmosphere, and out of the confusion in Ravenna, certain responsible men were now coming to the fore; and they were very interested in ending the confusion. They knew, of course, that the Emperor Honorius was, and always would be, incompetent. They had no objection to seeing a competent man installed as co-Emperor with him, if that man should be in all ways acceptable; and they were inclined to accept Attalus as that man.

Attalus had been known to them for years. He had been a leading senator in Rome, and had held various high offices before becoming Praefect of the city of Rome. He was one of the few Old Romans, a *Quinquagesimus* (one of fifty generations), related to at least two of the old Imperial dynasties. There was no man in the Empire with more blood right to be Emperor, though there were perhaps a score with equal right.

There was still the pressing threat of the pretender Emperor Constantine who held much of Gaul and Spain. If the Empire was to be restored, Constantine would have to be eliminated. It was felt in Ravenna that Alaric, if other matters should be settled, was competent to defeat Constantine; and that no other general was.

Alaric had demonstrated his loyalty to the Empire by his fair treatment of the city of Rome which he had twice in his power. He had a good record of late years. Materially, he had restored the rotten province of Illyricum in his years there; he had resettled its farms with his people and others, and had brought it to a hard state of prosperity. Possibly he could do the same thing for Noricum and Venetia, which had been all but abandoned by settled life. The Empire needed another Stilicho—they who had killed him realized it—and Alaric was the nearest approach.

Many of the greatest master generals had had a touch of the brigand in them in their greener years. There were even reports that Stilicho had been an adventurer not entirely within the law before his falling under the strong influence of the Emperor Theodosius. A master general who had committed his breaches of the peace early, and then reformed of them, was less likely to go astray in his maturity.

Alaric, on his side, had resolved to negotiate with long patience; but also he had resolved not to leave the matter unsettled. It had

continued too long in intolerable confusion. Should every negotiation fail, and there was no reason why they should, he would then
assail the unassailable city of Ravenna. He had accomplished the
impossible before. He was certain that he could, somehow, take
the fortress. But he had hardly an idea of failure, now that accord
seemed so near.

An explanation must be given why it was always so readily assumed that Ravenna was unassailable. Ravenna at that time stood
on the Adriatic Sea, on a lagoon. Today it is five miles from the
Adriatic; the land has risen in the fifteen and a half centuries since.
It is still somewhat swampy in the countryside around Ravenna;
but the present state gives no real indication of the horrifying
morasses that surrounded the fortress at the beginning of the fifth
century.

Ravenna, on the left of the Montone and Ronco rivers where
they come together just before going into the Adriatic, was surrounded on every land side by a belt of bog from twelve to thirty
miles wide, absolutely bottomless quicksand. This was crossed by
no real road. No proper Roman road had ever led into Ravenna.
There were horse paths by which one could be conducted by guide.
There were roads where, by much logging and shoring, wagons
could go in single file, but two of them could not pass. There were
firm meadows scattered through the swamps, but seldom of a size
of more than five or ten acres.

An approaching army would have to camp at fifteen or twenty
miles from the city, as the army of Alaric had done before and was
doing now; or it would have to be split up into dozens of small en-
campments of one hundred to two hundred men each on the precarious meadows.

There was one place right under the city walls where perhaps
three thousand men could be assembled, tightly formed and drawn
up, and in easy range of the archers on the walls. But an assault on
the fortress could not even be contemplated with less than ten times
that number assembled; and this one firm spot could be entered
only in single file, by men or horse.

Alaric had competent guides, of course, to the paths through the quicksand; but the bottom of the bogs was full of the bodies of competent guides who had gone down, for the land that was firm yesterday might not be firm today.

The bogs around Ravenna were peopled with ghosts and ghost stories, of a flavor that would later be called Gothic. There were false guides and ghost guides. One might meet a man in the bogs and speak with him; and after speaking to him for some time one would realize that the man was unsubstantial. The man would finally say that it was time he was going home; and would then wave farewell, and sink smiling into the bog, but making no ripple in it. One of the old bog dead who had been out for a walk in the upper air—such stories as that. Also, as is common with many swamps from the decomposed matter they contain, luminescent gas would hang over certain spots of it at night, of the size and shape of a man, glowing palely like ghosts indeed. There were the stories and there were such phenomena, and the men of Ravenna had found it to their advantage to let it be known that the dangerous bogs were haunted.

Ravenna was provisioned by sea, and had sea contact with every port of the Empire. Rimini, twenty-five miles to the south of her, was reached by sea and never by land. It would seem that Ravenna could be controlled only by one who had complete control of the sea; and Ravenna was the main station of the Imperial fleet. Alaric hardly had contacts in the fleet. The Roman Imperial army had become largely German; but the Imperial fleet had remained Roman. To the fleet, the Empire was embodied in Ravenna.

The Emperor Augustus had made Ravenna a station of the Imperial fleet; the Emperor Tiberius had made it the first station; and it was he also who built the great common wall surrounding both the city of Ravenna and the port of Classis. *Classis,* the fleet, was the name of the Port. The Emperor Trajan had built the aqueduct; Ravenna was in the middle of water, but it had sometimes been disease-carrying. Every following Emperor had added something to the strength of the fortress, until the Emperor Honorius moved his Court there.

The city was ornate within, and crisscrossed with canals—the most important of them the Augusta—so that Ravenna of that day resembled the Venice still to be built. It was a cosmopolitan city, and had close ties with Constantinople, even in the years of enmity between the brother Emperors.

Its greatest building was the Anastasis, the basilica of the Resurrection of our Lord, on the site of the present Cathedral, which contains remnants of the Anastasis built into it. San Giovanni in Fonte was the baptistery of the Catholics; and the church of Santo Spirito was that of the Arians. Later in the century the greatest building in Ravenna would be the mausoleum of Galla Placidia, containing the finest mosaics in the world. But at this time she was still very much alive.

The fortress of Ravenna must not be set too low, for all that it had an incompetent Emperor and no true ruler. The city commonly had more than fifty thousand men under arms within its walls, more than any other city in the world. It was a fortress; and it had been built to be an unassailable fortress by better Emperors than Honorius.

But Alaric believed that he could take it somehow, should the negotiations not succeed. His people on the opposite Adriatic coast, of Illyricum, had discovered an aptitude in themselves for the salt sea. They had been the finest river boat men in the world in the generation before. They learned new techniques from the pirates who had always been endemic to those shores; and their small swift Viking-like boats might have disconcerted the Imperial fleet.

The negotiations went well. Alaric was staggered by the mass of detail brought up both by the men of Ravenna and the men of his own party. The Empire was more intricate than he had imagined; and many of the affairs were brought to the fore and threshed out for his own education. But the Goths themselves were a nation of councils; and Alaric knew how to debate, to consult, and to abstract information from the various minds around him. He leaned heavily on John, the First Tribune of the Notaries from Rome, and on his own Emperor Attalus. He knew that an agreement is something that must be forged and hammered out, and re-heated and tempered more than once before it is final.

But two side events occurred in the time of the negotiations that were to affect their results. The first, right at the start of the parleys, was the disappearance of a person of some importance. The second, when the dialogues had almost come to successful fruition, was the appearance of a person of extreme importance.

These two did not meet at the time of the negotiations at Ravenna; but later they would be closely linked together.

Galla Placidia, the royal prisoner, out of perversity and likely not in truth, had written to Stairnon in Noricum. She told the wife of Alaric that Alaric had had relations with her, and that he had promised to make her Queen of Rome, after he had divorced Stairnon. Placidia wrote with her peculiar arrogance, and she had early learned the tricks of insulting Stairnon. She wrote as a high Roman, and made the Goths out to be dirt. Possibly the girl had found the time heavy on her hands in her captivity, and had enticed a rider into carrying her letter.

Stairnon replied in wrath and by special messenger, not to Galla Placidia, but to her husband Alaric. It was a furious missive, and it announced that she was following it in person. The letter was in Gothic, for Stairnon in her sudden anger had ceased to be a Roman. To her the symbol of Rome was no longer Serena, but the hated Galla Placidia. In losing Stairnon by such a circumstance, Rome lost an adherent badly needed.

Alaric, reading the letter from his wife which had been sent by special messenger, went howling to find the wayward wench Placidia, knowing that she had to be at the bottom of such nonsense. He learned then that she had made her escape that very hour.

Galla Placidia had broken out of her captivity, killed a forbidding Gothic matron set to guard her, stolen horse, and ridden out on the dangerous paths through quagmire and quicksand, towards Rome. So far as is known she made her escape alone and rode alone.

In six days she covered the two hundred and twenty miles to

Rome. She was apprehended by no one. She was in the process
of becoming a legend, and she had caught the popular fancy. Even
the German irregulars, still ravaging central Italy in revenge of the
massacres, offered no harm to the Imperial minx. And the
Italian people began to feel new hope, kindled by the knowledge
that there was still somebody like Placidia alive. The Spanish-
Greek girl now became the symbol of an arisen Rome.

She rode into the city of Rome, and was given certain honors.
This was late in May of the year 410. She began a highly partisan
campaign for the outlawing of the Goths and the restoration of
the Roman prestige. She denounced the Emperor Attalus as a tool
of the Goths, and swore that there could be no Emperor in the
realm but her brother Honorius. Her campaign would have some
effect. Rome was in a particularly dry and waiting mood, and she
kindled it to brightness. She brought the City up to a fever pitch
in those last one hundred days of the world.

The escape of Galla Placidia was a propaganda defeat for Alaric,
but not a serious one. The talks went along most auspiciously.
Alaric still could not meet the Emperor Honorius in person—his
ministers may have feared Alaric's magnetic influence over him
that went back to the time when Alaric was the boy giant and
Honorius was an unregarded princeling. Alaric was not permitted
to talk to the Emperor Honorius, but he was permitted—along
with his own Emperor Attalus—to meet all the important men
of Ravenna and to treat with them on all subjects. And they spoke
with him, not to put him off, but to reach a settlement.

These men were Jovius the Praetorian Praefect; Valens the
Master of Cavalry and Infantry; Potamius the Quaestor; and Julian
the First of the Notaries; this latter office seemed to involve everything from Attorney General to Secretary of State.

It was not a rapid thing; it went on for many weeks. The sincerity of both parties was attested by the many hundreds of questions proposed, discussed, and settled. There would be nothing left
to chance. It was not merely a question of whether Attalus should
be recognized in Ravenna as co-Emperor with Honorius. The
councilmen were drawing up a master plan for the restoration

of the Empire. Should Alaric be given a contract as guardian of the Empire, and it would amount to that, it would be a contract with every clause thoroughly defined.

The first rift was not between the party of Alaric and that of Ravenna; it was within Alaric's own party. Alaric was still without real experience in these matters. In taking Stilicho as his model for Master General, Alaric had thought of having such relations with an Emperor as Stilicho had had. But Attalus made it clear that he had not consented to be Emperor to be puppet. He would fill that high office to the best of his considerable ability; but it must be understood that he himself was Emperor, and that Alaric was but Master General. Alaric was humbled, but he came to see that Attalus was right. Stilicho had never set himself above the Empire, and Alaric must not.

Alaric had intended to bring his brother-in-law Singerich from Constantinople to see to the detail of administration; but he came, in the long weeks, to understand that administration is more than a detail. Basilius and John, brought up from Rome to Ravenna to add finesse and intellectual prestige to the party of Alaric and Attalus, were invaluable. Alaric moved freely within Ravenna with a small group. He was shown the glories of the fortress city and treated royally. He talked twice with Pope Innocent, but he was not allowed to see the Emperor Honorius who was kept practically a prisoner by his dealing ministers. And Alaric, with a military eye, noted every detail of the fortress city.

Accord was in the air. Difficulty after difficulty was erased as the weeks went by. As Stilicho had said, the Empire did not have to fall. Never, in those last years, had the hope for the restoration of the Empire been higher.

Then Fate began to play her last cards.

The Weird Eagle perched beyond the high Alps had become impatient. Athaulf the feral Goth had his own system of intelligence, and he knew that for the success of his own program he could not allow the negotiations to succeed. He saw his instrument Alaric slipping away from him should that instrument, *as a*

Roman, succeed to the highest appointive office of the Empire and have military control of that entire world.

Athaulf came quietly into Italy, if one may come quietly with twenty thousand men. He brought with him his own sister Stairnon, the wife of Alaric. He also brought various Gothic elders, and trans-Danubian Goths who were untainted by Rome. He concealed his army, insofar as such a thing may be concealed, in the great belt of pine forest that reached all the way from a dozen miles north of Ravenna up to Aquileia. And with a very small party he was brought by guides to Alaric before Ravenna.

The feelings of Alaric were many ways mixed. For no two people in the world did he have such affection as for Stairnon and Athaulf. They were the marrow of his bones and the blood of his liver; but he suffered a curious hepatitis at the sight of Athaulf who recalled to him his own suppressed Gothic personality. And this was a reverted Stairnon, who spoke only Gothic and who no longer believed in Rome. She proclaimed that Rome amounted to no more than the harlot Galla Placidia, and accused Alaric of having consorted with such; and Alaric was unable to explain.

Alaric was committed to Rome, and he could not allow family love or marital embarrassment to interfere with the larger business. He told the two of them that he loved them beyond all else except God and the Empire; like Stilicho, he had now come to see the Empire as the chief handiwork of God in this world.

Stairnon he would now keep with him forever, he said; but Athaulf must go back, and his forces with him. They were unreconstructed Goths, and they could not be allowed to remain in the Empire on any terms. Athaulf would return at once out of the Empire, with his army, and under the escort of the men of Alaric; or Alaric would have him slain on the spot, and would then drive that army out with his own full force.

Athaulf and his small escort laid their arms at Alaric's feet, and stated that they would abide by whatever Alaric should command.

At once, said Alaric. They must go at once.

In the morning, said Stairnon. Her brother would leave in the morning. For evening was now coming on, and it was dangerous to attempt to traverse the swamps in the darkness.

With great misgivings Alaric agreed that they might remain the night; but they must leave at dawn, on pain of death for Athaulf and the harrying and destruction of his men.

Alaric had further misgivings when he saw that the party was setting up for a Gothic feast, for they had brought cattle in with them. During the night, at the feasting on the roasted oxen, Alaric was subjected to a sort of pressure that he had almost forgotten. The old sayings which he had put aside as toys now assumed a real importance when they were stated by real Goths. He was shaken in the security of his mind, and felt his inbred Gothic feeling rise up like an old lust in him. Nevertheless, he would have surmounted all the pressure and stood fast had not Fate now played her last wild card.

An independent person in the Empire, riding at the head of no more than one hundred men as he commonly rode at the head of small groups, entered the fortress of Ravenna under the cover of darkness. The gate opened to his call, as every gate opened to his hard call. It was Sarus come in to give his last allegiance to the retarded Emperor Honorius, and to the party of Ravenna.

The brother of Sarus who was no longer his brother, Athaulf, had entered the Empire. In the eyes of Sarus this broke every pact, and meant war to the death on the Goths. Sarus knew that there could never be any sort of truce between the Goths of Athaulf's sort and the Empire. And Alaric in accepting Athaulf—and Sarus would not wait for an explanation of this—had likewise become an outlaw to be killed.

While Alaric was subject to one sort of pressure during the night, the city of Ravenna and its leading men were subjected to another. Sarus absolutely set them on fire with the eloquence he found in his anger; and the cause he pleaded was aided by two comings into Ravenna on the day that had just ended.

Two fleets had arrived that day in the port of Ravenna, both sent by the Count Heraclian from Africa. There was a group of troop transports bearing six thousand excellent and untainted Imperial legionnaires for the defense of the already well-defended Ravenna. With these was a large gift of money from Heraclian; for an extra bonus in gold will always stiffen a soldiery under siege. With the money was the admonition that Ravenna should not treat with Alaric at all; and the advice that negotiations should be broken off if they had begun. There came also the news that the Senate in Rome had repudiated both the Master General Alaric and his Emperor Attalus. This was as a result of the popular feeling stirred up by Galla Placidia and others.

And the second fleet was the grain transports, bringing so much wheat and produce into the city that the already adequately filled depots could hardly accommodate it. With this Ravenna could stand a siege of several years, even if blockaded by both land and sea.

Ravenna simply could not be cut off to starve as could Rome. She had not a million and a half persons to feed; she had only the soldiery and the Court and a small citizenship, less than a hundred thousand all inclusive. Even the disrupting of the aqueduct could not force into submission the fortress built in the middle of the waters. She had survived for centuries before she had an aqueduct; though, it is true, epidemic had then been frequent.

There was further news conveyed by Count Heraclian that additional units of the Imperial fleet were at the mouth of the Adriatic, that they would blockade the sea completely to any battle force, and that they would quarantine the entire Illyricum shore.

It is probable that not even this new accretion of force would have disrupted the negotiations, had not the incendiary Sarus ridden into the fortress during the night. The repudiation of Alaric and Attalus by Rome had not been known in Ravenna, nor was it believed by all. As a matter of fact it was not completely true. There had been such a proclamation proposed to the Senate, but it had not carried. It would not carry till Alaric was once more under the walls of Rome, and the Senate brought up the matter once more. It isn't known whether someone in the fleet of Count Heraclian had falsified the news, or whether it had been given falsely out of Rome. But the wave started by Galla Placidia was very powerful, and it made itself felt even in Ravenna.

But the Roman Goth Sarus, aided by the true assistance and the false rumor, appealed over the heads of the Ravenna leaders to the soldiers; and he brought much of the town to his way of thinking in a sudden surge of emotion. And Sarus had a plan to stampeed the town in the morning.

At dawn the party of Alaric had drawn itself up on the small meadow near the fortress walls. Alaric had shaken off the Gothic nightmare that beset him during the wakeful night of feasting: the folk dreams of the people who remembered Rome after many centuries, and remembered her for revenge.

He ordered brusquely that the period of delay be over, and that Athaulf must leave at once.

After breakfast, said Athaulf, who had been feasting all night.

At once, insisted Alaric.

But Athaulf gazed at the walls of Ravenna as one rapt, and seemed to be listening for a noise from within. Athaulf understood both his brother-in-law who was his friend, and his brother who was his deadly enemy. Athaulf had seen to it that Sarus had known of his quiet coming into the Empire; he himself had sent the emissary, under the guise of a traitor to himself, to inform Sarus of his coming.

Athaulf knew that Sarus had followed him the day before to kill him, trying to close the gap before Athaulf should reach Alaric; and he knew how many miles Sarus would fall short of coming up to him. He had correctly guessed at what time Sarus would enter the fortress after dark, and he had listened to the noises of the city during the Gothic feasting. The ears of Athaulf had been sharpened in the wilderness north of the Danube; he interpreted the murmurs reaching them from the fortress as the roaring inside, and he understood at what hour Sarus had finally swayed the most of them.

Moreover, on the afternoon before, coming through the forest from the north, picked men of Athaulf climbing the hill-topping pine had seen the fleets in the harbor; and Athaulf had known what they bore.

Athaulf was listening and waiting for the charge that would bring his enterprise to life.

When the near gate of the fortress was opened under the flag of the truce of the ambassadors, Athaulf was the only one of the Goths who suspected that the truce would be violated. The men of Ravenna, still not completely brought to his views, had trusted Sarus in his statement that he must go out with only his own band for a last parley with the Goths. He had said that he believed he could cut the knot which they had spent many weeks trying to untie.

But violated the truce was, and by Sarus. He emerged suddenly with the wildest of all his mad-dog charges. With less than one hundred men—always with less than one hundred men—he charged two thousand horrified Goths.

There is something unreal in the Homeric or early Irish accounts of the resplendent chief gallantly assaulting the enemy and striking down with his own hand a hundred men. One wonders what the ninety-nine were doing while he assaulted the first one. But here there was no time to wonder for there was always something unreal and Homeric about Sarus.

He rampaged with his men into the Goths and slaughtered them by the score before they could raise shield; trampling them to death with horse, transfixing them with lances, and slashing them to death with sword and scimitar—for there were Huns also in his small mixed force. He cut his way through the unarmed and half-armed Goths where stood Alaric mad with amazement, and Athaulf uncontrollable with black laughter.

For Athaulf had calculated wisely. He cared nothing for the deaths of a few hundred if they should further his plan; and he saw clearly that Sarus would not be able to reach them, no matter what the fury of his charge. Moreover, he believed himself the equal of Sarus in combat. Sarus was the most feared fighter of the Empire, but his brother Athaulf was not of the Empire. Athaulf had known all his life who would kill whom in the final showdown between them, which had not yet come. He had dreamed of Sarus dead too many times to have any apprehension of dying at his hand.

Nor was Sarus able to reach them. He rode to the end of his momentum, saw with hatred that he would not be able to accomplish it, then wheeled and cut a new path through the reeling Goths, and back into the fortress of Ravenna. The entire episode had not lasted five minutes; and two hundred and fifty Goths, many of them unarmed, had been slaughtered.

Ravenna had violated the truce, and that was the end of all negotiations. It made no difference that the leaders of Ravenna had not anticipated or approved of the violation; they were the leaders no longer. The Imperial soldiers inside the town, brought to a fever by Sarus, approved the violation; and they would raise leaders who approved.

Before Alaric had found voice, there appeared on the walls of Ravenna, on the ends of pikes, the heads of Alaric and Athaulf, the replicas of them—horribly caricatured.

Sarus himself surged to the walls and harangued them in ringing hatred, till his voice broke. Then a herald took it up: first transmitting the invective of Sarus; then crying out the official proclamation of the Emperor Honorius, of which Honorius may have been ignorant, that Alaric and Athaulf and Attalus were all outlaws under sentence of death, and that they would be destroyed.

Alaric, shaking with anger, withdrew his party into the swamps to contact his scattered army on its separated plots of firm ground. He ordered that the assault of the fortress should take place that very day. Then, realizing the folly of such haste, he ordered that it be one week from that day. He commanded the construction of great log roads and giant battering rams to begin.

Athaulf had a week to influence his brother-in-law Alaric, and influence him he did. Athaulf had no interest at all in the fortress of Ravenna. He called it the small second head such as monsters are sometimes born with. But the monster itself was the city of Rome. It was against Rome that the weird lineage of the Goths had vowed vengeance forever; and it was for the destruction of Rome that Athaulf had plotted all his life.

He had to convince Alaric that Ravenna could not be taken by direct assault—as under rational conditions it could not be. It would be necessary first to take the city of Rome and strike a death blow at the Empire; then take the provinces of Sicily and Africa—towards one or the other of which the Goths had an old homing instinct. After this, its base of provisions gone, Ravenna would wither, and then fall.

Athaulf pledged that they would have Ravenna within one year, and by the long way around; and that in the meanwhile they would have much greater things, Rome and the world.

Had it not been for the presence of Sarus inside the fortress, Alaric might have found a way to compel Ravenna into submission. He felt himself to be full of resources, and he knew all that the most expert Romans knew about sieges. He could have broken the spirit of Ravenna, but Sarus' was the one spirit he could never break. With such a firebrand as Sarus to inspire the numerous and well-provisioned defenders, Ravenna, the strongest fortress in the world, could not be taken by assault.

It took three days for Athaulf to work the change in Alaric; he and Stairnon and the unreconstructed Goths. But they did bring about a partial change in that time. Alaric prayed for guidance, but he complained that God had deserted him.

He would find God again on the road towards Rome, Stairnon told him. It was God who wished him to cast out the old leaven and bring in the new. It was the barm of the Goths that must yeast the new world.

Alaric agreed to lead his army to Rome, but not for an assault. He would reassure the City, he said, and order an end to the disturbances there. He would then have the faction of Ravenna declared outlaw, and would see about the blockade of that city; and about the replacement of Count Heraclian in Africa.

It could not be done, his Emperor Attalus told him. They must remain before Ravenna; they must compel Athaulf to leave the Empire as a show of their good faith; and they must treat for the reopening of negotiations, if it should take a year. Attalus commanded this as Emperor.

"Of what are you now Emperor?" Alaric asked him, and ordered the march to Rome.

A further change was worked in Alaric during the route march. There was brought to bear on him every pressure, from childhood memory to charismatic incantation; from the reference to his own father dead to his ghostly father to whom he had spoken on the island in the Danube. The entire Gothic mystique was raised: the legends of the old people broken by Rome centuries before and fleeing by sea to the north; the blood cry for revenge that would never be stilled; the entire secret cult that had gone underground but had not died.

Athaulf even brought cold reason to bear. Alaric, once unable to deal with a defective Emperor, had created his own Emperor in his place. Now, unable to deal at all with a defective people—the Romans perfidious from the beginning and who had attacked under a truce—should he not put another people in their place, his own people? And Stairnon, who at times had an almost total control over her man and who now hated Rome for one girl, brought him along that way.

The exterior Goths of Athaulf, now mixed with the Empire Goths of Alaric, worked a yeasty change in these latter during the march to Rome. One could see the Empire Goths shed their Roman exterior as a snake sheds its skin. From clean-shaven Romans, they became in a week fur-faced Goths. They sawed the Roman crests off their helmets and became as they had been a generation before, untamed Goths in their iron sheath caps. They shifted their *vaginae,* their scabbards, from the right to the left side. The Romans had always worn their scabbards on the right and had drawn swords straight up awkwardly, and the Empire Goths had followed them in this conformity. But the untamed Goths wore the scabbards on their left, and cross-drew. Their blacksmiths fashioned battle axes at night, for the Roman Goths had abandoned this old weapon, and now desired it again.

The men of Alaric changed, and their leader changed with them.

His devotion to the Empire had been shattered by the perfidy of what was left of the Empire at Ravenna. Under the shock he regressed to the atmosphere of his childhood; and in his childhood Stairnon had been everything to him. It was back to the early children's tale, that they should break open Rome as if it were a box of treasure.

For somewhere on the roads between Ravenna and Rome, Alaric the Boy Giant, who had matured into a Roman general, left off being a Roman and became once more a Goth. To him it did not seem treason. The Empire had degenerated into a cruel joke. He would supersede the old Empire by a new. The man who departed from the swamps of Ravenna was not the same man who approached the walls of Rome.

This was no longer a Roman army under a Roman general. It had become a Gothic force led by the King of the Goths; a foreign, barbarian invasion bearing down on Rome. The change in the men was complete. Hafras reports that they spoke Low Latin when they left Ravenna, but Gothic as they approached Rome. Among the five families of the Goths, it was the Amali who were descended from wolves, and the Balthi of Alaric who were descended from bears; but the change in this Balthi was now a werewolf sort; the animal came up in Alaric, and it had always been very strong.

The invading Gothic army was joined by the German irregulars who had been roaming Italy for nearly two years following the slaughter of their families after the death of Stilicho. Alaric did not refuse any recruit. He received slaves and refugees from the Gaul ravaged by the false Emperor Constantine, deserters of every race from the Roman legions, Spanish troops who had been garrisoned in Italy, marauders who had left Africa for hatred of the Count Heraclian. With his own considerable force; with Athaulf's initial force that had come into the Empire to near Ravenna, and his further force which now joined them on confident instructions previously given; with the addition of a dozen groups, Alaric now had the largest army that had been gathered in Italy for several generations—not counting the inconsequential mob of Radagais— somewhere between seventy-five and a hundred thousand men.

The Rome they came onto was frightened witless, but had formed an absolute resolve to resist to the death of every citizen. It had been an empty dream that Alaric might ever have reassured the City and ordered the end of the disturbances there. The arisen Rome was his enemy forever.

Galla Placidia inside the City had control of the Senate, and her incandescent oratory inflamed a real resistance. *"Roma, Roma, Roma Sacra!"* Holy Rome! was the chant they set up. There were torches burning by the tens of thousands every night till a heavy haze hung over the City. Bells tolled and clanged day and night. The giant bronze bells, a medieval thing already in existence with them, were a new and Christian appearance in the City.

A hundred thousand persons were put to brick making, and ramparts and causeways and catwalks were added to the walls, and old ones repaired. Citizens from the villas outside the walls had entered the City, and the outside buildings that backed too conveniently against the walls had already been battered down. Unaccustomed hands were torn at the work and new blood was added to the bricks of Rome.

But it was a desperate resistance that could be of no avail. Orders and appointments were being issued by the seventeen-year-old Galla Placidia who had declared herself Consul and Tribune and Praefect, without understanding what pertained to any of the offices.

And yet, the first Gothic assaults on the walls were repulsed by a defense so savage that the Goths reeled back from it bewildered, leaving their dead attackers and their broken scaling ladders.

Inside was hysterical defiance. But outside were the Goths.

There is a term placed on everything, even the world. On the night of August 24 of the year 410 the term was finished. One account states that it was at midnight; but a more trustworthy version states that it was about an hour after dark, and that it had begun to rain. At that time the Salarian Gate of Rome was secretly opened by Gothic slaves in the City. The troops of Alaric entered, and their entry was signaled by a giant trumpet blast such as will never be heard again till the last day.

And, on the terrible blast of the Gothic Trumpet, the world came to its end.

It had endured, in the central core of it that mattered, for eleven hundred and sixty-three years.

19. Which Is Epilogue

Sero Te amavi, pulchritudo Tam Antiqua—
Too late have I loved Thee, Thou of ancient beauty,
Too late have I loved Thee!

St. Augustine

In Latin writing there is a peculiar literary form that we can only call the Lamentations. Deaths of great men and good men brought out such. They were stylized in form, but they do not seem artificial. Deep grief is apparent in many of them.

The death of the Roman world brought out many such Lamentations, for everyone understood at once that this was the final event. St. Augustine in Hippo Regius in Africa mourned the end of the world, as did St. Jerome in Bethlehem. We have deep Lamentations on the event from Orosius, Salvianus, Rutilius Namatianus and others. The end was felt in all lands like muted thunder. It was like no earlier disaster. It was final death.

There was no more Western Empire, though it might continue in shadowy name for fifty more years. The heart was killed; and the limbs were unstrung, and fell away. It could no more be put together than can the pieces of a dismembered animal.

The sub-title of this study "The Day the World Ended" is not meant to be extravagant. It was not the *orbis terrarum,* the globe, that ended; but the *mundus,* the ordered world. *Mundus,* as an adjective, means clean, neat, or elegant. As a noun it may mean the ornamentation, the vesture; but it also means the world. It is like the Greek *cosmos* which not only means the world and the universe, but likewise means the order, the arrangement, the beauty: for cosmetic, the beautifier, and cosmos, the beauty, are of the same root.

Both before and after the *mundus,* the ordered world, there is chaos. But in its bounds it was one thing. It is redundant to speak of the Roman world; the *mundus* was the Roman world, and there was no other. It was one of the great things that have happened but once. It had been a living person, and now there were but the sundered limbs.

The story of Pandora's Box, the most profound of all the fairy tales, had been the story of the *mundus*. This, the Roman Thing, had truly been a chest of hidden treasures; and three children traveling from the north had come and opened the box. They were three Gothic children from the land over the edge of the world; they were Alaric and Stairnon and Athaulf. They opened the box of most curious construction. And when they lifted the lid the world came to an end.

What follows the end of a world? Why, chaos again, which is another name for legend. All that happened in the next five hundred years to the great area where the world had stood is legend. Whatever reality can be found in it must be found by probing, as an analyst attempts to find reality behind dreams. The acts of the Goths in the following weeks and years are strictly legendary. Had the eunuch Eutropius been alive and permitted to add further chapters to his history, he would have gently set these things into the realm of legend, as he did many of the first things of Rome.

When we now write that the Goths did such a thing, we use a short form. It is understood that we mean "It is the legend that they did such a thing."

The Goths remained but six days in Rome, a city from which all the fire had gone, a dead town of empty-eyed people watching mutely. There was no great slaughter, only the deaths of such misled men as chose to resist, who did not understand that it was all ended. The Goths took few lives, but they took much else—all the wealth they could carry, five hundred wagon loads of loot. It was the gold and jewels of Rome, the fine ornaments and the art; and they carried it away to the south when they left.

There is a legend within a legend that it turned to ashes, that the boxes of it when opened later for examination held only cinders, and were so abandoned. But the great known pieces have been turning up ever since in every land where the Goths went, and they went everywhere. The pieces are in the still preserved crowns of the later kingdoms and in their crown jewels, in the museums and in private vaults. They have a life of their own, and all of them did not turn to ashes. They represented the secret golden hoards of Europe for the next thousand years.

The Goths left a garrison in Rome and went into south Italy. They were in a daze. They had fulfilled one aspect of their old destiny: they had killed Rome and been revenged on her. Nobody doubted that now she was dead, who had come living through more serious things. The Goths had a rational program to take the provinces of Sicily and Africa and so have a key to all the resources of the Empire. But this rational program was only an excuse; it was a homing instinct that drew them south. Elements of the Goths had come from one of these two provinces many centuries before, and they felt the call to return.

They built a great fleet in South Italy, and the first ships of it went to sea. There arose then a tempest more severe than any that is recorded in history, for this was a thing outside such bounds. Waves more than three hundred feet high, and bearing whole islands and towns on their crests, shattered the fleet. And every time thereafter that the Goths laid even one keel for a new fleet, the great waves came ashore, even into the hills and forests, and destroyed their work. They would not be allowed to go home. They must wander.

Alaric died of a fever in the same year, three months after the taking of Rome. He was buried (it is the legend that he was buried) in the bed of the River Busento, which torrent was said to have been diverted from its bed and a great mausoleum built for Alaric. He was placed there with all the treasure, and the Busento

River turned into its bed once more to flow over him. Thereupon the slaves who had performed this labor were killed, that the secret of the place might not be found.

It has not been found, and there is likely no such place; but Italians still come on holiday and wade and drag the river; and of late years they use ticking instruments that might indicate the presence of golden metal, should they be the lucky ones.

Three stories are told of the end of Stairnon the Valkyrie, two of them unlikely, and one of them most probable. The first is that she expected that Alaric, like Christ, would rise from the dead on the third day; and that she killed herself with sword when he did not. The second is that she had herself immured alive in the mausoleum with the dead Alaric; and that she is alive there yet, her keening still to be heard above the thunder on stormy nights.

The third story is that she acquired land and slaves in South Italy and remained there as a great estate proprietor through a long lifetime, that she wore always the long bull whip coiled about her arm as she had in Little Moesia, and that she became somewhat unbending and cruel in her later years. The latter account is from Hafras who visited her, on such estate and in such condition, many years after the death of Alaric.

The horrible double fratricide that came to the Balthi family after the death of Alaric is like a murky dream inside a dream. Athaulf, in possession of Galla Placidia taken at the conquest of Rome, had in turn been possessed by her, and had married her. He became by this the brother-in-law of the shadowy Emperor Honorius. Athaulf and Galla Placidia then began, too late and with insufficient base, a sincere attempt to restore the Empire, not realizing that it was dead forever. Athaulf now bore the title of King of the Goths, and he took the field against the pretender Emperor Constantine, who was now actually the King of Gaul. It was an inconsequential campaign of the Low Middle Ages, and had nothing to do with the vanished Empire.

Sarus, coming still to kill his brother Athaulf, found him in South France, and attacked him in the last of his memorable charges. Once more Sarus rode furiously with less than one hundred men, calling out his intent in a loud voice in broad daylight, and launching into the middle of thousands of guards. Athaulf stood, as he had once before near Ravenna, waiting with black laughter, which, it is said, turned to fear in an instant when Sarus cut a path impossibly to the very core of the guard.

But Sarus had horse killed under him, and was himself driven clear through the upper body with lance as he continued his charge on foot. But it took eight men to pinion the dying lion as he still came on in fury; and it was not till he was so held that Athaulf came and sank his great fingers into his brother's throat.

Athaulf continued to throttle Sarus long after he was dead; till long after dark, it is said, when everyone had left them. Then he gave the body of Sarus to the dogs.

Singerich came one year later. It had taken that time for the news to come to him in Constantinople, and for himself to come and find Athaulf. He found him in Spain, in what is now Barcelona, and killed him; how he killed him is not known.

Singerich himself then reigned as King of the Goths—for seven days. The second brother had been killed for the murder of the first, and the third must follow. Singerich, after his one week's reign, was in turn murdered by an unnamed partisan of Athaulf. There followed as King of the Goths a man named Vallia, a more distant cousin from among the Balthi family. And there followed a hundred other Gothic kings in a dozen kingdoms for a thousand years. By the time that the remembered name Athaulf had evolved into its modern form of Adolph, the Goths had themselves so evolved and been assimilated that no one could say who was Goth and who was not.

But we are all Goths, for all that, whoever we are; which is to say, Outlanders. And like the Goth Sarus we still owe loyalty to an Empire, but we no longer know of what the Empire consists. We are still bound by the statement of Stilicho that the highest duty in the World is the proper ordering of the World. There will be, and are, other worlds; and perhaps it is not a terrible thing that a world should end. But we are still in admiration at the great corpse of it.

Index

Abrasi, 33

Adrianople, 30, 32, 38, 42

Africa, 267, 270

Alani, 214

Alareidar (father of Alaric), 19, 26

Alaric, King of the Goths: at Aquileia, third battle of, 105–7, 109–14; against Arbogast, 70, 83; birth and childhood, 18–28; in Constantia, 81–83; on the Danube, 83–84, 93–94; death of, 91, 295; described, 83–84, 165; and Eastern Empire, 129–31, 158–59, 232; in Epirus, 156–57, 183–84; and Eutropius, 127, 129; fame of, 190–91; first command, 58–59; and Galla Placidia, 57–58, 273, 274, 279–80; and Gothic revolt, 129–31, 135–65; in Greece, 135–56; and Honorius, 262; and Illyricum, 162–64, 202, 232, 234; against Inconstant Constantine, 247; and Italy, 203–4, 207–19 *passim,* 236–37, 243–44, 262; as King, 162–66; mentioned, 294; mother of, 19–20; and oracular voice, 168–69; and Ravenna, 267–68, 274–88; and Roman Senate, 245–47, 262, 265, 266–68, 270, 284; and Rome, 168–69, 244–45, 264–67, 269–73, 289–92; and Rufinus, 126, 132; and Sarus, 160–61, 264; at School for Generals, 37–47; on Shade Island, 84–89; and Stairnon, 26–27, 46–47, 74–81, 167, 184, 234, 282; and Stilicho, 48, 56, 132–36, 157, 160–61, 202, 237, 261; and Uldin, 236

Alavivus (Visigothic leader), 29

Allobich, 269

Amali, 33

Ambrose, Archbishop of Milan, 36, 45, 50, 54, 71, 120

Annibalianus (nephew of Constantine), 62

Anthemius, Consul, 233–34, 248

Antiochus, Proconsul of Greece, 135

Appian, 224–25

Aquileia: first battle of, 62; second battle of, 96; third battle of, 66, 99–119

Arbogast, Count of the Franks, 65, 66, 67; at Aquileia, third battle of, 99–100, 108, 118, 119; as usurper, 69–71, 95–98; Valentinian II overthrown by, 67–69

Arcadius, Emperor, 51, 120, 133; and Alaric, 124–25, 163; and the Constantinople riots, 195; death of, 247; described, 123, 125–26; and Gainas, 195–96; and the Gothic revolt, 127, 129; and Honorius, 232; mentioned, 198; and Rufinus, 123–24; and Singerich, 159; and Stilicho, 157–58

Athanaric (Gothic leader), 33

Athaulf (cousin of Alaric), 20, 22, 24, 25, 37, 77, 294; and Alaric, 26, 33, 78, 82, 89, 90–91, 94, 164–65, 264, 282–83, 285–88; attempts to restore the Empire, 296; described, 21, 49; and the Eastern Empire, 234; Galla Placidia married by, 296; and the Gothic invasion of Italy, 204; and Sarus, 23, 264, 297; Singerich kills, 297

Athens: invaded by Alaric, 140–41

Attalus, Praefect of Rome, 272–73, 275, 278, 281, 288–89

Augustine, Saint, 120, 193

Augustus, Emperor, 277

Aurelian, Master of Empire, 193–96

Bacurinius, 45, 72, 73, 113

Bacurius (Spanish general), 80, 113, 272